Study Guide to accompany

Guttman and Hopkins'

UNDERSTANDING BIOLOGY

Prepared by

Ruth L. Hays
Clemson University

Gordon E. Uno
University of Oklahoma

David R. Voth
Metropolitan State College

for

P.S. Associates, Inc.
Sterling, Massachusetts

Harcourt Brace Jovanovich, Inc.
New York   San Diego   Chicago   San Francisco   Atlanta
London   Sydney   Toronto

CONTENTS

TO THE STUDENT

The purpose of this *Study Guide* is to help you master the factual information, terms, and concepts presented in UNDERSTANDING BIOLOGY, by Burton S. Guttman and Johns W. Hopkins and to give you an opportunity to think about and use the information you are acquiring from this text. Learning is an active process. You must work with new terms, facts, and ideas in order to understand and remember them, and in order to be able to apply them to new issues in biology. The *Study Guide* provides you with a carefully planned sequence of exercises that will actively involve you in learning and using the information in your text.

ORGANIZATION OF THE STUDY GUIDE

Each chapter of the *Study Guide* corresponds to a chapter in the text and is divided into five sections (plus an answer key) designed to guide you through the steps of the learning process in a meaningful sequence.

What's in This Chapter gives you an overview of the chapter. It highlights major topics and issues and points out potential trouble spots. At the end of this section there is a list of specific learning goals to keep in mind as you read the chapter.

What You Should Already Know reviews the major concepts and issues covered in earlier chapters that are directly relevant to the current chapter. The purpose of this section is to reinforce your understanding and memory of biological concepts you learned earlier and to alert you to themes that run throughout the book. It includes a brief Pre-Test on the relevant material from earlier chapters.

The Guided Review of the Chapter uses sentence-completion items, true-false statements, and short-answer questions to test your understanding and memory of the facts, terms, and concepts introduced in the chapter. You need to be sure that you understand and remember new terms and facts before you try to apply them in new situations.

The Practice Quiz contains from 10 to 20 multiple-choice questions that cover as many of the major concepts in the chapter as possible. It includes both factual and concept-oriented questions.

The section entitled Review Questions contains several exercises designed to help you pull together and apply what you have learned from the chapter. It tests your understanding of text information and helps you to see the implications of the facts you have learned. In short, this section should help you think about what you have learned.

In the Answers to Chapter Exercises you will find the answers to the questions in the Practice Quiz and to the Review Questions.

HOW TO USE THE STUDY GUIDE

Read the first two sections of each *Study Guide* chapter before you read the text. Use What's in This Chapter first to preview the material you are about to read and then to help you organize the material in the chapter as you read it. Return to the list of learning goals at the end of this section periodically as you read, to see whether you can relate the material in the text to the list of goals.

Use What You Should Already Know to refresh your memory of important facts you learned earlier and to prepare for new encounters with familiar ideas. The answers to the Pre-Test in this section are provided on the left-hand side of the page, one frame below each question. Be sure to write out the answers to the Pre-Test before you check the answers. In this way you can test how well you remember what you have already learned.

Work through the remaining *Study Guide* sections after you have read the text. Use the Guided Review of the Chapter to test your understanding and memory for facts, terms, and concepts. As in the Pre-Test, the questions in the Guided Review are posed on the right-hand side of the page and the answers are given on the left-hand side of the page, one frame below each question. Be sure to write out the answer in the space provided before you look at the answer on the left. You may want to use a piece of paper to cover the answers until you are ready to look at them. The answers are readily available to give you immediate feedback, but if you skip the step of thinking through the answer yourself, you will defeat your purpose. If you miss several questions in a row, read the relevant section in your text again. The Guided Review is also structured so that you can use it to help you organize the information in the chapter. In many cases the answers on the left-hand side of the page provide a list of essential terms and concepts in the chapter. You can return to this list later to review and rehearse what you have learned.

Use the Practice Quiz to test how well you have done your work up to this point. If you have picked the wrong answer on some questions, read the relevant topics in your text again. Be sure that you understand why you did not choose the best answer.

Work through the Review Questions after you feel you have mastered the key terms and concepts in the chapter. This section will help you see relationships among terms and ideas and will give you an opportunity to think about and apply what you have learned. Although this section is designed to make you think, the exercises are not open-ended. Correct answers are given in the Answers to Chapter Exercises. Specific answers are given for matching, fill-in-the-blank, and short-answer questions. In the case of exercises that require short essay answers, you may regard the answers as guidelines. They are based on the material in your text. You may also find that you can draw upon material from lectures and other sources to elaborate on these answers.

The *Study Guide* is not intended to act as a substitute for reading your text and attending lectures. Nor will the *Study Guide* be very helpful if you use it only the day before an examination. Read your text and use the *Study Guide* on a regular basis. It takes time to master new concepts and ideas in biology. Regular use of the *Study Guide* should help you spend this time efficiently and effectively. It should also help you become involved in your classes. Studying on your own will prepare you to understand and take notes on the lectures and to formulate questions and participate actively in class discussions and laboratory sessions.

Chapter 1

INTRODUCTION AND ORIENTATION

WHAT'S IN THIS CHAPTER

This chapter introduces you to the study of biology and the world of living organisms. Biology is a science and, like all sciences, its development is based on observations. How do we make these observations and how do we account for them? We gain our observations through our perception of the world and our perception is biased by what we already know. We develop hypotheses, or educated guesses, about the causes of our observations, and we test the validity of these hypotheses through experimentation. This testing helps weed out unacceptable hypotheses, leaving us with well-supported statements that in turn help us build our paradigms--our common beliefs. Each of us makes observations and hypotheses every day, whether we are conscious of it or not, but the organized process is developed in this chapter.

You should be able to recognize and form a hypothesis and be able to see how its validity could be tested. You should also realize the logic and power of the scientific method of investigation, but also the difficulties and limitations imposed by the strict standards of this investigation. A biological paradigm has now developed that is based on several major concepts supported by years of experimentation. The brief introduction to each of these concepts prepares you for your entry into this biological paradigm--concepts to which we will return in future chapters--and provides you with a framework on which to build your knowledge of the living world.

By the end of the chapter you should be able to:

1. Define the word biology.

2. Explain the importance to all organisms of knowing and retaining knowledge about the world.

3. Develop and explain how to test a hypothesis based on a set of observations.

4. Recognize and explain the difference between a synthetic statement and an analytic statement.

5. Describe how humans perceive objects.

1

6. Discuss the relationship between paradigms and science.

7. List the major concepts in the modern paradigm of biology.

WHAT YOU SHOULD ALREADY KNOW

In each "What You Should Already Know" section, you will be asked to review some of the important concepts and information you gained in previous chapters--concepts that are necessary for you to gain complete understanding of the chapter you are about to read. Because this is your first chapter in a series designed to give you a broad basic training in biology, no review is necessary. You carry into this course a background in the biological and physical sciences that is different from that of other students, but anyone can achieve his or her desired level of understanding using this text without any previous science courses. This is an introductory text, so the chapters will introduce you to science and biology at a well-designed pace, providing you along the way with all the chemistry and physics background you will need. Although this guide will help you identify the major concepts in the accompanying text, always keep a pen or pencil handy to write down any questions you may have--and then get them answered.

GUIDED REVIEW OF THE CHAPTER

Introduction

1. The word "biology" comes from the Greek words *bios*, mean-

   ing (a)_____, and *logos*, meaning (b)_____.

1. (a) life;
   (b) word

2. The literal meaning of the word "science" is _____.

2. knowledge

3. True or False: Human life is occupied to a great extent with the acquisition of knowledge.

3. True

4. True or False: Most people have little understanding about what science is.

4. True

5. A _____ is a way of thinking and acting that is shared by a population of people.

5. culture

1-1 "Knowing" is an essential part of being alive.

1. True or False: To gather information about the surrounding world is one of the most important things an organism can do.

1. True

1-2 Knowing depends on hypothesis formation.

1. All statements that we know to be true by definition and

   whose meanings offer no alternatives are called _____.

1. analytic

2. The difference between analytic statements and synthetic statements is that synthetic statements _____
_____ .

2. cannot be proved true or false simply by examining them

3. One major problem with the use of authorities as a source of information is that _____
_____ .

3. authorities often contra- dict one another

4. One major problem with the use of intuition as a source of information is that _____
_____
_____ .

4. truths re- vealed in this way too often turn out, on further inves- tigation, to be false

5. True or False: Intuition plays an important part in science.

5. True

6. Intuition is important in science because _____
_____ .

6. it may pro- vide a sudden insight into a problem

7. True or False: Most humans use the process of observation and experimentation every day in one form or another to solve their problems.

7. True

8. A hypothesis is _____
_____
_____ .

8. an educated guess that will explain a set of observations and that can be tested through experimentation or further observation

9. True or False: It is possible to prove a hypothesis true.

3

9. False

10. True

11. True

12. (a) retroduc-
    tively; (b) de-
    ductively;
    (c) confirmed;
    (d) false

1. (a) hypotheses;
   (b) theory; (c)
   everything we
   know about
   these objects

1. (a) a time
   when a new
   viewpoint is
   introduced
   which causes
   science to go

---

10. True or False: It is possible to disprove a hypothesis.

11. True or False: The truths established in science are universal statements that say something is always true, not merely that it is sometimes true.

12. An investigator might reason (a)_____ (retroductively / inductively) in saying, "I could explain this observation if my hypothesis, H, is true." The investigator would then reason (b)_____ (inductively / deductively) that, if H is true, and if I do the following experiment, I will observe O. If O is observed, the H is (c)_____(confirmed / rejected). Other experiments are conducted to test the hypothesis and to try to prove it (d)_____ (true / false).

1-3 Perception itself is apparently theory-laden.

1. The act of perceiving occurs through the formulation of (a)_____. When we see an object, we see it through a (b)_____ about what the object is, called by Hanson "spectacles behind the eyeballs." Hanson also says we see objects not only "as" but also "that." By this Hanson means that the process of seeing is informed not only by our knowledge that there are certain kinds of objects but also by (c)_____
_____.

1-4 Science often proceeds through radical changes in theory and outlook.

1. In science, a revolution is (a)_____
_____
_____

Name two such revolutions: (b)_____

and (c)_____.

2. A _____ is the whole body of basic assumptions, beliefs, aims, and methods that are shared by a group of people in some field of science.

off in a different direction; (b) Copernican revolution (when astronomers shifted from a geocentric universe to a heliocentric universe); (c) Darwinian revolution

2. paradigm

3. True

4. A crisis develops when the theory is inadequate, and then a new paradigm must be invented to account satisfactorily for all of the available information.

1. it is a way of seeing the world and investigating it, just as a culture is a way of thinking and acting

2. (a) organisms;
(b) genetic;
(c) parent;
(d) inherits

3. True or False: Both the geocentric and the heliocentric models of the universe are paradigms.

4. What happens to a theory when too many anomalies develop (observations that the theory cannot explain)?

_____

_____

_____

1-5 The modern paradigm of biology.

1. A scientific paradigm is like a small culture because

_____

_____.

2. The major objects of study in biology are (a)_____, so named because they are highly organized structures.

They are (b)_____ systems, a term related to "genesis" and "generate" that refers to the origin of a new organism. Every organism is formed by some previous organism, a (c)_____, and from this organism it (d)_____ all the information it needs for its own structure and operation.

3. Genetic information is carried in the physical form called the (a)_____, which is the (b)_____

_____.

5

3. (a) genome;
   (b) total set
   of genetic
   material car-
   ried by every
   organism

4. A _____ is like a computer program,
   because both are coded, dictating exactly the structure of
   the organisms.

4. genetic
   program

5. (a)_____ are the occasional errors that are

   made during the (b)_____ process of the genome.

5. (a) Mutations;
   (b) replication

6. _____ is the ultimate source of variation among
   organisms and the basis of the evolutionary process.

6. Mutation

7. There are many different kinds, or (a)_____, of
   organisms on earth, and they are all related to one

   another (b)_____, meaning that they have
   evolved one from another over the long period of the
   earth's history.

7. (a) species;
   (b) phylo-
   genetically

8. True or False: All the various species of organisms that
   now exist are related to one another back through time.

8. True

9. Natural selection is _____

   _____

   _____.

9. the process by
   which those
   organisms in
   a population
   that are bet-
   ter adapted to
   their ways of
   life leave the
   largest pro-
   portion of
   offspring in
   the next
   generation

10. True or False: Darwin was successful in presenting his
    theory of evolution because he was able to present
    arguments for the importance of mutations and the method
    of inheritance.

10. False

11. True or False: All living organisms consist of one or
    more cells.

11. True

12. In 1665, (a)_____ examined a thin slice of cork

    and called the small compartments he saw (b)_____
    because they reminded him of monks' chambers in a monas-
    tery.

12. (a) Hooke;
    (b) cells

13. List the four parts of the cell concept.

(a)_____

(b)_____

(c)_____

(d)_____

13. (a) All organisms are made of cells and produced by cells. (b) All cells, in all organisms, are very similar. (c) The activity of a multicellular organism is primarily the combined activity of its constituent cells. (d) All cells are derived from pre-existent cells.

14. True or False: A cell in an organism living today is related to the first simple cells on earth.

14. True

15. True or False: Viruses do not consist of cells.

15. True

16. Living organisms are made from a small number of essential materials and are made mostly of the common compound

(a)_____ and of (b)_____ compounds, which

are made largely of carbon. Two materials, (c)_____

and (d)_____ constitute most of an organism's nonaqueous mass. Both of these materials are

giant molecules called (e)_____, which are made by stringing together many small molecules called monomers.

16. (a) water;
    (b) organic;
    (c) proteins;
    (d) nucleic acid; (e) polymers

17. Proteins and nucleic acids have specific shapes that allow them to recognize other shapes. This recognition occurs

through (a)_____, wherein one molecule attracts another in a particular way and fits into it. Two molecules that fit together specifically are

said to be (b)_____.

17. (a) chemical interaction;
    (b) complemen-

18. One large class of proteins called (a)_____, can effect chemical reactions, changing one molecule into another by adding, removing, or rearranging atoms. This

7

tary   is the foundation for all of the chemical activity, called

(b)_____, by means of which an organism grows

and maintains itself. (c)_____ is the concept
that describes the way various molecules fit into proteins
and alter their shape and activity.

18. (a) enzymes;   19. Homeostasis is _____
    (b) metabolism;
    (c) Parataxis   _____.

19. the relatively   20. Cells owe much of their structure and properties to thin
    stable set of
    conditions that   sheets of material called (a)_____, which
    all organisms
    maintain   are thin layers of (b)_____ with embedded

                         (c)_____. Membranes are important because

                         they (d)_____

                         _____

                         _____

                         _____.

20. (a) membranes;   21. In relation to the capture of energy for use to drive
    (b) lipids;   chemical reactions, there are two major types of
    (c) proteins;
    (d) restrict   organisms: (a)_____, which capture energy from
    what can move
    through them   light, and (b)_____, which capture energy from
    and can permit   certain chemical compounds.
    one kind of
    material to
    pass through,
    but not others.

21. (a) photo-   22. True or False: There are many species that live in isola-
    trophs;   tion from other organisms.
    (b) chemotrophs

22. False   23. All organisms exist in complex (a)_____ that
                          contain a variety of interacting organisms. In these,
                          phototrophs capture some of the sun's energy and are in

                          turn eaten by (b)_____. This series of "who
                          eats who," through which energy and material are trans-

                          ferred, is called a (c)_____.

23. (a) ecosystems;   24. An ecological niche is _____
    (b) chemo-

8

trophs; (c)
food chain

_____

_____ .

24. a specific
    habitat in
    which a species
    lives, together
    with its way of
    life

PRACTICE QUIZ

1. Each of the following statements is true about biology <u>except one</u>. Which
    statement is <u>incorrect</u>?
    a. It means "words about life."
    b. It is a science.
    c. It is organized information about the world.
    d. It is a series of facts.

2. Which of the following statements is <u>not</u> true about knowing?
    a. Organisms must "know" about their environment to survive.
    b. Knowing depends on hypothesis formation.
    c. All knowledge comes from the study of synthetic statements.
    d. Observation and experimentation are the only reliable source of knowledge.

3. All of the following statements about hypotheses are true <u>except</u>:
    a. A hypothesis is an educated guess about the cause of a set of
        observations.
    b. A hypothesis must be tested by experiment.
    c. A hypothesis can only be proven false, not true.
    d. The statement "Humans are the best organisms on earth" is a hypothesis.

4. Which of the following statements about perception is <u>not</u> true?
    a. The act of perceiving occurs through the formulation of many hypotheses.
    b. Scientists in different paradigms still share similar perceptions about
        the world.
    c. Perceiving is one way of gathering information about the world in which we
        live.
    d. Our perception of an object depends on what we already know about the
        object.

5. Which of the following statements about revolution and paradigms is <u>not</u> true?
    a. Most scientists disagree with Darwin's revolutionary idea of evolution.
    b. A revolution marks the changing of paradigms.
    c. The history of science has been marked by the changing of paradigms
        through time.
    d. Scientists living in the same country always share the same paradigms.

6. Which of the following statements is <u>not</u> true about a paradigm as applied to
    biology?
    a. The longer a paradigm exists, the greater its validity.
    b. The greater the number of experiments that support a paradigm, the greater
        its validity.

9

    c. A paradigm is based on intersubjective testability.
    d. If most scientists believe a paradigm, it is acceptable without testing.

7. All of the following are major concepts in the modern paradigm of biology <u>except</u>:
    a. Organisms are genetic systems.
    b. Humans lack similarities with plants.
    c. Populations of organisms evolve.
    d. Organisms are made of cells.

8. Which of the following is <u>not</u> a major concept in the modern paradigm of biology?
    a. Plants are chemotrophs and animals are autotrophs.
    b. Organisms use chemical reactions to construct themselves.
    c. Membranes play an important part in the life of an organism.
    d. Organisms capture energy from either light or certain chemical compounds.

9. Which of the following statements is <u>not</u> true of molecules?
    a. All organisms are made, in part, of organic molecules.
    b. Some organic molecules are made up of polymers.
    c. The most important organic molecule to an organism is water.
    d. Organisms operate through the interaction of organic molecules and their fit into one another.

10. Which of the following statements about ecosystems is <u>not</u> true?
    a. All organisms live within an ecosystem.
    b. All organisms occupy their own niche within an ecosystem.
    c. All organisms are connected with other organisms through food chains in an ecosystem.
    d. All ecosystems have distinct boundaries.

REVIEW QUESTIONS

I. Base your answers to the next four questions on this situation: Suppose you slowly pour Solution A (which is clear) into Solution B (which is clear) and the mixture bubbles vigorously and turns red.

    1. Which of the following is an <u>observation</u>?
        a. Solution A is the same as Solution B.
        b. Bubbles formed when Solutions A and B were mixed.
        c. Solution A caused Solution B to bubble.
        d. The temperature of the room was not a significant factor in the reaction.

    2. Which of the following is a reasonable hypothesis about your observations?
        a. A chemical reaction occurs when Solutions A and B are mixed together.
        b. Water is a liquid at room temperature.
        c. An increase in temperature causes a chemical reaction to increase in its rate.
        d. When hydrochloric acid is added to a calcium carbonate solution, carbon dioxide gas is formed.

    3. When Solution C (which is clear) is added to Solution B, the mixture bubbles vigorously and turns red. Which of the following statements is true?

    a. Solutions A and C are the same.
    b. Solution B is water.
    c. Solution B reacts with all solutions in the same manner.
    d. A test for the identity of Solution A may yield similar results for
        Solution C.

  4. Design a simple experiment to determine the effect, if any, of increased
      temperature on the reaction rate of Solutions A and B.

  _____

  _____

  _____.

II. Consider the following words and phrases:

                    The sun is going down in the West.
                    The moon is rising.
                    sunset
                    The sun is coming up.

All of these point to an old, and incorrect, perception of the world and its
relationship to the movement of planetary objects.

  1. What was the old paradigm in which these phrases might have been accurate,
      and what is the modern paradigm?

  _____

  _____

  2. What role did prevailing perceptions of the importance of humans play in
      the development of these phrases?

  _____

  _____

  3. How would you describe a sunset to a blind person? What experiences might
      all people share that would be a basis for your description and the blind
      person's perception of the event?

  _____

  _____

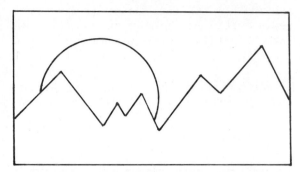

4. What do you perceive the accompanying drawing to be? _____

5. Basically, only two lines were used to form this drawing. How did your prior experience affect your perception of this fact?

_____

_____

6. How might measurements be important in the description of observations made by one person and communicated to another, such as those made in an experiment?

_____

_____

III. Use the following key to answer the next six questions. The key is based on concepts of the modern paradigm of biology. All of the statements that follow the key are beliefs that were held by some people at one time or another. Indicate in the blanks which of the modern concepts has replaced each of the old beliefs.

Key: a. Most organisms capture their energy from light or organic compounds.
b. Populations of organisms evolve from generation to generation on the basis of intraspecific variation and differential reproduction.
c. Organisms are genetic systems that inherit characteristics via nucleic acids.
d. All organisms are made of cells derived from preexisting cells.
e. All organisms occupy some ecological niche in an ecosystem with many food chains all based on producers.

_____ 1. If organisms cannot tolerate their living conditions, they change their physical structure to make their lives better and then pass this better condition on to their offspring.

_____ 2. Mice come from dirty rags left in the corner of a room for several weeks.

_____ 3. All organisms of a species are alike.

_____ 4. Plants get all of their weight from the soil.

_____ 5. Humans can live without plants as long as they have domesticated animals such as chickens, pigs, and cattle.

_____ 6. Organisms pass their characteristics on to their offspring through certain special proteins.

ANSWERS TO CHAPTER EXERCISES

Practice Quiz

1. d	3. d	5. a	7. b	9. c
2. c	4. b	6. d	8. a	10. d

Review Questions

I. 1. b
   2. a
   3. d
   4. Control--the time it takes for the reaction between A and B to go to completion. Experimental setup--the time it takes for the reaction between A and B to go to completion after heating solutions A and B. Students can heat the solutions to different temperatures and watch the reaction rate.

II. 1. The old paradigm included the belief that the sun traveled around the earth--that the sun moved and the earth was stationary.

   2. All of the phrases include reference to this idea that the earth is the center of the universe, based on the human egocentric perception of planetary motion.

   3. We will not try to suggest any single answer to this question.

   4. Many students should perceive this line drawing as a sunset behind a moutain range or forest.

   5. Prior experience, in the form of personally witnessing a sunset or seeing a photograph or drawing of a mountain range and the sun, is necessary before the student could come to the same conclusion.

   6. Measurements help to give definite, nonsubjective form to a person's perception of an event. This is especially critical if two people are both to understand an event that only one observed.

III. 1. b   3. b   5. e
    2. d   4. a   6. c

Chapter 2

THE DIVERSITY OF LIFE

WHAT'S IN THIS CHAPTER

This chapter introduces you to the great variety of organisms in the world, all of which share a common ancestry and have been shaped by evolutionary forces. Evolution, as postulated by Charles Darwin, involves a random "experimentation" in which the best adapted of a variety of organisms survive, reproduce, and pass on their characteristics to their offspring. This is the heart of natural selection, or differential reproduction, but the acceptance of Darwin's ideas was not easy.

In this chapter, the link between speciation and extinction, and evolution, will be outlined. The great diversity of organisms arising from speciation has been systematized in the development of a nomenclature system wherein each kind of living organism is given its own binomial epithet. Each then is placed at a point in a classification hierarchy that reflects the organism's phylogeny and the evolutionary forces that have shaped it.

After reading this chapter you should understand the action of evolution, the people who played important roles in its emergence as a theory that forms an underlying theme in biology, the misconceptions about it, and how it relates to the diversity of life. You will also be introduced to the diversity of organisms and the methods that scientists have developed to organize this diversity.

By the end of the chapter you should be able to:

1. Explain how all existing organisms are related by evolution, based on the evidence of homologous structures and on the succession of organisms through time.

2. Outline the four tenets of natural selection and explain how they relate to evolution.

3. Identify the genus, species, and family names of organisms and explain how these taxa fit into the classification hierarchy.

4. List two criteria used to define species of organisms, point out the difficulty in the use of these criteria, and describe an ideal classification system.

5. Use examples of adaptive radiation to illustrate evolution, including the ideas of reproductive isolation, speciation, and extinction.

6. Compare phyletic to punctuated equilibrium models of evolution and explain how some people may incorrectly suggest that evolution is directed.

WHAT YOU SHOULD ALREADY KNOW

The first chapter in this text provided an overview of the basic concepts in biology and how scientists go about perceiving, studying, and revising these concepts. Before beginning this chapter you should review the sections in the previous chapter on the process of hypothesis formation and testing, and the idea of a paradigm (Sections 1-2 and 1-4). To better understand evolution, you should review the discussion of the paradigms of genetic structure, phylogeny, and ecosystem structure (Section 1-5).

Pre-Test

    1.   A _____ is a whole body of basic assumptions, beliefs, aims, and methods that are shared by a group of scientists.

1. paradigm   2.   Use the following words to fill in the blanks: mutations, parents, inherit, offspring, reproduction. (a)_____ produce (b)_____, which (c)_____ genetic information through a process called (d)_____ _____. Occasionally this information is slightly different from that of the parents. An important source of this variation in genetic information is (e)_____ _____.

2. (a) parents;   3.   There are many different kinds, or (a)_____,
   (b) offspring;   of organisms in the world. These are all related to one
   (c) inherit;   another phylogentically, meaning that they have (b)_____
   (d) reproduc-
   tion; (e)   _____ one from another.
   mutations

3. (a) species;   4.   No species lives alone, but rather in an (a)_____,
   (b) evolved   in which a variety of interactions occurs. Each species
    has a specific habitat and way of life that makes up its

    ecological (b)_____.

4. (a) ecosystem;
   (b) niche

15

Introduction

1. For at least 500 years, Japanese fishermen have been

    practicing _____(natural / artificial)
    selection on crabs found off the coast of southwestern
    Japan.

1. artificial

2-1 All existing organisms are related by evolution.

1. True or False: To a typologist, variation between
    individuals of the same species is important.

1. False

2. True or False: To a typologist, common ancestry of two
    closely related species is important.

2. False

3. Give two important reasons why organic evolution was slow

    to be accepted by scientists: _____

    and _____.

3. belief in
   typology;
   misconception
   of age of
   earth

4. A (a)_____(catastrophist / uniformitarian)
    believed that the earth's history consisted of a series of
    geological events that wiped out all life on earth, or at
    least some large part of it. This differed from the views

    of a (b)_____, who believed that geologic

    forces are constantly at work. Of the two, a (c)_____

    _____ would be more likely to predict an older age
    of the earth.

4. (a) catastro-
   phist; (b) uni-
   formitarian;
   (c) uniform-
   itarian

5. Different kinds of organisms replace one another through

    time by means of the process of _____.

5. succession

6. Place the following groups of organisms in the order of
    their appearance in the fossil record. In other words,
    which evolved first? (1 = appeared first, 5 = appeared
    much later)

    _____ fishes with jaws

    _____ frogs

    _____ invertebrates

    _____ birds

    _____ fishes without jaws

16

6. 3, 4, 1,
   5, 2

7. Many rocks are deposited in (a)_____ or layers, laid down one upon the other with the (b)_____ (oldest / youngest) stratum on the top. The most primitive fossil plants are all very simple (c)_____ (algae / vascular plants) and would be expected to be found in (d)_____ (deep / shallow) strata.

7. (a) strata;
   (b) youngest;
   (c) algae;
   (d) deep

8. True or False: An individual organism can become extinct.

8. False

9. If we can identify two structures in different species as being equivalent to each other, these structures are (a)_____. This is different from (b)_____ _____ structures, which are structures that are found in organisms, and resemble one another superficially but are not derived from the same ancestral structure.

9. (a) homolo-
   gous; (b)
   analogous

10. Name one structure that is homologous to a human leg: (a)_____. Name one that is analogous to a human leg: (b)_____ _____.

10. (a) monkey
   leg, back leg
   of a dog;
   (b) insect leg,
   chair leg

2-2 *Evolution is explained generally in terms of natural selection.*

1. What are the four tenets (basic ideas) of natural selection?

   (a)_____

   (b)_____

   _____

   (c)_____

   _____

   (d)_____

   _____

1. (a) overpro-
   duction of
   offspring; (b)

2. In 1858 both (a)_____ and (b)_____ announced a mechanism

17

variation in population and inheritance of characteristics; (c) differential reproduction based on differential survival; (d) increase in successful traits in succeeding generations

2. (a) Charles Darwin; (b) Alfred Russel Wallace; (c) *On the Origin of Species*; (d) Darwin; (e) Malthusian

3. 1

4. (a) English peppered moth; (b) dark; (c) camouflaged on the soot-covered bark; (d) light; (e) natural selection

5. Every organism is adapted to living in a particular niche, and those organisms that survive and reproduce are the most fit for their way of life.

to account for evolution. However, it was a year later that the book entitled (c)_____,

written by (d)_____ provided so much evidence and argued so convincingly in favor of evolution. Many of

the ideas about evolution were based on the (e)_____ principle: each population has enormous reproductive potential that is held in check by environmental factors.

3. In a population of maple trees, each tree may produce 1,000,000 seeds in its lifetime. If the population is neither shrinking nor growing, how many of these 1,000,000

seeds live and grow into a tree? _____

4. Kettlewell studied the insect (a)_____

in England. From 1800 to 1950, the (b)_____(light / dark) form of the insect was favored because these indivi-

duals were (c)_____.
Today pollution is being cleaned up in the area, and the

(d)_____(light / dark) form of the insect is favored.

This is an example of (e)_____.

5. How is an organism's adaptedness related to its fitness?

_____

_____

_____

6. The definition of a niche is _____

_____

_____.

6. an account of an organism's way of life and a description of the habitat it lives in

7. True or False: An adapted organism is one that is fit.

7. True

8. True or False: An adapted organism is one that survives and reproduces.

8. True

2-3 Species are designated by a binomial nomenclature.

1. The field of biology that categorizes and names organisms is called (a)_____ or _____. Each organism is given two names under the (b)_____ system, the first name being the (c)_____ and the second name being the (d)_____. When writing them, the difference between these two names is that (e)_____.

1. (a) systematics taxonomy;
   (b) binomial;
   (c) genus;
   (d) species;
   (e) the genus is always capitalized and is placed first

2-4 Species are classified through a hierarchy of categories.

1. Linnaeus devised a system of classification with several different categories called (a)_____. In this hierarchy, several closely related species are grouped together into a single (b)_____. In this same hierarchy, several closely related genera are grouped into a single (c)_____.

1. (a) taxa;
   (b) genus;
   (c) family

2. For each blank, fill in one taxon. Humans are placed into the same (a)_____(family / class) as a house cat, the same (b)_____(superclass / order) as a canary, and the same (c)_____(subphylum superclass) as a goldfish.

2. (a) class;
   (b) super-class;
   (c) subphylum

2-5 A taxonomy is supposed to reflect phylogeny.

1. A family tree detailing relationships among various taxa is called a (a)_____ tree, and the history of evolution that it summarizes is called a (b)_____.

19

1. (a) phylo-
genetic;
(b) phylogeny

2. The aim of the modern taxonomist is _____

_____

_____.

2. to create use-
ful catalogs
of organisms
that look
alike and that
reflect common
ancestry

3. Taxonomists use (a)_____

and _____ as important in-
formation in determining whether two organisms should be
placed in the same species. In forming phylogenetic trees,

taxonomists hope to (b)_____(increase / decrease) polyphyletic relationships.

3. (a) morpholo-
gical charac-
teristics and
interbreeding
success;
(c) decrease

2-6 Species are defined on the basis of reproductive isolation.

1. Two individual plants are interbreeding if the (a)_____

_____ made by one of them (b)_____ the ovum
made by the other plant. If these two plants look quite

different, offspring called (c)_____ may be
formed, which are intermediate in appearance to the
parental types.

1. (a) sperm;
(b) fertilizes;
(c) hybrids

2. Speciation is _____

_____.

2. the process by
which one
species is di-
vided into two
or more species

3. In what three situations is it difficult to place a population in a particular species?

(a)_____

_____

(b)_____

_____

(c)_____

_____

3. (a) when there
is great morpho-
logical varia-
tion; (b) when
hybrids are
found between
two distinctly
different pop-
ulations; (c)
when there is
clinal varia-

2-7 Species diverge by taking advantage of new opportunities.

1. Hawaiian Drepanids are all closely related to one another,

as shown by their (a)_____ anatomy, but the variation in at least one morphological characteristic is ex-

treme. Two examples of this difference are (b)_____

_____ and _____

20

tion over a
wide geo-
graphic area _____. The Drepanids represent

an example of (c)_____ radiation, because one
original population took advantage of many new opportunities.

1. (a) internal;   2. True or False: Opportunism implies directed evolution.
   (b) massive,
   tough bill for
   crushing naio
   seeds and long
   bill to probe
   for grubs and
   insects;
   (c) adaptive

2. False   3. Flickers with one red mustache and one black mustache are

                      (a)_____ between eastern and western flickers.

                      They are in the (b)_____ (first / intermediate)
                      stage of speciation. The eastern and western flickers

                      (c)_____ (have / have not) acquired reproductive
                      isolating mechanisms. Such parents in this stage of

                      speciation are called (d)_____.

3. (a) hybrids;   4. (a)_____ is the pattern of evolution
   (b) inter-   wherein one original population of organisms separates
   mediate; (c)   into subpopulations that become adapted to new ways of
   have not;
   (d) semispecies   life. (b)_____ (Isolation / Interbreeding)
                       is a critical factor in this pattern, because without it,
                       all the subpopulations would continue to breed with each
                       other. Those physical features that can separate subpop-

                       ulations from each other are called (c)_____

                       barriers, one example of which is (d)_____.

4. (a) Adaptive
   radiation;   *2-8 Evolution consists primarily of speciation and extinction.*
   (b) Isolation;
   (c) geographic; 1. A (a)_____ tree illustrates an organism's evolu-
   (d) islands or   tionary history. Each branch point of the tree represents
   mountains

                        the process called (b)_____ (speciation / hy-
                        bridization), and each end of a branch represents a par-

                        ticular (c)_____ (species / race). The trunk of

                        the tree represents all the (d)_____ of the
                        organisms above, from which the organisms represented by
                        the branches were derived.

21

1. (a) phylo-
   genetic; (b)
   speciation;
   (c) species;
   (d) ancestors

2. True or False: More species have become extinct than now exist on the earth.

2. True

3. Extinction is _____

   _____.

3. the process
   by which
   species die
   out

2-9 *Evolution shows no evidence of being purposeful or directed.*

1. True or False: The forces of evolution direct organisms toward the goal of becoming better organisms.

1. False

2. True or False: Natural selection always results in individuals that are better adapted to their environment than their ancestors were.

2. False

3. Explain the following sentence: Evolutionary experiments are edited by natural selection.

   _____

   _____

   _____

3. The variation
   we see in na-
   ture is the
   experiment, and
   natural selec-
   tion selects or
   edits this so
   that only the
   best-adapted
   organisms
   survive.

4. The five kingdoms of organisms used in this text are

   (a)_____, (b)_____, (c)_____,

   (d)_____, and (e)_____.

4. (a) Plantae;
   (b) Animalia;
   (c) Fungi;
   (d) Protista;
   (e) Monera

PRACTICE QUIZ

1. The great variety of organisms on earth can best be accounted for by:
   a. several mass extinctions and subsequent creations.
   b. the extinction of different kinds of organisms over a long period of time.
   c. natural selection.
   d. speciation.

2. Which of the following does(do) not supply evidence that evolution has occurred?
   a. fossils
   b. hybrids
   c. succession of organisms through time
   d. homologous structures on different organisms

3. Which of the following is not a tenet of natural selection?
   a. adaptive radiation
   b. variation
   c. overpopulation
   d. struggle for existence

4. Charles Darwin is important because he:
   a. discovered the genetic basis for evolution.
   b. was first to point to the dangers of world overpopulation.
   c. linked variation and natural selection to evolution.
   d. proved that speciation occurred in many birds.

5. Which of the following is an example of a genus?
   a. *Hordeum*
   b. Monera
   c. *vulgaris*
   d. Chordata

6. Natural selection is most accurately defined as:
   a. speciation.
   b. evolution.
   c. differential reproduction.
   d. directed selection.

7. Which of the following undergoes evolution?
   a. a kingdom
   b. an individual
   c. a cell
   d. a population

8. In the phrase "survival of the fittest," the fittest are those individuals that:
   a. live the longest.
   b. leave the most offspring.
   c. are the strongest.
   d. are the most healthy.

9. Speciation has occurred when:
   a. populations of one species become geographically isolated from each other.
   b. populations of two species come together in one area.
   c. populations of one species become reproductively isolated from each other.
   d. all variant individuals within a population die.

10. Which of the following is the taxon with the fewest species in it?
    a. order
    b. kingdom
    c. phylum
    d. class

23

REVIEW QUESTIONS

I. Use the following table to answer the next four questions.

	Individual 1	Individual 2	Individual 3	Individual 4
Phylum	Arthropoda			
Class	Hexapoda			
Order	Hymenoptera	Hymenoptera		
Family	Apidae	Adrenidae	Apidae	
Genus	*Bombus*	*Andrena*	*Apis*	*Bombus*
Species	*fraternus*	*carlini*	*mellifera*	*fervidus*

1. Which two individuals are <u>most</u> similar?
    a. 1 and 2
    b. 2 and 3
    c. 3 and 4
    d. 1 and 4

2. Which two individuals have the <u>fewest</u> similarities?
    a. 1 and 2
    b. 1 and 3
    c. 1 and 4
    d. 3 and 4

3. Which organism(s) belong(s) to the phylum Arthropoda?
    a. 1
    b. 1 and 2
    c. 1, 2, and 3
    d. 1, 2, 3, and 4

4. Which organism(s) belong(s) to the order Hymentoptera?
    a. 1
    b. 1 and 2
    c. 1, 2, and 3
    d. 1, 2, 3, and 4

II. Suppose you excavate and expose the side of a hill. You find five rock layers that are different thicknesses and different colors. Use this information to answer the next four questions.

1. Which of the following assumptions can be made about fossils found in the different layers?
    a. Animals could dig into any layer and become fossilized.
    b. Each layer contains fossils that are older as you go from the top layer to the bottom.

24

        c.   Each layer contains fossils that are younger as you go from the top layer to the bottom.

        d.   Each layer represents a fossil community with the same environment as the community above it.

2. If you found fossils of a lizard almost identical to a species now living on the hill, the best explanation would be that:
   a.   lizards can withstand great changes in the local environment.
   b.   many changes have taken place in the lizard population.
   c.   there were more lizards living in the past than at the present.
   d.   the evolution of this lizard species has been slow.

3. If you found very few fossils of flowers in any of the layers, the best explanation would be that:
   a.   fossils of flowers are difficult to detect in rock.
   b.   soft tissues such as flowers rarely become fossils.
   c.   flowering plants did not evolve until after the top layer of rock had been deposited.
   d.   all flowers had been eaten by the animals in each community.

4. Fossils are:
   a.   usually found only in the top layers of rocks.
   b.   the bodies of extinct organisms.
   c.   remnants or traces of plants and animals of the past.
   d.   our only clue to relationships among different organisms.

III. Consider two populations of fish, and use the following key to answer the next five questions.

       Key: a.   Fish in the two populations have different sized fins and length of stripes along their bodies.
             b.   The two populations live in different isolated ponds.
             c.   The two populations have a common ancestor, based on fossil records.
             d.   The two populations can interbreed and produce fertile offspring.

_____ 1. Which statement in the key provides the best evidence that the fish all belong to one species?

_____ 2. Which statement suggests that the fish are in a situation that favors the evolution of two separate species?

_____ 3. A change in which of the observations in the key would eventually lead to two separate species?

_____ 4. Which observation is the <u>result</u> of adaptive radiation?

_____ 5. Suppose the two populations do become two different species. Which statement then provides information to help us build a phylogenetic tree?

IV. Use the following key to answer the next four questions. Fill in each blank with the most appropriate principle of Darwin's theory of natural selection for each statement.

Key: a.   Individuals of a species show variation in their character-
          istics.
       b.   A struggle for existence results among members of a species.
       c.   Favorable variations are passed on to offspring.
       d.   More offspring are produced than survive.

_____ 1.   Dark peppered moths are more abundant in a polluted forest than in an
           unpolluted forest.

_____ 2.   In a flower show, 16 different varieties of roses were displayed.

_____ 3.   In its lifetime, a female insect may lay 10,000 eggs.

_____ 4.   Out of 400 elm seeds that fall in a small clearing in the forest, 16
           live to become seedlings.

ANSWERS TO CHAPTER EXERCISES

Practice Quiz

1. d   3. a   5. a   7. d   9. c
2. b   4. c   6. c   8. b   10. a

Review Questions

I.   1. d   II. 1. b   III. 1. d   IV. 1. c
     2. a   2. d   2. b   2. a
     3. d   3. b   3. d   3. d
     4. d   4. c   4. a   4. b
                                    5. c

Chapter 3

BIOLOGICAL ORGANIZATION: CELLULAR AND GENETIC STRUCTURE

WHAT'S IN THIS CHAPTER

In this chapter you will learn how living organisms are <u>organized</u>. From the smallest unicellular bacterium to the largest multicellular tree, in all organisms the cell is the basic unit of structure and function. The genetic material within directs the activities of each cell and thus, ultimately, the activities of the entire organism. The directions for cell function come from genes, discrete hereditary factors, and we can determine the possible characteristics of offspring if we know the parents' genetic makeup.

You will see that, although they share the characteristics of cellularity and the genetic material DNA, all organisms can be divided into two large groups. Those that have their genetic material enclosed in a nucleus are called eucaryotes. The more primitive, single-celled organisms that lack a nuclear boundary between cell contents and genetic material are called procaryotes.

All organisms also share the characteristics of movement, growth, metabolism, and reproduction. In this chapter you will be introduced to the two types of reproduction: asexual reproduction, wherein the offspring produced are essentially identical to the one parent involved, and sexual reproduction, wherein two special sex cells (typically sperm and egg) fuse to form a new offspring. Sometimes when organisms reproduce, mistakes are made in the formation of the genetic material that controls the functioning of the cell. You will see that these mistakes, called mutations, may have a positive or negative effect on the organisms that possess them.

By the end of this chapter you should be able to:

1. List several characteristics of living organisms.

2. Name and describe the basic unit of all organisms.

3. Explain the difference between a eucaryote and a procaryote.

4. Explain how sexual and asexual reproduction differ.

5. Define <u>gene</u>, <u>genetics</u>, and <u>genome</u>.

27

6. Describe Mendel's work and its importance.

7. Explain how characteristics are passed on from parents to offspring.

8. List and describe the two main functions of a genome.

9. Explain the relationship between imprecise replication and evolution.

10. Describe both experimentation and editing in terms of evolution.

11. Give an example of a teleological statement and an anthropomorphic statement.

12. Design a test to distinguish genetic effects on the appearance of an organism from environmental effects.

13. Define genotype and phenotype.

Most important of all, you should have a general conceptual model of what an organism is and how it operates. You should be able to relate your whole study of biology to this broad concept.

WHAT YOU SHOULD ALREADY KNOW

In the previous chapter you were introduced to the great diversity of living organisms and the process through which the different species are created. You should know what this process is and understand its importance in the study of biology. This process involves changes in the genetic makeup of a population through time and selective forces that operate on the variation found within the population. Although evolution appears to be directed and purposeful, it is not. You should be able to explain this lack of purposeful direction in terms of natural selection and how all organisms are related through their evolutionary history. In this chapter you will learn about the biological structures that provide this continuity through time.

Pre-Test

1. Genera are placed into categories called phyla, and phyla are placed into taxa called _____.

1. kingdoms

2. All organisms are related through their evolutionary history, or their _____.

2. phylogeny

3. Evolution can be defined as (a)_____ _____. It occurs through the process of (b)_____, the four basic tenets of which are as follows:

(c)_____.

(d)_____.

(e)_____.

(f)_____.

3. (a) the change
in the genetic
makeup of a pop-
ulation through
time; (b) na-
tural slection;
(c) organisms
produce more
offspring than
can survive;
(d) competition
for resources
results; (e)
best-adapted
variants sur-
vive and repro-
duce; (f)
characteristics
that allowed
survivial are
passed on to
offpsring

GUIDED REVIEW OF THE CHAPTER

3-1 The activity in a handful of hay.

1. Organisms are basically _____(alike /
   different) in their fundamental structures and in the ways
   in which they operate.

1. alike

2. If you threw a handful of hay into a jar of water, after a
   few days you would be able to tell that the jar was full

   of living organisms because (a)_____

   _____, (b)_____

   _____, and (c)_____

   _____.

2. (a) the water
develops a
pungent odor;
(b) the water
begins to cloud
up; (c) there
is movement
in the water

3. _____ are "first animals," so named because
   they were once considered the simplest kinds of animals.

3. Protozoans

4. The five kingdoms of life are (a)_____,

(b)_____, (c)_____, (d)_____,

and (e)_____.

4. (a) Plantae;
   (b) Animalia;
   (c) Protista;
   (d) Fungi;
   (e) Monera

5. When organisms increase in size, they are (a)_____

_____(growing / proliferating); when they increase

in number they are (b)_____(growing / proliferating).

5. (a) growing;
   (b) pro-
   liferating

6. The difference between a mixed and a pure culture is that

_____

_____

_____.

6. a mixed culture
   is made up of a
   variety of or-
   ganisms, where-
   as a pure cul-
   ture has only
   one species
   in it

7. A (a)_____ is a substance that an organism
   needs for its growth. Bacteria will grow well in a
   solution of water, salts, and sugar. This solution is

   called a (b)_____, because it is an
   appropriate mixture of nutrients.

7. (a) nutrient;
   (b) nutrient
   medium

8. Describe the multiplication pattern of an organism that
   shows exponential growth.

   (a)_____

   _____

   Another name for exponential growth is (b)_____
   growth. If a bacterium shows exponential growth and
   divides every hour, how many bacteria will you have at the

   end of 24 hours? (c)_____

8. (a) One or-
   ganism grows
   into two,
   these two grow
   into four, the
   four grow into
   eight, and so
   on; (b) geo-
   metric;
   (c)2^{23} cells

3-2 The basic unit of every organism is a cell.

1. The basic unit for every organism is the (a)_____.
   The most prominent structure in the cell is the

   (b)_____.

1. (a) cell;

2. The cells of a plant or a fungus are (a)_____

(b) nucleus (boxlike / irregular) in shape with (b)_____ (thick / thin) walls. A (c)_____ is a mass of similar cells.

2. (a) boxlike; (b) thick; (c) tissue

3. Bacteria and protozoa are unicellular, meaning that (a)_____, but plants and animals are (b)_____, meaning that they are made up of many cells.

3. (a) they are made of just one cell; (b) multicellular

4. Cells grow by increasing in (a)_____ and (b)_____.

4. (a) size; (b) number

5. The difference between sexual and asexual reproduction is that, in sexual reproduction, a (a)_____ and an (b)_____ join to form a zygote.

5. (a) sperm; (b) egg

6. A (a)_____ may be considered the "atom of biology" because (b)_____

_____

_____.

6. (a) cell; (b) it is the smallest piece of matter that carries out all the necessary biological activities

3-3 *There are two major types of cells.*

1. A _____ forms the boundary of every cell, separating the inside from the outside environment.

1. membrane

2. Inside a plant or animal cell you will find a pair of membranes called the (a)_____ that forms the boundary of the nucleus and separates everything inside the nucleus, called the (b)_____ _____, from the rest of the cell, called the (c)_____ _____.

2. (a) nuclear envelope; (b) nucleoplasm; (c) cytoplasm

3. A procaryote is a cell that lacks a (a)_____ _____, an example of which is (b)_____. Non-procaryotes are called (c)_____. Two king-

doms of organisms that belong to this group are (d)_____

_____ and (e)_____.

3. (a) nuclear
   envelope; (b)   *3-4 Information is required to specify biological behavior.*
   a bacterium;
   (c) eucaryotes; 1. A group of cells that is formed from one cell by repeated
   (d and e)
   plants, ani-   division is called a (a)_____. This term also
   mals, fungi,   refers to any collection of multicellular plants that are
   protista
                       derived (b)_____(sexually / asexually).

1. (a) clone;   2. Body cells are called (a)_____ cells. Sperm
   (b) asexually
                      and eggs are called (b)_____ cells.

2. (a) somatic;
   (b) sex or germ *3-5 Heredity is determined by discrete, conserved "factors."*

                   1. The science of heredity is called (a)_____; the

                      "father" of heredity was (b)_____, who

                      worked on (c)_____ plants.

1. (a) genetics;   2. Mendel's work marked a whole new way of thinking about in-
   (b) Gregor   heritance for several reasons, including the following:
   Mendel;
   (c)pea   (a)_____.

                      (b)_____.

                      (c)_____.

2. (a) He studied 3. A purebred strain of plants is one that _____
   only a few char-
   acteristics   _____
   that showed
   only one de-   _____.
   finite form or
   another. (b) He
   studied each
   characteristic
   independently.
   (c) He used
   quantitative
   data and
   statistics to
   study
   inheritance.

3. breeds only   4. When two plants are crossed, hybrids are formed; hybrids
   plants similar
   to itself gene-   are defined as (a)_____

ration after
generation _____. The F_1 generation is the

(b)_____ generation.

4. (a) offspring
that have some
combination of
characteristics
from each
parent; (b)
first hybrid
or filial

5. The law of conservation in genetics states that

_____

_____

_____.

5. hereditary
factors are
conserved from
generation to
generation,
even if their
effects cannot
be seen

6. Every diploid organism carries two hereditary factors for
each characteristic. If these are different from each
other and only one of them is expressed visibly, it is

called the (a)_____ factor; the other, not

expressed, is called the (b)_____ factor.

6. (a) dominant;
(b) recessive

7. A somatic cell has two hereditary factors for each char-

acteristic, whereas a germ cell has (a)_____ (one /
two / four). When germ cells are formed, the hereditary

factors separate or (b)_____ from each other.

7. (a) one;
(b) segregate

3-6 Genes are located on chromosomes.

1. The factors of inheritance are called (a)_____

and are located on the (b)_____ found in

the cell's (c)_____.

1. (a) genes;
(b) chromo-
somes;
(c) nucleus

2. In 1902 Sutton and Boveri inferred that genes were on the

chromosomes because _____

_____.

2. chromosomes
behave exactly
as genes are
supposed to

3. Hämmerling's experiments with *Acetabularia* showed that the

_____ is stored
in the nucleus.

3. genetic infor-
mation for cell
structure

4. When the nucleus is removed from an amoeba, the amoeba

_____.

4. loses its
ability to

33

move and
degenerates

3-7 *An organism operates on the basis of instructions in its genome.*

1. The full set of structures bearing all the genes in an organism is called the _____.

1. genome

2. The two major functions of the genomes are to (a)_____

_____

_____

_____ and to (b)_____.

2. (a) provide
a genetic pro-
gram that
specifies the
structure of
the whole
organism and
how it is to
operate; (b)
inform new
copies of
itself.

3. Replication is _____

_____

_____.

The significance of replication is that (b)_____

_____

_____.

3. (a) the process
in which the
genome makes a
new replica of
itself; (b)
both daughter
cells end up
with genomes
identical to
those of the
parent cell

3-8 *Imprecise replication is the basis for variation and evolution.*

1. Changes in the genome are called (a)_____.
The chance of one of these mistakes occurring in a single gene during one replication is approximately 1 out of

(b)_____. Cite an example wherein one of these mistakes gives the possessor an advantage over other members of its species. (c)_____

_____

_____.

1. (a) mutations;

(b) 10^5 to 10^8;
(c) any muta-
tion that
allows an
organism to
produce more
offspring than
other members
of its species

2. The chief activity of an organism is to _____

_____

_____.

2. synthesize more of its own structure from materials in the environment so that it maintains itself, grows, and reproduces.

3. (a) mutates; (b) best-adapted variants

1. (a) mutation; (b) natural selection

2. recombination

3. (a) survival value; (b) the number of offspring that survive to form the next generation

4. the forces of evolution

5. All biological structures are shaped by processes of mutation and selective editing to perform their functions efficiently.

---

3. The key elements of evolution are: (1) an organism reproduces itself and (a)_____ so that there will be some genetic variation in the population; and (2) in an environment that produces competition, only the (b)_____ survive.

3-9 Organisms are shaped through evolution by a kind of editing process.

1. Evolution occurs through "experimentation." This experimentation occurs through the process of random (a)_____. Evolution operates through a kind of "editing process" known as (b)_____.

2. The genetic process called _____ permits portions of genomes to be arranged in new combinations, producing variations.

3. An organism's fitness is its (a)_____, which is measured by (b)_____ _____.

4. Biological structures have evolved through _____ _____ (a rational, intelligent process / the forces of evolution).

5. What is the Principle of Efficient Design?

   _____

   _____

   _____

3-10 Systems that are following a program appear to be purposive.

1. The difference between the efficient cause and the final cause of an event is that the efficient cause is (a)_____ _____, whereas the final cause is (b)_____.

35

1. (a) the event that is responsible for something happening; (b) the purpose that an action is to serve or the goal for which it is aiming

2. (a) explains the present in terms of the future; (b) casts all things in human form, giving human qualities to objects or lower organisms

3. unacceptable

4. teleonomic

5. (a) strategy; (b) a pattern of behavior or a particular path of evolution

1. (a) sperm; (b) eggs

2. genome

3. (a) Viruses; (b) plasmids; (c) inhabiting the functioning cells of living

2. The difference between a teleological and an anthropomorphic statement is that a teleological statement (a)_____ _____, whereas an anthropomorphic statement (b)_____ _____.

3. Teleological explanations are _____(acceptable / unacceptable) in science.

4. An explanation of apparently purposeful behavior in terms of an evolutionary history is referred to as _____.

5. A consistent course of action that some species follows is known as its (a)_____. An example is (b)_____ _____.

3-11 The genome's view of the world.

1. The two different kinds of germ cells are (a)_____ and (b)_____.

2. The _____(somatic cell/ genome) is really the only thing that is capable of reproducing.

3. (a)_____ and (b)_____ are not organisms but genomes that are like intracellular parasites. They can reproduce themselves only by (c)_____ _____ _____.

3-12 Variation comes from both genetic and environmental sources.

1. Every natural population of organisms is _____

organisms, where they find all the apparatus necessary to reproduce themselves. (variable / uniform).

1. variable

2. A normal distribution curve is shaped like a (a)_____, showing that most of the organisms cluster around the average or (b)_____. The (c)_____ _____ of the distribution curve are described by the variance of the population. If all the organisms in a population were exactly alike, the variance would be (d)_____.

2. (a) bell;
   (b) mean;
   (c) width and shape;
   (d) zero

3. The two sources of variability in a population are
   (a)_____ and
   (b)_____.

3. (a) differences in the genomes of the organisms; (b) environmentally caused differences

4. The characteristics that are observed in an organism are called its (a)_____; the information coded in its genome is called its (b)_____.

4. (a) phenotype;
   (b) genotype

5. The phenotype of an organism is determined in part by the (a)_____ of the organism and in part by (b)_____. The (c)_____ _____ is the range of possible phenotypes that may be expressed in a particular environment.

5. (a) genotype;
   (b) environmental influence;
   (c) norm of reaction

6. Natural selection operates only on those variances that _____ (have a genetic basis / are environmentally induced).

6. have a genetic basis

PRACTICE QUIZ

1. Which of the following is <u>not</u> a characteristic of all living organisms?
   a. growth
   b. movement

37

c. multicellularity

d. reproduction

2. Which of the following is <u>not</u> found in a cell?
   a. tissue
   b. nucleus
   c. plasma membrane
   d. cytoplasm

3. Which of the following <u>best</u> describes a procaryotic cell?
   a. lacks DNA
   b. lacks a nuclear membrane
   c. lacks a cell wall
   d. less than 1 μm in diameter

4. Which of the following is <u>directly</u> involved in sexual reproduction?
   a. somatic cell
   b. daughter cell
   c. clone
   d. egg

5. Select the <u>best</u> definition of the word "gene."
   a. the science of heredity
   b. a pattern of inheritance characteristic of all sexually reproducing animals
   c. a factor of inheritance
   d. the sum of all the genetic information of an organism

6. Which of the following statements about the way characteristics are inherited is <u>not</u> true?
   a. Hereditary factors are conserved from generation to generation.
   b. Plants and animals carry at least two hereditary factors for each characteristic.
   c. The dominant characteristic is better than the recessive.
   d. Hereditary factors for one characteristic segregate from each other during the formation of germ cells.

7. The primary function of the genome is to:
   a. inform the structure of an organism.
   b. segregate independently.
   c. eliminate recessive characteristics.
   d. mutate.

8. _____ is a mutation.
   a. A recessive characteristic
   b. A change in the genome
   c. An infertile organism
   d. A hybrid

9. Which of the following is a teleological statement?
   a. The horse was frightened by the lightning.
   b. The small plant grows toward the light.
   c. Female salmon swim upstream in order to lay their eggs.
   d. The boy climbed up the tree.

10. The phenotype of an organism is:
    a. the sum of all its genetic information.

b. the width and shape of its distribution curve.
c. the characteristics observed in it.
d. its selfish gene.

REVIEW QUESTIONS

I. Fill in the blanks with the appropriate characteristics of procaryotes and eucaryotes.

	Procaryotes	Eucaryotes
Presence or absence of an organized nucleus		
Approximate diameter of cells		
Primitive or advanced		
Multicellular, uni-cellular, or both		

II. Indicate whether each of the following statements is <u>True</u> or <u>False</u>.

_____ 1. A cell has more chromosomes than genes.

_____ 2. A recessive characteristic never benefits the organism possessing it.

_____ 3. Characteristics that do not appear in the F_1 generation but do appear in the F_2 generation must be recessive.

_____ 4. A sperm cell has the same number of chromosomes as does a somatic cell.

_____ 5. The nucleus contains the genome in eucaryotes.

III. Correct those of the following statements that are either teleological or anthropomorphic.

1. A seedling grows tall quickly to reach the sunlight before other seedlings.

_____

2. Birds build their nests above ground to avoid predators prowling on the

ground. _____

_____

39

3. A seed remains in a dormant state until the appropriate rainfall and temperature conditions come about. _____

_____

4. Genes are selfish because their only interest is in survival and replication. _____

_____

IV. Briefly explain how a population of short, mature plants could be derived from a population made up of mostly tall individuals.

_____

_____

_____

ANSWERS TO CHAPTER EXERCISES

Practice Quiz

1. c	3. b	5. c	7. a	9. c
2. a	4. d	6. c	8. b	10. c

Review Questions

I.

Procaryotes	Eucaryotes
absence	presence
1 μm	10 – 30 μm
primitive	advanced
unicellular	both

II. 1. False   2. False   3. True   4. False   5. True

III. 1. A seedling that grows tall quickly reaches the sunlight before other seedlings.
2. Birds that build their nests above ground escape predators prowling on the ground.
3. No change is required.

4. Genes may be considered "selfish" because only the genome reproduces itself.

IV. Suppose a selective agent such as a lawn mower or a grazing animal were introduced into the area where the plants were growing. Tall plants would be moved down or eaten first, leaving only shorter plants. These shorter plants would reproduce; the taller ones would not. Thus, in the next generation, you would expect to find many more short plants than tall ones at maturity.

Chapter 4

BIOLOGICAL MOLECULES

WHAT'S IN THIS CHAPTER

Biology requires some understanding of chemistry because organisms are made up of molecules, which are atoms that have been joined by chemical bonds. In this chapter you will be introduced to the chemical concepts necessary for you to understand and appreciate biological systems. You will learn about the important kinds of atoms--the elements--that make up the bodies of all organisms, and how these atoms are arranged and bonded together into the large macromolecules of life.

Water is one of the most important substances necessary for life, and all organisms are mostly bags of water with organic and inorganic compounds making up and filling up the bag. Carbon, hydrogen, oxygen, and nitrogen are the most important elements in organic compounds of living organisms, and they (with a few other elements) are combined into large numbers of small, similar monomers. These monomers are then combined into complex polymers with distinctive shapes: proteins, nucleic acids, and polysaccharides. The shapes of complex polymers determine their function, which may include controlling the body's chemical reactions, carrying the genetic information, or serving as an energy-storage unit.

You may come to appreciate the amazingly consistent production of complex structures that works perfectly most of the time. However, occasional errors in nucleic acid structure create mutations that can have dramatic effects on the function of other polymers. You will see that, though often deleterious, these mutations are the stuff that evolution is made of.

By the end of this chapter you should be able to:

1. Describe an atom.

2. Define noble gas and explain why atoms that are like noble gas atoms are quite stable.

3. Name and describe two different types of chemical bonds.

4. Differentiate between an atom, an ion, and a molecule.

5. Compare an acid to a base.

42

6. Distinguish between a chemical reaction and a physical process.

7. List three characteristics of water that make it important to life.

8. Compare macronutrients to micronutrients.

9. Explain how shape is important to the functioning of a molecule.

10. Name the three important macromolecules of life and their subunits.

11. Explain how information can be stored in the length of a DNA molecule.

12. Define <u>mutation</u> and tell how it is related to evolution.

WHAT YOU SHOULD ALREADY KNOW

In the previous chapter you learned about the basic units of all living organisms and the internal structures necessary for the units' proper function. Information to construct these units and their internal parts and to direct their function comes from a large, special organic molecule. This same information is passed on to an organism's offspring, usually in a precise manner. However, occasional mistakes occur. You learned that these mistakes can be deleterious or may give the possessor an advantage over other members of its species. You were introduced to the idea that the selection of positive variants is the basis of evolution.

Pre-Test

1. The basic unit of every organism is the (a)_____.
    The most prominent internal structure of this unit is the

    (b)_____, which houses the material of heredity

    called (c)_____.

1. (a) cell;
    (b) nucleus;
    (c) DNA

2. The science of heredity is called (a)_____ and

    the factors of inheritance are called (b)_____.

2. (a) genetics;
    (b) genes

3. The small changes in the genetic material are called

    (a)_____ and they are important because

    (b)_____.

3. (a) mutations;
    (b) they pro-
    vide variation
    for evolution

43

GUIDED REVIEW OF THE CHAPTER

Introduction

1. Organic compounds are compounds that are made up of the elements (a)_____ and (b)_____. Many organic compounds are huge molecules called (c)_____, which are made by stringing together many small molecules called (d)_____.

1. (a) hydrogen;
   (b) carbon;
   (c) polymers;
   (d) monomers

4-1 A chemistry lesson in four molecules.

1. Each atom has equal numbers of positively charged particles called (a)_____ in its (b)_____ and negatively charged particles called (c)_____ in its orbitals.

1. (a) protons;
   (b) nucleus;
   (c) electrons

2. There can be no more than (a)_____ (one / two) electrons per orbital. Each electron must go into the (b)_____(lowest-energy / highest-energy) orbital available.

2. (a) two;
   (b) lowest-
   energy

3. Atoms have a special stability if their orbitals (a)_____ _____(are filled / have only single electrons in them). A noble gas is (b)_____ _____ _____ _____.

3. (a) are filled;
   (b) an element
   that has no
   tendency to
   combine with
   other elements
   because its
   orbitals are
   filled with
   electrons at
   a certain
   energy level

4. What is the difference between an atom and a molecule? _____ _____

4. A molecule is
   a structure

5. Carbon atoms have six electrons. This means that the

44

made up of two or more atoms and held together with chemical bonds.

lowest-energy orbital is (a)_____(empty / full) and that in the next highest-energy orbitals there are (b)_____(two / four) electrons. A carbon atom therefore requires (c)_____ additional electrons to make it stable like a noble gas atom.

5. (a) full;
   (b) four;
   (c) four

6. The chemical bond involving the sharing of an electron between two atoms is called a (a)_____ bond. The molecules held together by such bonds are relatively (b)_____(stable / unstable).

6. (a) covalent;
   (b) stable

7. The atomic number of nitrogen is 7. This means that a nitrogen atom has (a)_____(one more / one less) electron than a neutral atom. It also means that the nitrogen atom needs to gain (b)_____ electrons to become like a noble gas atom.

7. (a) one more;
   (b) three

8. A water molecule is (a)_____(more / less) polar than a hydrogen gas molecule. A polar bond is (b)_____

_____

_____.

Water molecules have the form of (c)_____: structures with positive and negative charges short distances apart. This is because the oxygen atom attracts electrons more strongly than do the hydrogen atoms and is therefore more (d)_____ than the hydrogens.

_____

8. (a) more;
   (b) a bond in which there is an unequal distribution of charge along its length;
   (c) dipoles;
   (d) negative

_____

_____.

9. a weak bond formed by a hydrogen atom being held between two more negative atoms

10. An atom or molecule that has a positive or negative charge is called an (a)_____. When a molecule dissociates, it (b)_____.

10. (a) ion;
    (b) splits to

11. An (a)_____ is a compound that releases hydrogen

form two or
more ions

ions in solution. A (b)_____ is any compound
that can combine with a hydrogen ion.

11. (a) acid;
    (b) base

12. An atom that tends to lose electrons becomes a positive

ion or (a)_____. An atom that tends to gain

electrons becomes a negative ion or (b)_____.

12. (a) cation;
    (b) anion

13. Cations and anions combine to make _____ with a
balance of positive and negative charges, such as NaCl,
KI, and NaF.

13. salts

4-2 Atoms are rearranged in chemical reactions.

1. Heating   and   cooling   are   (a)_____   processes
because they change the property of a material without

changing its composition.   A   (b)_____   process
is a process in which one material is changed into quite
different materials.

1. (a) physical;
   (b) chemical

2. A (a)_____ is 6×10^{23} molecules of a particular
kind, which is also a number of grams equal to the

(b)_____ weight of the molecules.

2. (a) mole;
   (b) molecular

3. It is important in biology that molecules and ions dis-

solve in water so that _____

_____.

3. chemical
   reactions can
   take place

4. It is important to living organisms in lakes that ice

floats because _____

_____.

4. life can con-
   tinue in liquid
   water under the
   ice in winter

4-5 Organisms are composed of a small group of elements.

1. The four elements that make up over 90% of a living
organism and are components of organic molecules are

(a)_____, (b)_____,

(c)_____, and (d)_____.

1. (a) nitrogen;
   (b) oxygen;
   (c) hydrogen;
   (d) carbon

2. (a)_____ are elements required by an organism
in abundance of 1,000 to 100,000 parts per million.

Three examples of these elements are (b)_____,

(c)_____, and (d)_____.

2. (a) Macronu-
trients;
(b, c and d)
calcium, iron,
phosphorus,
potassium,
nitrogen

3. (a) Micronu-
trients;
(b and c)
zinc, copper
cobalt, nickel

1. (a) hydro-
carbon;
(b) saturated

2. aromatic

3. (a)_____ are those elements required in the range of 1 to 1,000 parts per million. Two examples of these are (b)_____ and (c)_____.

4-6 Organisms are built of organic molecules with distinctive shapes.

1. Methane is a (a)_____, a molecule made up of only carbon and hydrogen. Such a compound that contains as many hydrogen atoms as possible is referred to as (b)_____.

2. An _____ compound is one that has molecules with a flat ring shape.

4-7 Hydrophilic and hydrophobic molecules have very different properties.

1. Polar molecules dissolve in water. These molecules that "love water" are said to be (a)_____. Nonpolar molecules do not dissolve in water. These molecules that "fear" water are said to be (b)_____. Charged particles, like ions, dissolve in water because of (c)____

_____.

1. (a) hydro-
philic; (b)
hydrophobic;
(c) the
attractive
forces between
ions and the
water dipoles

2. van der Waals
forces

2. Oil molecules form droplets in water that are held together by weak interactive forces called _____

_____.

4-8 Different molecules may be made with different arrangements of groups.

1. Two molecules made with different arrangements of the same atoms are called (a)_____. (b)_____ are two molecules that have the same atoms arranged differently in space. (c)_____ are molecules that are mirror images of each other. A binding site is said to be (d)_____ if it interacts differently with different stereoisomers.

47

1. (a) isomers;
(b) Stereo-
isomers; (c)
Enantiomers;
(d) stereo-
specific

4-9 Biological materials are primarily macromolecules.

1. All cells contain a fraction called (a)_____, which can be extracted from the cell by using hydrophobic organic solvent. One type of these compounds is primarily made of (b)_____, which are hydro-carbon chains with a carboxyl group at one end. These molecules are combined with a (c)_____ molecule, which is a triple alcohol. These compounds are found in animals, where they are important in (d)_____ _____ and (e)_____. A related molecule is a (f)_____, in which a phosphate has re-placed one fatty acid. These make up a large part of the structure qf (g)_____.

1. (a) lipids;
(b) fatty
acids; (c)
glycerol;
(d) energy
storage; (e)
insulation;
(f) phospho-
lipid;
(g) membranes

2. Most of the cell is made of very large molecules called (a)_____. There are three basic types of these large molecules: (b)_____, (c)_____ and (d)_____.

2. (a) macro-
molecules; (b)
polysaccha-
rides; (c)
nucleic acids;
(d) protein

3. The macromolecule that contains most of the cell's phosphate is the (a)_____. The macro-molecule that contains most of the cell's sulfur is the (b)_____.

3. (a) nucleic
acid;
(b) protein

4. Cytosol is _____ _____.

4. a solution
of ions,
proteins, and
small organic
molecules that
fills most of
the cell.

4-10 Macromolecules are polymers.

1. All macromolecules are (a)_____, made by joining many similar or identical small molecules called (b)_____ _____.

1. (a) polymers;
(b) monomers

2. All proteins break down into the same assortment of small molecules called (a)_____. These small molecules are joined together in a polypeptide by

the removal of water molecules in (b)_____
reactions. When subjected to hot acid, the protein is
broken as water is added back to each residue in

(c)_____ reactions.

2. (a) amino
   acids; (b)
   condensation;
   (c) hydrolysis

3. Plastics are (a)_____ because each of them is
   made from many identical monomers. A biological example

   of a homopolymer is (b)_____, which is made
   up of many glucose molecules linked one to another. Pro-

   teins are (c)_____ because each is made from
   20 different kinds of amino acids.

3. (a) homopoly-
   mers; (b)
   starch or gly-
   cogen or cellu-
   lose; (c) het-
   eropolymers

4. DNA and RNA are both (a)_____, made

   up of monomers called (b)_____. Each of these

   monomers is made of three smaller units: (c)_____,

   (d)_____ and (e)_____.

4. (a) nucleic
   acids; (b)
   nucleotides;
   (c) sugar;
   (d) base;
   (e) phosphate

4-11 Proteins are heteropolymers of 20 types of amino acids.

1. Proteins and nucleic acids are (a)_____ because
   their monomers are not all identical. Amino acids differ

   from each other in their (b)_____.
   The specific sequence of amino acids is called the

   (c)_____ of the protein.

1. (a) hetero-
   polymers; (b)
   side chains;
   (c) primary
   structure

4-12 Proteins have basically helical structures.

1. Proteins have two basic shapes. They are either a long,

   thin (a)_____ protein used primarily for struc-

   ture or a compact, rounded (b)_____ protein
   that is used mainly for chemical activity. Proteins are
   frequently coiled into a helical form, a shape known as

   the protein's (c)_____.

1. (a) fibrous;
   (b) globular;
   (c) secondary
   structure

2. A protein is held in shape by many interactions between
   its side chains. Its three-dimensional shape is known

   as the _____structure of the protein.

2. tertiary

4-13 The primary structure of a protein determines its three-
dimensional shape.

1. Once the proper sequence of amino acids has been made, a

49

protein folds up (a)_____(spontaneously / with added energy). If the shape of a protein has been severely changed by salt or acid treatment, it has been (b)_____. This causes the protein to (c)_____(increase / lose) its biological activity.

1. (a) spontaneously;
   (b) denatured;
   (c) lose

4-14 *Polypeptides associate to make larger protein structures.*

1. Proteins commonly bind to one another to make larger structures whose shape is described as their _____ _____ structure.

1. quaternary

4-15 *Polymeric structure provides a simple mechanism for obtaining variety.*

1. If there are 20 different kinds of amino acids, how many different ways can they be assembled to make chains 4 amino acids long? (a)_____. A typical protein is a chain of a few (b)_____(hundred / dozen) amino acids.

1. (a) 160,000;
   (b) hundred

2. Linkages between monomers are generally all _____ (identical / different) in heteropolymers.

2. identical

4-16 *Polymeric structure provides information storage and retrieval.*

1. The sequence of nucleotides in the DNA forms a coded message that specifies the sequence of (a)_____ _____ to be laid down in a protein. Each DNA molecule can be divided functionally into shorter sequences called (b)_____, which are regions of the DNA that specify the structure of one polypeptide.

1. (a) amino
   acids;
   (b) genes

4-17 *Polymeric structure permits the subtle changes of evolution.*

1. The typical mutation changes (a)_____(one / many) amino acid(s) in one type of protein. The gene for human (b)_____ can have a mutation that causes sickle-cell anemia.

1. (a) one;
   (b) hemoglobin

PRACTICE QUIZ

1. An atom is:
   a. any molecule with equal numbers of electrons and protons.
   b. a noble gas.
   c. held together with a covalent bond.
   d. the smallest particle of an element.

2. Which of the following statements about noble gases is true?
   a. Hydrogen is a noble gas.
   b. Noble gases combine easily with other elements.
   c. Noble gas atoms do not easily form bonds with other atoms.
   d. Noble gases have one electron in the highest-energy orbital.

3. Which of the following is <u>not</u> an important type of chemical bond?
   a. voltaic
   b. ionic
   c. hydrogen
   d. covalent

4. Which of the following statements is true of acids and bases?
   a. Any molecule that dissociates is an acid.
   b. An acid releases hydrogen ions.
   c. A base reacts with noble gases.
   d. Acids tend to combine with hydrogen ions.

5. Which of the following properties makes water an important substance for life?
   a. Water freezes
   b. Water changes temperature quickly.
   c. Water is made of hydrogen and oxygen.
   d. Many materials dissolve in water.

6. Which of the following statements about the nutritional requirements of organisms is true?
   a. Most organisms can live without micronutrients.
   b. Carbon, hydrogen, oxygen, and nitrogen are the most important elements.
   c. Macronutrients are required in amounts of 1 to 1,000 parts per million.
   d. Sodium, magnesium, and potassium are trace elements.

7. Which of the following statements about organic molecules and their shape is <u>not</u> true?
   a. Hydrophobic and hydrophilic forces help determine a molecule's shape.
   b. Amino acid chains fold spontaneously into their functional shape.
   c. Isomers may react differently to a stereospecific binding site.
   d. Nucleotides come together spontaneously to form nucleic acids.

8. Which of the following is an important macromolecule of living organisms?
   a. nucleic acid
   b. amino acid
   c. fatty acid
   d. aspartic acid

51

9. Which of the following statements about DNA is <u>not</u> true?
   a. DNA informs the structure of a cell.
   b. Nucleotides are the subunits of DNA.
   c. Genes in DNA code for the formation of proteins.
   d. Hundreds of different nucleotides are necessary to code for all the different proteins.

10. Which of the following statements about mutations and evolution is true?
    a. Most mutations result in dramatic changes in the appearance of an organism.
    b. A mutation is the change in the amino acid sequence of a protein.
    c. Mutations cannot be inherited.
    d. Mutations provide variation for evolution.

REVIEW QUESTIONS

I. Use the following key to answer the next seven questions about macromolecules of living organisms.

        Key: a. protein
              b. nucleic acid
              c. starch
              d. a and b only
              e. a, b, and c

_____ 1. A heteropolymer

_____ 2. The subunits are nucleotides.

_____ 3. Contains carbon

_____ 4. Contains genetic information

_____ 5. Glycogen, starch, and cellulose are examples.

_____ 6. An organic molecule

_____ 7. Contains most of the cell's nitrogen

II. Use the following key, which gives qualities of water that are important to life, to answer the next eight questions. For each phenomenon listed, indicate the most appropriate quality of water.

        Key: a. ice floats
              b. excellent solvent
              c. high specific heat
              d. high heat of vaporization
              e. high heat of fusion

_____ 1. Evaporating water has a cooling effect.

_____ 2. Air temperatures change gradually from fall to winter.

_____ 3. Photosynthesis by pond algae takes place during the winter in Michigan.

_____ 4. Organic materials required for life move from cell to cell in an organism.

_____ 5. Water freezes at lower temperatures than organic solvents.

_____ 6. Trout live in high mountain lakes.

_____ 7. Ions are insulated by layers of water molecules.

_____ 8. Chemical reactions take place primarily between dissolved materials.

III. If the characteristic on the left pertains to the item listed at the top, place an X in the appropriate box.

	Atom	Electron	Ion	Molecule
Found in an orbital.				
Has or may have a negative charge.				
A bond may form between two of them.				
An example is water (H_2O).				
A particle with equal numbers of postive and negative charges.				
Contains protons.				

ANSWERS TO CHAPTER EXERCISES

Practice Quiz

1. d		3. a		5. d		7. d		9. d	
2. c		4. b		6. b		8. a		10. d	

Review Questions

I. 1. d   2. b   3. e   4. b   5. c   6. e   7. a

II. 1. d   2. c   3. a   4. b   5. e   6. a, e   7. b   8. b

III.

	Atom	Electron	Ion	Molecule
Found in an orbital.		X		
Has or may have a negative charge.	X	X	X	X
A bond may form between two of them.	X		X	X
An example is water (H_2O).				X
A particle with equal numbers of postive and negative charges.	X			
Contains protons.	X		X	X

Chapter 5

ENERGY AND THE ECOSYSTEM

WHAT'S IN THIS CHAPTER

In this chapter the energetic foundation of biology will be discussed. Energy is the ability to do work, and therefore all organisms must have energy to live. Also, all organisms live within communities, assemblages of different species, and they are tied together in energy pathways involving producers and consumers. Although the use of energy within the individual organism will be discussed in detail in other chapters, the foundations of all energy-related reactions will be outlined here. You will see that all communities are based on the activites of green plants, which are autotrophs that convert sunlight into useful chemical energy. These plants are eaten by consumers and much of the energy is passed through the community via food chains. However, because all systems tend to become disordered and because the transfer of energy from one organism to another is not efficient, much energy is lost to heat and waste. You should be able to follow the path of energy through the community, all the way to the decomposers, the organisms of decay. Although this path is not always easy to map, the chemical reactions involved are predictable. As energy is passed from organism to organism and from one state into another, there are reactions that give off energy and some that require energy. But these reactions can be coupled together to drive the energy-requiring reactions. You will learn that building a living organism out of inorganic materials requires energy and that in order to be useful to organisms, the stored energy in organic materials must be released slowly. All this requires series of chemical reactions, the bases of which will be dealt with here.

By the end of this chapter you should be able to:

1. Define what a community is and describe one example.

2. Describe the functions of producers, consumers, and decomposers in a community.

3. Compare potential, kinetic, chemical, and heat energy, and explain how they relate to biological molecules.

4. Define and explain the first and second laws of thermodynamics and outline their importance in biological systems.

5. Distinguish between endergonic and exergonic reactions and describe their occurrence in nature.

6. Define <u>entropy</u> and explain how it relates to a biological system.

7. Describe what coupling is and how it is used in biological systems.

8. Describe the relationship between the sun, plants, and communities.

9. Compare autotrophic and heterotrophic organisms, describing their positions in a food chain and the flow of chemical energy through a community.

10. Trace the development of the modern concept of respiration.

11. Describe the carbon cycle in terms of photosynthesis and respiration.

12. Give an example of an oxidation reaction and a reduction reaction and describe their importance to biological systems.

WHAT YOU ALREADY KNOW

In the previous chapter, you were introduced to the principles of chemistry that are important to biological systems. In this chapter you will employ that chemical background while learning about energy use by organisms living in ecosystems around the world. You should have gained an appreciation for and an understanding of the chemical structure of living things and the similarity of molecules from one organism to the next. Organisms are <u>organized</u> atoms, and energy is required to put them together. You should be able to describe an atom, how atoms are put together, and the kind of chemical reactions involved in these syntheses.

Pre-Test

1. Organisms are made up of approximately (a)_____ different kinds of elements. Most of the mass of or-

ganisms is (b)_____; the rest consists of

(c)_____ compounds, which are made of carbon

and (d)_____.

1. (a) 30;
   (b) water;
   (c) organic;
   (d) hydrogen

2. An atom is defined as the (a)_____

_____. Noble

gases are (b)_____

_____. Most elements tend to combine so that, by gaining or losing electrons, their atoms achieve

a condition similar to that of the (c)_____.

2. (a) smallest
   unit of an
   element with an

3. Two characteristics of water that make it important to

life are that it (a)_____

55

equal number of
protons and
electrons; (b)
stable elements
with no tendency
to combine with
other elements
to make com-
pounds;
(c) noble gases

3. (a) is close
to a universal
solvent; (b)
has a high
specific heat

4. The three most important macromolecules of life are

(a)_____, (b)_____ and

(c)_____.

4. (a) nucleic
acids; (b)
proteins; (c)
polysaccharides

GUIDED REVIEW OF THE CHAPTER

Introduction

1. In the school of thought called _____, it was
believed that life transcended the principles of physics
and chemistry.

1. vitalism

2. In 1828, Wöhler synthesized the organic compound urea from
inorganic material, ammonium cyanate. This was important

because _____

_____.

2. it demonstrated
that no myster-
ious gap sepa-
rated the two
realms of
matter

3. The principle of parsimony states that _____

_____

_____.

3. complex, ob-
scure explana-
tions should
not be used
if simpler
explanations
are satis-
factory

5-1 All organisms live in communities.

1. Populations of different organisms that live together and

interact create a (a)_____. Such a group of

organisms runs on (b)_____, which the group
gets from the surrounding physical environment--mainly

from the (c)_____.

1. (a) community;
   (b) energy;
   (c) sun

2. (a) a community plus its physical environment;
   (b) a pond;
   (c) a forest
   (See the text for other examples.)

3. (a) producers;
   (b) consumers;
   (d) decomposers

1. the ability to do work.

2. (a) potential;
   (b) kinetic;
   (c) can

3. (a) remains constant;
   (b) are interconvertible in atomic reactions

4. (a) energy can be transformed from one state to another but not created or destroyed;
   (b) the entropy of an isolated

---

2. An ecosystem is (a)_____

   _____. Two examples of an ecosystem are

   (b)_____ and (c)_____.

3. Use the words <u>consumers</u>, <u>decomposers</u>, and <u>producers</u> to fill in the next three blanks. Green plants are

   (a)_____ that bring energy into the ecosystem

   by capturing sunlight. Animals are (b)_____, passing energy one to another as they eat. Molds and

   bacteria are (c)_____, decaying and reducing dead organisms to simpler materials.

5-2 Energy can be transformed, but not created or destroyed.

1. Energy can be defined as _____

2. Two important types of energy are (a)_____ energy, which is the energy an object has by virtue of its

   position, and (b)_____ energy, which is the energy of an object in motion. One type of energy

   (c)_____(can / cannot) be transformed into the other type.

3. The total energy in a closed system (a)_____

   _____(remains constant / decreases with time).

   Mass and energy (b)_____

   _____(are interconvertible in atomic reactions / cannot be interconverted).

4. The first law of thermodynamics is that (a)_____

   _____.

   The second law of thermodynamics is that (b)_____

   _____.

5. Name five different forms of energy. (a)_____,

   (b)_____, (c)_____, (d)_____,

   (e)_____, and (f)_____.

57

system tends to
increase

5. (a) kinetic;
   (b) potential;
   (c) heat;
   (d) sound;
   (e) electro-
   magnetic;
   (f) chemical

6. A calorie is _____

_____.

6. the amount of
   energy required
   to raise the
   temperature of
   1 gram of water
   1 degree C.

7. An object raised above the ground (a)_____(gains / loses) potential energy as it gets higher. When an object

falls, (b)_____ energy is converted into

(c)_____ energy. When an object hits the ground, kinetic energy is converted into the energy of

(d)_____ and (e)_____.

7. (a) gains;
   (b) potential;
   (c) kinetic;
   (d) heat;
   (e) sound

8. _____ is the kinetic energy of molecules in random motion.

5-3 Chemical reactions entail changes in energy.

8. Heat

1. The natural tendency of matter is to go from a position of

(a)_____(higher / lower) potential energy to

a position of (b)_____(lower / higher) potential energy.

1. (a) higher;
   (b) lower

2. In an (a)_____(endothermic / exothermic) reaction, energy is released. An opposite process, called

an (b)_____ reaction, requires that energy be put into the system.

2. (a) exothermic;
   (b) endothermic

5-4 All systems tend to become more disordered.

1. Entropy is (a)_____

_____.

A living organism has relatvely (b)_____(high / low) entropy.

1. the tendency
   for things to
   become dis-
   ordered;
   (b) low

2. In a spontaneous process, free energy will (a)_____ (increase / decrease). A compound with a high free energy

can perform (b)_____(a great deal of / only a little) work.

2. (a) decrease;

3. Entropy (a)_____(increases / decreases) as

(b) a great
deal of

ice melts. As ice melts many (b)_____ bonds
are broken.

3. (a) increases;
(b) hydrogen

5-5 *Endergonic processes can be driven by coupling to exer-gonic processes.*

1. The process of making biological material from nonbio-

logical material is (a)_____(endergonic /

exergonic). Free energy must be (b)_____(put
in / taken out) to make an organism grow.

1. (a) endergonic;
(b) put in

2. When an organism grows, it appears to violate the laws of
thermodynamics. Two explanations for this false appearance

are that (a)_____

and that (b)_____

_____.

2. (a) the second
law applies only
to an isolated
system;
(b) within an
isolated system
it is only the
<u>sum</u> of all pro-
cesses that
must be
exergonic

3. Two different processes can occur together if the two re-

actions are (a)_____--where the energy
release from one reaction is used to drive an energy-
requiring reaction. This linking of reactions can occur

only if the reactions share (b)_____

_____. The reaction linking two others is called a

(c)_____ reaction, because some
atoms are transferred from one molecule to another.

3. (a) coupled;
(b) some chem-
ical component;
(c) group
transfer

4. The most important carrier of a phosphoryl group is a

nucleotide called _____.

4. ATP

5-6 *Ecosystems operate on a flow of energy that comes from the sun.*

1. The pigment that gives plants their green color is called

(a)_____. Green plants use this pigment in

the process of (b)_____, or light-driven

synthesis, where light is important because (c)_____

_____

_____

_____.

59

1. (a) chloro-
phyll; (b) pho-
tosynthesis;
(c) its energy
is used to
drive chemical
reactions in
which organic
molecules are
formed

2. There are two main types of organisms. Some make their own organic compounds and are called (a)_____, and some live on organic compounds already made by some other organisms and are called (b)_____.

2. (a) autotrophs;
(b) hetero-
trophs

3. Use these four terms to fill in the blanks: Photo-autotrophs, Chemoautotrophs, Chemoheterotrophs, Photoheterotrophs. (a)_____ use light and carbon dioxide to make their own organic compounds.

(b)_____ extract structural material from organic compounds and their energy from light. (c)_____ use carbon dioxide, with inorganic compounds as a source of energy. (d)_____ extract energy and structural material from organic compounds.

3. (a) Photo-
autotrophs;
(b) Photo-
heterotrophs;
(c) Chemo-
autotrophs;
(d) Chemo-
heterotrophs

4. Consumers that eat a mixture of plants and animals are called (a)_____. In an ecosystem, a series of organisms that eat one another is called a (b)_____, but such organisms actually form a complicated tangle of feeding relationships called a (c)_____.

4. (a) omnivores;
(b) food chain;
(c) food web

5. A biosphere is _____
_____.

5. all of the
ecosystems
taken
together

6. Energy taken in by an organism may follow several pathways. Three different pathways that energy may follow are: (a)_____ (b)_____, and (c)_____.

6. (a) loss as
waste heat;
(b) conversion
into the or-

7. If you have 10,000 grams of plant material, approximately how many grams of carnivores will this be able to support?

_____(1,000 / 100 / 10 / 1)

ganism's struc-
ture; (c) use
to maintain
the organism

7. 100

8. (a) consumer;
   (b) producer

1. respiration

2. (a) Priestley;
   (b) phlogiston

3. (a) Lavoisier;
   (b) oxygen

4. (a) De
   Saussure;
   (b) carbon
   dioxide

5. combustion

6. $C_6H_{12}O_6$ +
   $6O_2$ ---> $6CO_2$ +
   $6H_2O$

7. (a) photo-
   synthesis;
   (b) respiration

8. A bird can be a (a)_____(consumer / decomposer),

   but it can never be a(an) (b)_____(omnivore /
   producer).

5-7 The biosphere operates on cycles of reactions.

1. In the process called _____, energy stored by
   phototrophs is used.

2. In 1771, (a)_____ studied respiration of animals.

   He believed in the material (b)_____, which
   was supposed to be a kind of material ingredient of fire
   and to be produced by living animals.

3. (a)_____ showed that the gas named

   (b)_____ was removed from the air during
   respiration and replaced by carbon dioxide.

4. (a)_____ demonstrated that, as plants grow,

   they incorporate the gas (b)_____
   into their bodies.

5. According to the experiments of Lavoisier and de Laplace,
   respiration is just a slow form of another process called

   _____.

6. Using the following molecules, write a balanced equation
   for respiration: CO_2, O_2, H_2O, $C_6H_{12}O_6$.

   _____

7. The two main processes involved in the carbon cycle are

   (a)_____ and (b)_____.

8. The difference between cellular respiration and breathing
   is that cellular respiration is (a)_____

   _____

   _____,

61

whereas breathing is (b)_____

_____.

8. (a) the complex series of re- actions in which carbon compounds are combined with oxygen to make CO_2 and to release stored energy, (b) the physi- cal intake of oxygen in the air

9. In the carbon cycle, energy from the (a)_____

is captured in the organic molecule (b)_____

via the process called (c)_____.

5-8 Useful energy can be obtained from oxidative reactions.

1. A substance is (a)_____ when electrons are re-

moved from it, and it is (b)_____ when electrons

are added to it. In combination, the two reactions in

which electrons are added or removed are called (c)_____

9. (a) sun; (b) glucose; (c) photo- synthesis

_____. An atom or molecule that picks up an electron

is called the (d)_____ agent, whereas one that

loses an electron is called the (e)_____ agent.

1. (a) oxidized; (b) reduced; (c) oxidoreduc- tion; (d) oxidizing; (e) reducing

2. What is the oxidation state of carbon in each of the

following molecules? (a) CH_4 _____; (b) $C_6H_{12}O_6$ _____;

(c) CO_2 _____; (d) HCN _____

2. (a) -4; (b) 0; (c) +4; (d) +2

3. The process of building biological structure is intrinsic-

ally a process of _____(oxidation / reduction).

3. reduction

4. Every cell contains structures in which minute (a)_____

_____ are created as electrons flow from

one point to another. In respiration, electrons flow from

a reduced compound, usually (b)_____, to an

oxidizing agent, (c)_____. In photosynthesis,

electrons flow from (d)_____ that has gained
extra energy by absorbing light. In both processes,
electron flow is directed through reactions that store

some energy in the form of (e)_____.

4. (a) electric currents; (b) sugar; (c) oxy- gen; (d) chloro- phyll; (e) ATP

PRACTICE QUIZ

1. A community:
    a. is primarily made of consumers.
    b. is a group of populations living and interacting together in one area.
    c. obtains most of its energy from the action of decomposers.
    d. has more consumers than producers.

2. The <u>primary</u> function of a decomposer is to:
    a. reduce dead organisms back to simpler materials.
    b. capture sunlight and produce sugars.
    c. eat both plants and animals.
    d. pass energy from one trophic level to the next.

3. Which of the following has the <u>greatest</u> chemical energy?
    a. a molecule of carbon dioxide
    b. a molecule of oxygen gas
    c. a molecule of water
    d. a molecule of sugar

4. Which of the following is an example of the first law of thermodynamics?
    a. An organism increases in entropy after death.
    b. Heat is given off by an organism after death.
    c. Decomposers return nutrients to the soil.
    d. Light energy is converted to stored chemical energy in photosynthesis.

5. Which of the following statements about endergonic and exergonic reactions is <u>not</u> true?
    a. Exergonic reactions occur spontaneously in nature.
    b. Living organisms require a number of endergonic reactions.
    c. Endergonic reactions release energy upon completion.
    d. Molecules with stored chemical energy are formed through endergonic reactions.

6. Entropy:
    a. increases after an organism dies.
    b. decreases after an organism dies.
    c. increases through endothermic reactions.
    d. decreases as kinetic energy is lost by an organism.

7. Coupling links:
    a. potential and kinetic energy reactions.
    b. ions to molecules.
    c. exergonic and endergonic reactions.
    d. photosynthesis and respiration.

8. In a community you may find that 500 grams of plant material will support only 50 grams of herbivore. The <u>least</u> acceptable explanation for this is that:
    a. much of the food energy taken in by the herbivores is used up in maintenance reactions.
    b. much of the food taken in cannot be digested.
    c. much of the food energy taken in is wasted as heat energy.
    d. additional energy may be brought into the ecosystem from outside.

9. _____ is <u>not</u> an important part of the carbon cycle.
    a. Photosynthesis
    b. Phlogiston

63

c. Respiration

d. Glucose

10. Which of the following involves a reduction in carbon?

a. $C_6H_{12}O_6 \longrightarrow CO_2$

b. $CO_2 \longrightarrow C_6H_{12}O_6$

c. $CH_4 \longrightarrow CO_2$

d. $CH_4 \longrightarrow C_2H_4$

REVIEW QUESTIONS

I.

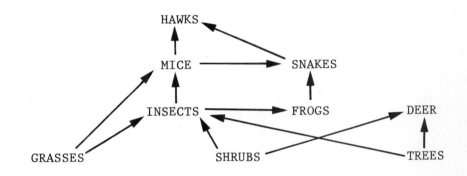

1. This diagram best illustrates a:
   a. carbon cycle.
   b. food chain.
   c. food web.
   d. biosphere.

2. In the diagram, which of the following are herbivores?
   a. grasses
   b. deer
   c. frogs
   d. hawks

3. In the diagram, which of the following are carnivores?
   a. deer
   b. insects
   c. trees
   d. mice

4. In the diagram, which of the following are omnivores?
   a. deer
   b. insects
   c. frogs
   d. mice

5. In the diagram, which group would have the greatest total biomass?
   a. grasses
   b. mice
   c. snakes
   d. hawks

6. Grasses, trees, and shrubs are <u>most</u> important in supplying _____ for the community.
   a. seeds
   b. shelter
   c. nests
   d. energy

7. In this community, which of the following would you expect to find in the <u>smallest</u> number?
   a. grasses
   b. frogs
   c. mice
   d. hawks

II.

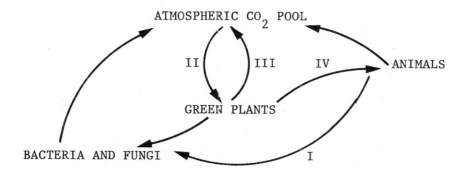

First, consider this question: There is a certain amount of plant biomass, but only a small part (say, 10-20%) ever becomes animal biomass. To what chemical form is the other 80%-90% converted? Now, assuming that most plant material becomes food for animals, rather than simply decaying, you should be able to answer the following mutliple-choice questions.

1. In the carbon cycle shown in the diagram, which of the following is responsible for returning the most carbon dioxide back to the atmospheric pool?
   a. bacteria and fungi
   b. sunlight
   c. green plants
   d. animals

2. In this carbon cycle, _____ use(s) the most carbon dioxide.
   a. bacteria and fungi
   b. sunlight
   c. green plants
   d. animals

3. Which one of the arrows represents decomposition?
   a. I
   b. II
   c. III
   d. IV

4. Which one of the arrows represents photosynthesis?
   a. I
   b. II

          c. III
          d. IV

     5. Which one of the arrows represents respiration?
          a. I
          b. II
          c. III
          d. IV

III. Use the following key to answer the next four questions about what happens to
energy in a forest community.

          Key: I.   Energy is brought into the community.
                II.   Energy leaves the community.
               III.   Energy goes to the next higher level in the food web.
                IV.   Energy goes to decomposers.

     1. Photosynthesis involves which energy pathway?
          a. I
          b. II
          c. III
          d. IV

     2. A tree dies. What happens to the energy stored in its body?
          a. I
          b. II
          c. III
          d. IV

     3. Which pathway represents a food chain?
          a. I
          b. II
          c. III
          d. IV

     4. A deer runs through a forest. Which pathway represents the route of
         energy?
          a. I
          b. II
          c. III
          d. IV

ANSWERS TO CHAPTER EXERCISES

Practice Quiz

1. b   3. d   5. c   7. c   9. b
2. a   4. d   6. a   8. d   10. b

Review Questions

  I.   1. c   3. d   5. a   7. d
       2. b   4. d   6. d

II. 1. d   2. c   3. a   4. b   5. c
     (To answer the questions you were asked to consider 80-90% of plant biomass as
     converted to CO_2 and water.)

III. 1. a   2. d   3. c   4. b

Chapter 6

ENZYMES AND THE ORGANIZATION OF METABOLISM

WHAT'S IN THIS CHAPTER

In this chapter you will learn about the importance of proteins to the functioning of individual cells and organisms. Organisms are made up of organic molecules, and they grow because they can transform these molecules through metabolic pathways, some of which are for the manufacture, or biosynthesis, of metabolites and others of which are for their degradation (catabolism). These pathways are all controlled by special proteins called enzymes, which catalyze a wide range of chemical reactions by lowering activation energies. Enzyme function will be discussed in this chapter.

You will see that the shapes of all proteins, including enzymes, are essential to their proper functioning. They interact with other molecules, which also have specific shapes, including other proteins as well as all kinds of small molecules called ligands. (A ligand is not a special type of chemical--it is just the name we give to molecules when they are interacting with proteins, as we will describe here). Proteins can do many things with ligands, including the whole range of things that organisms must do to stay alive (the main exception being those things that the genome itself does). For instance, proteins can recognize the existence of ligands, so they serve as sensory devices to tell organisms that these particular molecules are present. This is what happens when you smell or taste some substance, but even simple bacteria have the ability to detect molecules in this way. Proteins can transport ligands across cell membranes, so they can get in or out of cells. And proteins are used in a variety of ways to maintain a kind of internal balance, both in single cells and in multi- cellular organisms. This balancing act involves the inflow and outflow of materials and the detection of, and protection from, threats to the cells and larger organisms.

By the end of this chapter you should be able to:

1. List the three major phases of an organism's metabolism.

2. Describe an enzyme and explain how it functions.

3. Explain the importance of enzyme and substrate shape to their interaction.

4. Name three ways in which enzymes can be separated from a cell extract and thereby identified.

68

5. Explain the function of coenzymes and activators.

6. Define <u>homeostasis</u> and explain how feedback and feedahead mechanisms operate to maintain a steady-state condition.

7. Explain parataxis and allostery.

8. Describe the action of a drug.

9. Differentiate between chemotaxis, chemoreception, and chemosensing.

10. Name and describe three important paratactic interactions in living organisms.

11. Name four signal ligands and tell what their actions are.

WHAT YOU SHOULD ALREADY KNOW

In the last chapter you learned the importance of energy to an individual organism, how organisms get their energy, and how organisms are tied together in communities by their energy requirements. In this chapter we will see how the organic materials of living organisms are put together. Because energy is required for this process, before you proceed with this chapter you should understand what energy is and what forms it comes in (Chapter 5). As energy is taken in by an organism, used by an organism, or passed on, it may be transformed in a variety of chemical reactions, but it can never be created or destroyed (Section 5-2). Also recall the kinds of interactions between organisms involving energy flow and the kinds of chemical reactions on which these interactions are based.

Pre-Test

1. Every organism lives in a community, which is (a)_____

    _____

    _____. Those memebers of the community that bring energy into the system by capturing sunlight are

    called (b)_____. (c)_____ are fungi and bacteria, which decay and reduce dead organisms to

    simpler materials. (d)_____ are all the other organisms that pass energy from one to another as they eat.

1. (a) a group of populations of different organisms that live together and interact; (b) producers; (c) Decomposers; (d) Consumers

2. The first law of thermodynamics states that (a)_____

    _____

    _____. The second law of thermodynamics

    states that (b)_____

    _____.

2. (a) energy can be transformed from one state to another but it cannot be created or destroyed; (b) the entropy of an isolated system tends to increase.

3. The difference between an exergonic reaction and an endergonic reaction is that, in an exergonic reaction, (a)_____, whereas in an endergonic reaction, (b)_____ _____.

3. (a) energy comes out in the form of heat; (b) energy is required for its completion

4. In organisms, energy-requiring reactions can be linked to energy-yielding reactions in a process called (a)_____ _____. This is important to living organisms because (b)_____ _____ _____.

4. (a) coupling; (b) many of the reactions needed to make an organism require energy, which can be obtained only by coupling

5. Useful energy can be obtained from oxidative reactions in which highly (a)_____(reduced / oxidized) molecules are (b)_____(reduced / oxidized).

5. (a) reduced; (b) oxidized

GUIDED REVIEW OF THE CHAPTER

Introduction

1. An organism's metabolism involves three main processes: synthesizing (a)_____, polymerizing (b)_____ _____ in the right sequence to form (c)_____, and obtaining enough (d)_____ to carry out these metabolic reactions.

1. (a) monomers; (b) monomers; (c) polymers; (d) energy

2. The metabolism of a heterotroph consists of three main phases: organic molecules are broken down in the process of (a)_____, small molecules are rearranged and

70

built up to make monomers in the process of (b)_____

_____ or (c)_____, and monomers are put

together in the process of (d)_____.

2. (a) catabolism;
(b) biosyn-
thesis; (c)
anabolism; (d)
polymerization

6-1 Catalysts increase the rates of chemical reactions.

1. The amount of free energy lost in a reaction is (a)_____

_____(important / not important) in determining

reaction rate. Activation energy is (b)_____

_____.

1. (a) not
important;
(b) the energy
barrier im-
peding a chemi-
cal reaction.

2. Chemical reactions occur when molecules (a)_____
with each other. Name the three ways in which it is
possible to make a reaction occur faster.

(b)_____

(c)_____

(d)_____

2. (a) collide;
(b) Increase
reactant con-
centration.
(c) Heat the
reactants so
molecules
acquire greater
kinetic energy.
(d) Add a
catalyst.

3. A (a)_____ is a substance that speeds up a
chemical reaction but is not consumed in the process.
Each cell has many such substances that are proteins

called (b)_____. These special proteins are

highly specific; each operates on one type of (c)_____

_____.

3. (a) catalyst;
(b) enzymes;
(c) substrate

*6-2 Organisms construct themselves through enzyme-catalyzed
pathways.*

1. Metabolism is organized into streams of chemical activity

known as (a)_____. Materials

moving through such a stream are (b_____.

1. (a) metabolic
pathways;
(b) metabolites

2. Each reaction in a pathway is catalyzed by _____
(one / several) enzyme(s).

2. one

3. An enzyme can work on only one kind of substrate molecule

because (a)_____

71

_____

_____.

An enzyme has a crevice called an (b)_____
into which a substrate can fit.

3. (a) the sub-   4. An enzyme is a powerful catalyst because it does two
   trate has a
   certain shape,   things at once. It holds (a)_____
   and the enzyme
   has a comple-   _____; and brings in (b)_____
   mentary crevice
   into which the   _____
   substrate can
   fit; (b) active   _____.
   site

4. (a) substrate   5. The active site of an enzyme changes its shape because the
   molecules in
   just the right   substrate _____ the enzyme to fit around
   orientation;
   (b) other chem-   it.
   ical groups
   that give them
   the energy
   needed to cross
   the activation
   barrier

5. induces   6. An intracellular pool is _____

                          _____.

6. the collection   7. What is the difference between metabolite pools in
   of all the
   molecules of a   procaryotic cells and in eucaryotic cells? _____
   given kind in-
   side a cell at   _____
   any instant
                          _____

                          _____.

7. In a procaryote,
   the different   *6-3 Every enzyme is a distinct protein.*
   metabolite
   pools are all   1. All (a)_____(enzymes / proteins) are (b)_____
   mixed together;
   in a eucaryotic   _____(enzymes / proteins), but not all (c)_____
   cell many pools
   are restricted   _____(enzymes / proteins) are (d)_____
   to special
   parts of the   (enzymes / proteins).
   cell by
   membranes.

1. (a) enzymes;
   (b) proteins;
   (c) proteins;
   (d) enzymes

2. (a) -in;
   (b) -ase

3. (a) how much
   of some mate-
   rials is pre-
   sent in a
   sample; (b)
   chemical re-
   action; (c)
   Determine
   whether the
   cell extract,
   when added to
   a reaction
   mixture, makes
   a particular
   reaction go
   faster. The
   faster the rate
   of reaction,
   the greater the
   enzyme activity.

4. (a) spectro-
   photometer;
   (b) Substrates
   and products
   may absorb a
   particular
   wavelength of
   light differ-
   ently. By com-
   paring the
   amount of light
   entering the
   sample with the
   amount leaving

2. The names of proteins generally end in (a)_____,

   whereas the names of enzymes generally end in (b)_____.

3. An assay is a method of determining (a)_____

   _____. An enzyme assay

   is a method of determining whether a (b)_____

   _____ is occurring. How can you tell whether an

   extract has a particular enzyme in it? (c)_____

   _____

   _____

   _____

4. A useful tool in an assay is the (a)_____,
   which is an instrument that creates a beam of monochro-
   matic light. Explain how this instrument measures the

   amount of material being sampled. (b)_____

   _____

   _____

   _____

   _____

5. If identical samples of a purified enzyme are mixed with
   increasing concentrations of substrate, the rate of the

   resulting reaction increases (a)_____
   (indefinitely / up to a point). The K_m is a measure of

   the (b)_____, and it

   is the concentration of substrate at which (c)_____

   _____.

73

it, the spec-
trophotometer
determines how
much light is
absorbed, which
is proportional
to the amount
of light-
absorbing
material.

5. (a) up to a
point;
(b) affinity
of an enzyme
for its sub-
strate; (c)
the velocity
of the reac-
tion is half
the maximum
velocity

6. To determine what the components of a cell are, we must
(a)_____ them, or divide them into more
homogeneous fractions. A (b)_____ is a
batch of cells that have been ground up and mixed with a
salt solution. Two methods of separating cellular components from each other are (c)_____, which
is based on the principle that large things fall faster
than small things in a liquid, and (d)_____,
which is based on the fact that different proteins have
different electrical charges.

6. (a) fraction-
ate; (b) cell
extract;
(c) centrifuga-
tion; (d) elec-
trophoresis

7. A typical cell probably requires on the order of _____
(100 / 1,000 / 10,000) different types of enzymes to
function properly.

7. 1,000

6-4 *Many enzymes operate with coenzymes.*

1. A common procedure used to purify enzymes is (a)_____
_____, where a partially purified cell extract is placed
in a thin plastic sac. During this procedure the enzyme
may lose its activity, but the enzyme function returns
when (b)_____
_____.

1. (a) dialysis;
(b) the small
molecules of
the cell ex-
tract are
added back to
the enzyme

2. Coenzymes are (a)_____
_____. An example of a coenzyme
is (b)_____. Heavy metal atoms are often
partners in enzyme activity and are called (c)_____
_____. Many enzymes have coenzymelike groups
attached so strongly that they can't diffuse away. These
groups are called (d)_____.

2. (a) small

74

nonprotein
molecules
essential for
enzymatic
activity;
(b) ATP or
some vitamins;
(c) activators;
(d) prosthetic
groups

1. remains rela-
tively constant

2. the flow of
materials
through an
organism is
balanced, so
that the con-
centrations of
all materials
remain essen-
tially constant

3. (a) internal;
(b) are power-
less to supply

4. the relatively
stable state in
which each
organism main-
tains itself

5. (a) feedback;
(b) feedahead;
(c) for feed-
back, a thermo-
stat linked to
a heater;
(d) for feeda-
head, a reflex
reaction to an
impending
danger

*6-5 Organisms maintain themselves in steady-state conditions
through homeostatic mechanisms.*

1. The inside of an organism _____

_____(remains relatively constant / changes
with changes in the outside environment).

2. Every organism is in a steady state, meaning that _____

_____

_____

_____.

3. In the words of the physiologist Claude Bernard, all cells

of a multicellular organism live within an (a)_____

_____ environment. The individual cells of a multi-

cellular organism (b)_____
(are powerless to supply / supply) all their own nutrients
needed for survival.

4. Homeostasis is _____

_____.

5. Control mechanisms may operate through either (a)_____

_____ or (b)_____ loops. An example

of the former is (c)_____. An

example of the latter is (d)_____

_____.

*6-6 Protein-ligand interactions are essential for biological
activities.*

1. Many proteins are paratactic to other molecules, meaning

that they (a)_____

_____. Such proteins have a highly
specific binding site where a small molecule called a

75

(b)_____ can fit.

1. (a) recognize
a ligand that
can fit into
the binding
site of the
protein;
(b) ligand

2. Proteins are flexible, going through (a)_____

from one shape or (b)_____ to another shape.
In parataxis, the protein has two shapes: one shape

before the ligand binds to it, called the (c)_____ _____

_____, and one shape after the ligand binds

to it, called the (d)_____.

2. (a) transi-
tions; (b)
conformation;
(c) relaxed
conformation
(d) tense
conformation

3. An enzyme may have two different binding sites, one for

its (a)_____ and a second site for a

ligand called an (b)_____, which controls
the activity of the enzyme. The second ligand may be an

(c)_____, which makes the active site of the
enzyme have little catalytic activity, or it may be an

(d)_____, which enhances the activity of the

enzyme. In (e)_____, a paratactic interaction at one site affects another interaction at a
different site.

3. (a) substrate;
(b) effector;
(c) inhibitor;
(d) activator;
(e) allostery

4. What is a domino-effect transition? _____

_____

_____

_____.

4. In some mem-
branes, several
proteins lie
next to one
another, one
of which is
paratactic to
some ligand.
When one pro-
tein shifts in-
to its T confor-
mation, it has
a similar
effect on a
neighboring
protein.

6-7 Drugs and inhibitors are "unnatural" ligands.

1. A (a)_____ is an "unnatural" ligand that
binds to a protein with a binding site paratactic to a
variety of similar molecules. Many of these substances

are known as (b)_____, because they stop
competing organisms from growing in their presence and
are effective in combatting the causes of infectious

diseases. Such substances may be produced by (c)_____

_____ and (d)_____.

1. (a) drug;
(b) antibio-
tics;

2. A competitive inhibitor is _____

_____

76

(c) fungi;
(d) bacteria

2. a substance that competes with the natural substrate of an enzyme for the active site and inhibits the enzyme's catalytic action

3. (a)_____ is the science of drug action.

Drugs fall into two general categories: (b)_____ are drugs that mimic the effect of a natural ligand, and

(c)_____ are drugs that block the natural effect.

6-8 Many cells can recognize and respond to external ligands.

1. Bacteria move through water by means of hairlike extensions called _____.

3. (a) Pharmacology;
(b) Agonists;
(c) antagonists

1. flagella

2. A (a)_____ is any object or change in the environment that an organism recognizes and responds to. The movement in response to a chemical stimulus is called

(b)_____. You can tell that a bacterial cell is swimming in the direction of a positive stimulus

because (c)_____

_____.

2. (a) stimulus;
(b) chemotaxis;
(c) it will swim in one direction for a long distance without changing direction

3. Sensory systems in bacteria are based on the activity of two distinct proteins: a (a)_____, which has an external site that is paratactic to one kind of

molecule, and a (b)_____, which directs the movements of the organism after receiving information about the ligand from the first protein.

3. (a) chemoreceptor;
(b) chemosensor

6-9 Three important paratactic interactions.

1. (a)_____ involves the movement of materials from one place to another in or out of a cell across its membranes. Protein flexibility accounts for

this process, because a ligand induces (b)_____

_____.

1. (a) Translocation;
(b) an R-T transition that pushes the

2. Specific regulatory proteins bind to the genome. These

proteins have two binding sites, one for (a)_____

_____ and one for (b)_____

77

ligand in the
right direction.   _____.

2. (a) the attach-   3. Birds and mammals can make special proteins called
ment site on
the genome;   (a)_____, whose binding sites are para-
(b) a ligand
that induces an   tactic to foreign materials known as (b)_____,
allosteric
change that   especially to two types of organic molecules: (c)_____
determines
which genetic   _____ and (d)_____. These special
messages can
be read   proteins are part of the (e)_____,
                         which is a homeostatic mechanism that provides a defense
                         against disease-causing agents.

3. (a) anti-
bodies;   *6-10 Protein-protein interactions are responsible for the for-*
(b) antigens;   *mation of biological structures.*
(c) proteins;
(d) polysaccha-   1. The region where two proteins bind to each other is called
rides; (e)
immune system   (a)_____. The proteins are held

                         together by complementary groups called (b)_____

                         _____. An example of proteins bound together through

                         identical bonding sets is (c)_____,
                         and an example of a structure that is formed when proteins

                         are bound through different bonding sets is (d)_____

                         _____.

1. (a) domain of
bonding; (b)   *6-11 Signal ligands are used for communication at several*
bonding sets;   *levels.*
(c) some
enzymes, or   1. The most basic medium of communication is (a)_____,
hemoglobin;   and all this type of communication is grouped under the
(d) a sheet
or helix   heading of (b)_____.

1. (a) chemical;   2. _____ are ligands that are
(b) chemore-   not catabolized but are important in carrying a specific
ception   signal from one place to another.

2. Signal ligands   3. A (a)_____ is a signal ligand that is pro-
                         duced by one type of cell in a multicellular organism and
                         promotes a specific response by other types of cells. A

                         (b)_____ is a signal ligand passed between
                         individuals of a single species. An example of such a

                         signal ligand is one that operates (c)_____

_____

_____.

3. (a) hormone;
   (b) pheromone;
   (c) to cause
   individuals of
   a species to
   come together
   as a group; or
   to help males
   and females of
   a species find
   and recognize
   each other and
   to induce
   mating between
   them

4. **There are at least two different intracellular signal ligands called (a)_____ that set off alarms inside bacterial cells whenever certain threatening conditions arise. One signals (b)_____ _____, and the other signals (c)_____ _____.**

4. (a) alarmones;
   (b) exhaustion
   of an energy
   source; (c)
   interference
   with protein
   synthesis

5. **(a)_____ are signal ligands that are produced by individuals of one species and have a detrimental effect on individuals of other species. One example of this is an (b)_____. (c)_____ _____ are signal ligands that are beneficial to the individual that detects them but not to the one that produces them.**

5. (a) Allomones;
   (b) antibiotic;
   (c) Kairomones

6-12 Putting it together: a perspective on the cell.

1. **A typical cell is measured in (a)_____ (µm / mm/ cm). A typical procaryotic cell is a cylinder about (b)_____ _____ in diameter by (c)_____ in length.**

1. (a) µm; (b)
   1/2 - 1 µm;
   (c) 1-4 µm

2. **A plasma membrane is a sheet made primarily of (a)_____ _____ molecules with many embedded (b)_____ molecules.**

2. (a) lipid;
   (b) protein

3. **The cell is largely filled with a viscous (a)_____ which is mostly (b)_____ with dissolved ions, proteins, and many small organic molecules. In this viscous part of the cell are many little balls of protein and ribonucleic acid called (c)_____, which are factories that manufacture (d)_____.**

3. (a) cytosol;
   (b) water;

4. **The genome of the procaryotic cell is made of a long**

79

(c) ribosomes;   molecule of (a)_____ that is about
(d) proteins
                     (b)_____(5 / 500 / 5,000) times longer than
                     the whole cell.

4. (a) DNA;   5. The main function of internal membranes in eucaryotic
   (b) 500
                     cells is _____.

5. compartmenta-
   lization   *6-13 Biological systems grow exponentially.*

                   1. A fundamental pattern of biological activity is _____

                     _____ growth. Cells grow this way because every
                     new cell mass consists of material that makes more cell
                     mass.

1. exponential

PRACTICE QUIZ

1. Which of the following is <u>not</u> an important chemical process in an organism's
   metabolism?
   a. catabolism of reduced organic compounds
   b. catabolism of inorganic molecules
   c. biosynthesis of monomers
   d. polymerization of monomers into polymers

2. An enzyme is:
   a. a substrate.
   b. the energy of activation of a chemical reaction.
   c. an organic catalyst.
   d. a metabolite.

3. The shape of an enzyme is important to its function because:
   a. only molecules with a certain shape can fit into the enzyme's active
       site.
   b. the enzyme induces the substrate to fit into it.
   c. ligands are large.
   d. a coiled protein provides many active sites.

4. Gel electrophoresis is based on the principle that:
   a. enzymes move faster than other proteins.
   b. larger molecules are pulled along faster than small molecules.
   c. individual proteins combine with starch in distinctive patterns.
   d. different kinds of proteins have different electrical charges.

5. A coenzyme:
   a. promotes dialysis.
   b. is a small, nonprotein organic molecule that complexes with enzymes and
       substrates.
   c. is a protein catalyst that lowers the energy of activation of a chemical
       reaction.
   d. is a heavy metal atom.

80

6. Which of the following is an example of a feedback system?
   a. At the approach of winter, migratory birds fly south.
   b. A chemical released by a male fly attracts female flies to him.
   c. As the temperature rises, the mercury in the thermometer rises.
   d. Products of reaction X cause the enzyme for the reaction to become inactive.

7. Which of the following does <u>not</u> involve a paratactic interaction?
   a. translocation of materials across a membrane
   b. regulation of the genome
   c. recognition and elimination of foreign material
   d. capture of sunlight by chlorophyll molecules

8. A drug could <u>not</u> be considered:
   a. an unnatural ligand.
   b. a product of certain bacteria and fungi.
   c. an enzyme.
   d. a competitive inhibitor.

9. Chemotaxis is:
   a. a movement in response to a chemical.
   b. a protein with an external site that is paratactic to one kind of molecule.
   c. a protein that directs the movements of a flagellum in bacteria.
   d. a protein involved in the movement of materials across a membrane.

10. Which of the following signal ligands is <u>least</u> likely to be found in plants as well as animals?
    a. pheromones
    b. hormones
    c. alarmones
    d. allomones

REVIEW QUESTIONS

I. The following graph shows the activities of two enzymes. Use the key to answer the next five questions.

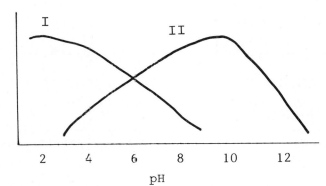

Key: a. Supported by the graph
     b. Refuted by the graph
     c. Unrelated to the graph

_____ 1. Coenzyme X increases the rate of enzyme II.

81

_____ 2. Enzyme activities increase with an increase in pH.

_____ 3. Different enzymes operate in different pH ranges.

_____ 4. The greater the temperature, the greater the enzyme activity.

_____ 5. The activity of enzyme I is greatest in acidic conditions.

II. Consider the following four test tubes containing starch and different substances. Answer the next five questions using the information given in the table.

Tube	Contents	Amount of starch in tube after 1 hour
1	5 gm starch + substance A	3 gm
2	5 gm starch + substance B	5 gm
3	5 gm starch + substances A and B	0 gm
4	5 gm starch + substance A that has been boiled	5 gm

1. Which two tubes provide the best evidence that substance A is an enzyme? _____

2. Substance B could be a(an) _____.

3. Which tube provides evidence that substance B is not an enzyme? _____

4. Which two tubes provide evidence that substance A is necessary for the breakdown of starch? _____

5. Which tube provides evidence that shape is important to the function of substance A? _____

III. Use the following key to answer the next five questions about signal ligands.

Key: a. allomones
     b. alarmones
     c. hormones
     d. kairomones
     e. pheromones

_____ 1. Beneficial to the organism that produces it

_____ 2. Used for sexual activities and aggregation

_____ 3. Internal ligand

_____ 4. Produced by one group of cells and affects another group of cells in an organism

_____ 5. Involves two different species of organisms

ANSWERS TO CHAPTER EXERCISES

Practice Quiz

1. b	3. a	5. b	7. d	9. a
2. c	4. d	6. d	8. c	10. a

Review Questions

I.   1. c   2. b   3. a   4. c   5. a

II. 1. 1 and 4   3. 2   5. 4
     2. coenzyme or activator 4. 2 and 3

III. 1. a, b, c, e   3. b, c   5. a, d
     2. e   4. c

Chapter 7

METABOLISM: RESPIRATION AND CHEMOTROPHY

WHAT'S IN THIS CHAPTER

The business of living involves the maintenance of the body, growth, and
reproduction. All of these require energy, and for most organisms the ultimate
source of that energy is the sun. In the next chapter you will see how green
plants use the energy from the sunlight to produce glucose, but in this chapter you
will see how organisms use this glucose as a source of energy and raw materials.
Energy reactions revolve around the production of ATP, and you will learn what this
molecule is and how it functions in the cell. Growth involves the addition of
materials to the existing body of an organism, so heterotrophs must bring in food
to be broken down and reassembled into new polymers. The five phases of this
process will be outlined, with a particular emphasis on respiration, a set of
catabolic reactions that produces ATP. Although most organisms require oxygen for
respiration, others function without it. You will be introduced to some of the
by-products of such anaerobic processes--beer, wine, cheese--and also to some
unusual bacteria whose respiration is based on inorganic materials.

By the end of this chapter you should be able to:

1. Name the parts of an ATP molecule and explain its importance to living
    systems.

2. Explain the use of nicotinamide-based coenzymes in oxidation-reduction
    reactions

3. List the five phases of heterotrophic metabolism.

4. Define digestion.

5. Describe (in outline) the oxidation of glucose to pyruvic acid.

6. Sketch a mitochondrion and explain its function.

7. Name the products of the Krebs cycle from the oxidation of acetyl groups.

8. Describe how an electron transport system operates, and relate the
    chemiosmotic model to the production of ATP molecules.

9. Explain how acetyl groups can be made into fatty acids, and vice versa.

10. Define fermentation, tell how it differs from aerobic respiration, and name two by-products of fermentation that are useful to humans.

11. Describe how energy-yielding pathways are regulated in the cell.

12. Distinguish between chemoheterotrophy and chemautotrophy.

WHAT YOU SHOULD ALREADY KNOW

This chapter begins the discussion of metabolism and focuses on the ways in which organisms obtain and use energy. Metabolism involves a group of interrelated chemical reactions that are controlled by catalysts called enzymes. You should thus have an understanding of what enzymes are and how they function and of their importance to organisms. An important point is the relation of protein shape to protein function. You should also be able to distinguish between catabolic and biosynthetic reactions and to explain how cells maintain a steady-state condition with all these chemical reactions taking place.

Pre-Test

1. Reduced organic molecules are broken down into smaller molecular fragments via the process called (a)_____. Small molecules are built up and their atoms rearranged to make monomers in the process called (b)_____. In the process called (c)_____, monomers are linked together to build large organic molecules.

1. (a) catabolism;
    (b) anabolism
    or biosynthesis;
    (c) polymeriza-
    tion

2. A catalyst is (a)_____

    _____.

    An enzyme is (b)_____

    _____.

    A coenzyme is (c)_____

    _____.

2. (a) a substance
    that speeds up a
    chemical re-
    action but is
    not consumed in
    the process;
    (b) a biological
    catalyst and a

3. The relatively stable state in which each organism main-tains itself is called _____.

85

special type of
protein; (c) a
small, nonpro-
tein organic
molecule that
is essential for
enzymatic
activity.

3. homeostasis

4. A (a)_____ is a small molecule that can fit into

the binding site of a protein. A protein is (b)_____

_____ to any such small molecule that can fit into

its binding site. Allostery is (c)_____

_____

_____

_____

4. (a) a ligand;
   (b) paratactic;
   (c) the situa-
   tion in which
   a protein has
   two different
   binding sites,
   each paratactic
   to a different
   ligand. The
   binding of a
   ligand to one
   site has a
   specific effect
   on the other
   site.

GUIDED REVIEW OF THE CHAPTER

7-1 Free energy is stored primarily in ATP.

1. Organisms   are   made   of   organic   compounds   that   have

   (a)_____(more / less) free energy than inorganic

   materials   and   are   more   (b)_____(oxidized /
   reduced) than the typical organic materials from which
   organisms construct themselves.

1. (a) more;   2. Autotrophs construct themselves from a (a)_____,
   (b) reduced

(b)_____, and (c)_____.

Heterotrophs use (d)_____ that are changed and reduced to make structural monomers.

2. (a) CO_2; (b) H_2O;
   (c) inorganic materials;
   (d) food polymers

3. Coupling occurs through a (a)_____ process in which some atom or group of atoms is (b)_____ _____.

3. (a) group transfer; (b) passed from one compound to another

4. (a)_____ is the major source of free energy because it can transfer the group (b)_____ easily and does so because it has a (c)_____(high / low) transfer potential.

4. (a) ATP;
   (b)-H_2PO_3;
   (c) high

5. The group transfer potential is _____ _____.

5. the energy released in removing a group by hydrolysis

6. A nucleotide is a monomer of (a)_____. Each nucleotide consists of a (b)_____, a (c)_____, and a (d)_____ _____.

6. (a) nucleic acid; (b) sugar;
   (c) phosphate;
   (d) ring-shaped nitrogenous base

7. Activating a compound means _____ _____.

7. giving the com-compound extra energy

8. Name three activities in which energy of ATP is used.

   (a)_____

   (b)_____

   (c)_____

8. (a) driving biosynthesis reactions; (b) moving; (c) transporting ions across cell membranes

7-2 Nicotinamide nucleotides are used as oxidizing and reducing agents.

1. A compound is reduced when (a)_____ or b)_____ are added to it. Biological oxidations are primarily (c)_____ in which a

87

pair of (d)_____ atoms are removed.

1. (a) hydrogens;
   (b) electrons;
   (c) dehydro-
   genations;
   (d) hydrogen

2. The nicotinamide ring (which animals derive from a (a)_____ vitamin) is important in (b)_____ and (c)_____ reactions.

2. (a) B;
   (b) oxidation;
   (c) reduction

3. An enzyme that catalyzes a reaction in which a hydrogen is removed is called a (a)_____. A reverse reaction, in which reduced nicotinamide can be used as a coenzyme, is catalyzed by an enzyme called a (b)_____.

3. (a) dehydro-
   genase;
   (b) reductase

4. The double nucleotide NAD^+, or (a)_____ _____ is commonly used as a (b)_____ _____ for dehydrogenation in catabolism.

4. (a) nicotin-
   amide adenine
   dinucleotide;
   (b) coenzyme

5. Animals have lost the ability to make the nicotinamide ring, so it must be taken in as part of the diet as a _____.

5. vitamin

7-3 Heterotrophic metabolism consists of five phases.

1. The five major phrases of metabolism are (a)_____, (b)_____, (c)_____, (d)_____ _____, and (e)_____. Catabolism and amphibolic pathways simultaneously provide (f)_____ and (g)_____ for growth.

1. (a) digestion;
   (b) catabolism;
   (c) biosynthesis;
   (d) polymeriza-
   tion; (e) amphi-
   bolic pathways;
   (f) energy; (g)
   raw materials

2. Why doesn't an organism just rearrange the monomers it gets from its food to make up its biological structure?

_____

_____

_____

2. Although some
   monomers from
   food are used,
   there are too
   much of one kind
   and too little
   of others.

3. Respiration is _____

_____

_____

_____

3. the energy-
   yielding process
   in which an
   organic energy
   source (such as
   glucose) is
   oxidized to CO_2,
   generally
   using oxygen as
   a final
   oxidizing agent

4. (a) Glucose is
   broken down into
   small molecules.
   (b) ATP is
   generated by the
   electron trans-
   port system.

5. oxidizing

6. $C_6H_{12}O_6 + 6O_2 +$
   $6H_2O \rightarrow 6CO_2 +$
   $12H_2O$

1. (a) polymers;
   (b) they are
   too large

2. the hydrolysis
   of large food
   polymers into
   monomers

3. (a) osmiotrophs;
   (b) saprobes;
   (c) Holotrophic

4. What are the two main parts of respiration?

   (a)_____

   _____

   (b)_____

   _____

5. In respiration, oxygen is used as the _____
   agent of the electron transport system.

6. The complete summary equation for the respiration of a

   glucose molecule is _____.

7-4 *Polymers must be digested into monomers.*

1. Food consists mainly of polysaccharides, proteins, and

   nucleic acids, which are all (a)_____. These
   food molecules cannot cross a plasma membrane very easily

   because (b)_____.

2. Digestion is _____

   _____.

3. Heterotrophs may be (a)_____ that pick up
   monomers directly through their plasma membranes from
   their environment. Examples of these kinds of organisms

   are (b)_____, or saprophytes, such as molds

   and bacteria. (c)_____ organisms are heterotrophs that pick up whole pieces of food in their digestive cavity.

7-5 *Glucose is oxidized to pyruvic acid.*

1. The two possible fates of glucose, once in the cell, are

   either to be (a)_____

   or to be (b)_____.

89

1. stored as a polysaccharide (if glucose is overabundant); (b) oxidized to release energy

2. The initial reactions in the oxidation of glucose must be activated by (a)_____ . The free energy of glucose is approximately (b)_____(6 / 600 / 6,000) kcal/mole.

2. (a) ATP; (b) 600

3. In the oxidation of each glucose molecule to pyruvic acid, (a)_____ extra ATP molecules are produced. These extra ATP molecules contain about (b)_____(2% / 20% / 60%) of the energy in the glucose molecule.

3. (a) 2; (b) 2%

7-6 *Pyruvate can be oxidized by a crystal of coordinated enzymes.*

1. Each pyruvic acid molecule has (a)_____ carbon atoms. To be converted to a C_2 compound, a (b)_____ must be removed from the pyruvate. The enzyme that catalyzes this reaction is (c)_____.

1. (a) 3; (b) CO_2; (c) pyruvic decarboxylase

2. Pyruvic decarboxylase works first with the coenzyme (a)_____. After a CO_2 moleule has been removed from pyruvate, the remaining C_2 fragment is attached to (b)_____. The C_2 fragment is then attached to the dinucleotide (c)_____.

2. (a) vitamin B_1 or thiamine; (b) lipoic acid; (c) coenzyme A

7-7 *Mitochondria are the principal sites of respiration in eucaryotes.*

1. In (a)_____(procaryotic / eucaryotic) cells, the Krebs cycle and electron transport are confined to the (b)_____, which have been called the powerhouses of the cell.

1. (a) eucaryotic; (b) mitochondria

2. Mitochondria are made of two membranes, and the inner one is folded into (a)_____. Between these folds is the (b)_____ space, which contains all the enzymes of the (c)_____.

2. (a) cristae; (b) matrix; (c) Krebs cycle

7-8 The core of metabolism is a cycle of reactions.

1. Metabolism centers around the _____ or citric acid cycle.

1. Krebs cycle

2. In catabolism, one glucose molecule is first oxidized and split to make two (a)_____ molecules. Each of these loses one CO_2 as it is converted to (b)_____. These are then oxidized to two more (c)_____ molecules in the Krebs cycle.

2. (a) pyruvate;
   (b) acetyl-CoA;
   (c) CO_2

3. The energy of each NADH molecule formed in the Krebs cycle can be used to produce three (a)_____ molecules. As succinate is oxidized to fumarate, electrons are fed directly into the (b)_____.

3. (a) ATP;
   (b) electron transport system

7-9 ATP is synthesized by the electron transport system.

1. In metabolism, sugars, fats, and amino acids can be oxidized to produce reduced (a)_____, primarily $FADH_2$, and (b)_____. These are then used in the synthesis of ATP in the process called (c)_____.

1. (a) coenzymes;
   (b) NADH:
   (c) oxidative phosphorylation

2. An (a)_____ operates on the principle of a bucket brigade, where the buckets are hydrogens or (b)_____.

2. (a) electron transport system;
   (b) electrons

3. The four major compounds that are used in all electron transport systems to carry hydrogens are (a)_____ that are lipid-soluble molecules; (b)_____ that carry a flavin ring; (c)_____ proteins; and (d)_____ that contain a heme group.

3. (a) quinones;
   (b) flavopro-
   teins;
   (c) iron-sulfur
   (d) cytochromes

4. In the electron transport system, oxygen combines with (a)_____ and (b)_____ to form (c)_____, one of the waste products of respiration.

4. (a) hydrogen;

5. All molecules tend to move from a region of (a)_____

91

(b) electrons;
(c) water

(high / low) concentration to a region of (b)_____ (high / low) concentration.

5. (a) high;
(b) low

6. In Mitchell's (a)_____ model of ATP synthesis, an electron transport system creates an unequal distribution of (b)_____ ions across a membrane. The (c)_____ stored in such a distribution is used to do (d)_____.

6. (a) chemiosmotic;
(b) hydrogen;
(c) energy;
(d) useful work

7-10 Acetyl groups can be made into fatty acids...

1. Fat is a better storage material than glycogen because

_____

_____.

1. one gram of fat yields much more energy than one gram of glycogen

2. The reason why fatty acids generally have an even number of carbons is that _____

_____.

2. they are made from acetyl-CoA, which is a 2-carbon fragment

7-11 ... and fatty acids are broken down into acetyl groups.

1. In (a)_____, fatty acids are broken into acetyl-CoA molecules that are then oxidized in the (b)_____ cycle.

1. (a) -oxidation;
(b) Krebs

7-12 Many organisms get their energy through fermentation.

1. Fermentation is _____

_____

_____.

1. incomplete oxidation in which the terminal electron acceptor is an organic compound

2. In fermentation by yeast, pyruvic acid is decarboxylated to produce _____.

2. ethanol

3. Three foods produced as a by-product of a fermentation pathway are _____, _____,

92

_____.

3. cheese, sauer-
   kraut, yogurt,
   dill pickles

4. Without oxygen, in animals glycolysis ends in the **produc-**tion of _____, **which** causes the **burning** feeling of muscle fatigue.

4. lactate

7-13 Many compounds are catabolized into the central pathways.

1. The general mechanisms for the **catabolism** of glucose are _____(different **from** / similar to) those for the catabolism of fats **and amino acids.**

1. similar to

2. The _____(**starting** compounds / end products) of catabolic pathways **are generally** pyruvate and intermediates of the Krebs cycle.

2. end products

3. _____ is an element that animals **get** too much of and must therefore excrete.

3. Nitrogen

7-14 Energy-yielding pathways are regulated by ATP and ADP levels.

1. The major energy-yielding pathways are (a)_____ (inhibited / stimulated) by an excess of ATP and (b)_____ _____(inhibited / stimulated) by an **excess of ADP.**

1. (a) inhibited;
   (b) stimulated

2. The hydrogens on the reducing agents (a)_____ **and** (b)_____ can be used for the production **of ATP** molecules.

2. (a) NADH;
   (b) FADH$_2$

7-15 Some organisms use other types of respiration.

1. Chemoheterotrophs and photoheterotrophs oxidize (a)_____ _____(organic / inorganic) molecules. Chemautotrophs oxidize (b)_____(organic / inorganic) mole-cules; for instance, the thiobacilli oxidize H_2S and S to (c)_____.

1. (a) organic;
   (b) inorganic;
   (c) sulfate

2. The most common terminal electron acceptor is (a)_____ _____. In nitrate respiration of some bacteria, nitrate is used as a (b)_____ _____ and reduced to (c)_____. The greater the potential difference between electron

93

donor and electron acceptor, the more (d)_____
molecules can be made.

2. (a) oxygen;
   (b) terminal
   electron accep-
   tor (c) nitrite;
   (d) ATP

PRACTICE QUIZ

1. Which of the following statements is not true of ATP?
   a. It is a nucleotide.
   b. It has a high group-transfer potential.
   c. It is used to drive exergonic reactions.
   d. It is a major source of free energy for the cell.

2. Nicotinamide is important to living systems because:
   a. it comes from a vitamin.
   b. it is part of two important coenzymes.
   c. ATP is produced as it is oxidized.
   d. no intracellular reduction reactions could take place without it.

3. Which of the following come(s) first in heterotrophic metabolism?
   a. digestion
   b. amphibolic pathways
   c. catabolism
   d. anabolism

4. Digestion is the:
   a. oxidation of glucose to pyruvic acid.
   b. production of ATP molecules from glucose.
   c breakdown of food to its atomic particles.
   d. hydrolysis of polymers into monomers.

5. _____ is not produced in glycolysis.
   a. Pyruvic acid
   b. ATP
   c. Carbon dioxide
   d. NADH

6. A distinctive characteristic of a mitochondrion is that it:
   a. is 0.5 μm wide.
   b. is the site of RNA synthesis.
   c. is the site of ATP production.
   d. contains chlorophyll.

7. _____ is not an important product of the Krebs cycle.
   a. Pyruvate
   b. Acetyl-CoA
   c. NADH
   d. ATP

8. The chemiosmotic model of ATP generation is based on the movement of:
   a. flexible proteins in membranes.
   b. ATP molecules along a transport chain.
   c. hydrogen ions across a membrane.
   d. glucose within a cell.

9. The terminal electron acceptor in fermentation is:
   a. ethyl alcohol.
   b. hydrogen.
   c. oxygen.
   d. an organic molecule.

10. Which of the following is a chemautotroph?
    a. mitochondrion
    b. thiobacillus
    c. green plant
    d. human

REVIEW QUESTIONS

I. Use the following key to answer the next nine questions.

        Key: a. fermentation
                b. cellular respiration
                c. neither a or b
                d. both a and b

_____ 1. The process can occur in the absence of oxygen.

_____ 2. More energy is released than is stored.

_____ 3. Carbon dioxide is (or may be) produced.

_____ 4. Oxygen is produced.

_____ 5. Glucose is produced.

_____ 6. ATP is produced.

_____ 7. Oxygen is used.

_____ 8. Glucose is used.

_____ 9. Alcohol may be produced.

II. Use the following key to answer the next five questions.

        Key: a. the same as
                b. more than
                c. less than

_____ 1. The amount of energy stored in glucose during photosynthesis is _____ the energy released as ATP in respiration.

_____ 2. The amount of energy in ATP is _____ the energy in ADP.

_____ 3. The amount of energy released in fermentation is _____ the energy released in cellular respiration.

_____ 4. The amount of energy stored in an ATP molecule produced in photosynthesis is _____ the energy stored in an ATP molecule produced in respiration.

_____ 5. The amount of energy in an ethyl alcohol molecule is _____ the energy in a glucose molecule.

III. Use the following graph and key to answer the next six questions.

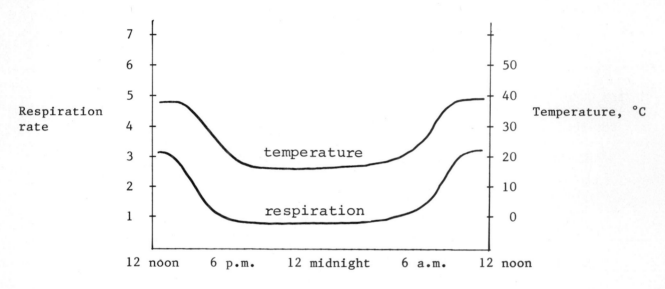

Key: a. reasonable interpretation of data
     b. refuted by data
     c. not enough information to tell

_____ 1. Respiration rate is not affected by temperature.

_____ 2. Respiration rate is greatest at 12 noon.

_____ 3. Respiration does not occur at night.

_____ 4. Respiration rate decreases with increasing weight of the organism.

_____ 5. The respiration rate graphed is one for a plant.

_____ 6. Oxygen use is lowest at midnight.

ANSWERS TO CHAPTER EXERCISES

Practice Quiz

1. c	3. a	5. c	7. a	9. d
2. b	4. d	6. c	8. c	10. b

Review Questions

I.   1. a   3. d   5. c   7. b   9. a
     2. d   4. c   6. d   8. d

II. 1. b   2. b   3. c   4. a   5. c

III. 1. b   3. b   5. c
     2. a   4. c   6. a

Chapter 8

METABOLISM II: PHOTOSYNTHESIS AND BIOSYNTHESIS

WHAT'S IN THIS CHAPTER

In the last chapter we saw how organisms use the chemical energy stored in glucose for their growth.   In this chapter you will learn how photoautotrophs use light energy to produce glucose in the series of chemical reactions called photosynthesis.   Light energy is used to produce ATP and NADPH, which in turn are used to reduce carbon dioxide.   You should become familiar with the light-trapping apparatus, which is made up of chloroplasts and chlorophyll.   You should know how light activates electrons and should be able to follow the path these electrons take as reducing agents are produced, inorganic compounds are reduced, and water is split apart to form oxygen gas.   Most autotrophs reduce carbon dioxide to sugar through a remarkable cyclical set of chemical reactions called the Calvin cycle, but some plants that live in hot, dry habitats have evolved a water-saving alternative pathway of carbon fixation.   Once sugars are produced by a plant, the carbon backbone of the sugars can be used as the basic structure of the other organic materials within the plant, and you will be introduced to the biosynthetic pathways in which these interconversions occur.

By the end of this chapter you should be able to:

1. Tell where photosynthesis occurs in eucaryotic and procaryotic phototrophs.

2. Describe what a chloroplast looks like.

3. Name three light-absorbing pigments and describe what happens when a pigment absorbs a quantum of light.

4. Explain the role of water in photosynthesis.

5. Describe the roles of ATP and NADPH in photosynthesis.

6. Compare cyclic and noncyclic photophosphorylation.

7. List, in order, the series of transformations that carbon dioxide goes through as it is incorporated into organic compounds in the Calvin cycle.

8. Compare C_3 to C_4 photosynthesis and describe the advantages of C_4 metabolism.

9. Define transamination and explain its relationship to biosynthesis, beginning with Krebs-cycle metabolites.

10. Describe a control mechanism of biosynthetic pathways.

11. Explain how polymers are made from activated monomers.

WHAT YOU SHOULD ALREADY KNOW

Chapters 7 and 8 are tied intimately together because, directly or indirectly, almost all living organisms obtain their energy and raw materials for their own bodies from phototrophs. Whereas Chapter 8 reveals the plant processes involved with the production of glucose, Chapter 7 outlines the catabolism of the sugar molecule. Before embarking on this chapter, you should be able to outline heterotrophic metabolism in general and the complete oxidation of glucose. You should know what ATP is and how it is formed in electron transport systems, because this compound is a product of both photosynthesis and respiration. Review the relationship between polymers and monomers. Also review what goes into and what comes out of the Krebs cycle, which plays an important part in the breakdown of organic compounds while simultaneously serving as the center of biosynthesis.

Pre-Test

1. ATP consists of a (a)_____, three (b)_____ _____ and a (c)_____. One of the main

   functions of ATP in a cell is to drive (d)_____ (exergonic / endergonic) reactions. In eucaryotic cells, ATP is formed primarily in the powerhouses called

   (e)_____. Here ATP is synthesized in a series of reactions that is analogous to a bucket brigade and is

   called an (f)_____.

1. (a) sugar;
   (b) phosphates;
   (c) base;
   (d) endergonic;
   (e) mitochondria
   (f) electron
   transport system

2. The five phases of heterotrophic metabolism are (a)_____

   _____, (b)_____, (c)_____,

   (d)_____ and (e)_____.

2. (a) digestion;
   (b) catabolism;
   (c) biosynthesis;
   (d) polymeriza-
   tion; (e) amphi-
   bolic pathways

3. Catabolism of sugar produces many metabolites, some of

   which can be oxidized in the (a)_____ cycle whereas some can be converted to other compounds in

   (b)_____ reactions.

3. (a) Krebs;
   (b) biosynthetic

99

8-1 Photosynthesis in eucaryotes occurs in chloroplasts.

1. The site of photosynthesis in eucaryotes is the (a)_____. In the upper portion of a leaf there may be (b)_____(50 / 500) of these in each cell. In procaryotes, the site of photosynthesis is (c)_____.

1. (a) chloroplast; (b) 50; (c) internal membranes

2. Each chloroplast is surrounded by (a)_____(one / two) membrane(s). Inside are flattened sacs of membrane called (b)_____ with about 20 of these sacs compressed into stacks called (c)_____. These membranes contain the green pigment (d)_____.

2. (a) two; (b) thylakoids; (c) grana; (d) chlorophyll

3. Around the thylakoids is a fluid-filled region called the (a)_____. In this region are enzymes that carry out the (b)_____ reactions of photosynthesis.

3. (a) stroma; (b) light-independent

8-2 Molecules absorb light through activation of their electrons.

1. A green plant reflects _____ light.

1. green

2. Each light wave is a package, or (a)_____, of electromagnetic energy. A short wave of light has (b)_____(more / less) energy than a long wave.

2. (a) quantum; (b) more

3. An electron in an atom moves from one level to another in a (a)_____ jump. The major source of energy for this jump is (b)_____.

3. (a) quantum; (b) light

4. Ultraviolet light waves have (a)_____(more / less) energy than visible light waves. X-radiation has (b)_____(more / less) energy than visible light.

4. (a) more; (b) more

5. An (a)_____ illustrates the amount of light absorbed at each wavelength. Chlorophyll a has a strong peak at (b)_____(red / green) light.

5. (a) absorption
   spectrum;
   (b) red

6. In photosynthesis an electron activated by (a)_____,

   is pulled from a (b)_____ molecule.

6. (a) light;
   (b) chlorophyll

7. If an excited electron is allowed to fall back to its
   original energy level, it may emit a longer wavelength of
   light than it absorbed. This phenomenon is called

   _____.

7. fluorescence

8-3 Chlorophylls are the major light-absorbing pigments.

1. Light that drives photosynthesis is absorbed primarily by

   (a)_____, but (b)_____,
   which are orange pigments, absorb light and then pass
   the energy on.

1. (a) chlorophyll;
   (b) carotenoids

2. All green plants have chlorophylls (a)_____ and (b)_____.
   Phototrophic bacteria have special chlorophylls called

   (c)_____.

2. (a) a; (b) b;
   (c) bacterio-
   chlorophyll

3. All plant pigments have alternating (a)_____ and

   (b)_____ bonds between their carbon atoms. The

   electrons are delocalized, meaning that they (c)_____

   _____

   _____.

3. (a) single;
   (b) double;
   (c) reside in a
   single orbital
   that extends
   over a large
   part of the
   molecule

4. An (a)_____ spectrum will illustrate what
   colors of light are absorbed by a compound such as chloro-

   phyll, whereas an (b)_____ spectrum illustrates the rate of photosynthesis with light of each
   wavelength.

4. (a) absorption;
   (b) action

5. In autumn the leaves of certain trees turn billiant

   orange, yellow, and red. This is due to the (a)_____

   _____ and (b)_____ pigments that had

   been masked by the pigment (c)_____ while the
   leaves were still alive.

5. (a) carotenoid;
   (b) xanthophyll;
   (c) chlorophyll

101

8-4 Photosynthesis requires a reducing agent, which is generally water.

1. Before 1890, people believed that the oxygen evolved during photosynthesis came from the molecule (a)_____

   _____. Today we know that this oxygen

   comes from (b)_____.

1. (a) carbon dioxide; (b) water

2. Purple sulfur bacteria carry out photosynthesis by oxidizing reduced sulfur compounds, such as (a)_____,

   to (b)_____.

2. (a) sulfide; (b) sulfate and sulfur

3. There are several kinds of photosynthesis that share the feature of using (a)_____ to split some reduced

   compound H_2X. After H_2X is split, the X becomes (b)_____

   _____, while the H atoms combine with (c)_____

   _____ to make a (d)_____.

3. (a) light; (b) waste; (c) carbon dioxide; (d) carbohydrate

4. The equation for green plant photosynthesis is as follows:

   _____

4. $6CO_2 + 6H_2O ->$

   $C_6H_{12}O_6 + 6O_2$

5. Sometimes water is written on both sides of the equation

   in photosynthesis. This is because _____

   _____.

5. it tells us that water is split by light to provide a reducing agent

6. Hill demonstrated that isolated chloroplasts would produce oxygen if they were provided with an appropriate electron acceptor. This is important because it showed that

   (a)_____

   _____

   _____.

   In the plant, the electron acceptor is (b)_____.

6. (a) oxygen comes from water and that chloroplasts can drive the endergonic reaction of

8-5 Light energy is used to drive the synthesis of ATP and NADPH.

1. In photosynthesis, carbon dioxide is (a)_____

102

splitting water;
(b) NADP$^+$

(oxidized / reduced)   to (b)_____

_____.

1. (a) reduced;
(b) glucose or
other organic
compounds

2. In eucaryotes, photosynthesis occurs in the (a)_____

_____. During photosynthesis, ATP is produced **through**

the   same   (b)_____   mechanism   **used   in**

oxidative phosphorylation, wherein (c)_____
ions are pumped from one side of a membrane to **another.**

The concurrent synthesis of ATP is called (d)_____

_____.

2. (a) chlorplasts;
(b) chemiosmotic;
(c) hydrogen;
(d) photophos-
phorylation

3. The dissociation of water into oxygen and hydrogen **is**

driven by _____.

3. light energy

4. The events of photosynthesis that center around electron

transport are (a)_____(light-
dependent / light-independent) reactions, whereas ATP and

NADPH are used to synthesize glucose in (b)_____

_____(light-dependent / light-independent) reactions.

4. (a) light-
dependent;
(b) light-
independent

8-6 Two photosystems must cooperate in plant photosynthesis.

1. The photosynthetic pigments and associated proteins are

organized into two complexes called (a)_____

and (b)_____. Each complex is organized
around a photosynthetic unit that consists of about

200-400 (c)_____ molecules.

1. (a) photosystem
I; (b) photo-
system II:
(c) chlorophyll

2. What is the Emerson enhancement effect? _____

_____

_____.

2. When chloro-
plasts are
irradiated with
far-red light
and light of a

3. Photosystem I absorbs most of the (a)_____

light, while photosystem II absorbs most of the (b)_____

_____ light.

103

shorter wave-
length, photo-
synthesis
reaches its full
efficiency.

3. (a) far-red;
   (b) shorter-
   wavelength

4. How are antenna chlorphylls and reaction centers related?

_____

_____

_____

_____

4. Antenna chloro-
   phylls are pack-
   ed together in
   photosynthetic
   units and ex-
   change energy
   with each other.
   The energy is
   passed along un-
   til it reaches
   a reaction cen-
   ter where the
   energy can be
   drained off.

8-7 *Cyclic photophosphorylation creates only ATP.*

1. In cyclic photophosphorylation, only photosystem (a)_____
   is involved. In this system a photon of light excites an

   (b)_____ of a (c)_____ molecule.

1. (a) I;
   (b) electron;
   (c) chlorophyll

2. In cyclic photophosphorylation, as the electron passes between two cytochromes, the electron transport chain pumps

   (a)_____ ions across the membrane. For every

   (b)_____ of these ions, (c)_____
   ATP molecule(s) can by synthesized.

2. (a) hydrogen;
   (b) three;
   (c) one

3. In cyclic photophosphorylation, light gives a reaction

   center enough energy to (a)_____(oxidize /
   reduce) the chain of electron carriers. Some of this

   energy is temporarily stored in (b)_____.

3. (a) reduce;
   (b) ATP
   molecules

8-8 *A noncyclic pathway creates both ATP and NADPH.*

1. NADPH is generated in the _____(cyclic / noncyclic)
   photophosphorylation pathway.

1. noncyclic

2. Water is split when light is absorbed by photosystem

   _____.

2. II

3. If the excited electron from a chlorphyll molecule is used

104

to reduce $NADP^+$ to (a)_____, then an electron

from (b)_____ is used to replace the electron
in the reaction center.

3. (a) NADPH;
   (b) water

8-9 *Sugar is made from CO_2 in the Calvin cycle.*

1. The Calvin cycle involves the formation of (a)_____

   from carbon dioxide and water using the (b)_____

   and (c)_____ that are formed using light energy.

1. (a) glucose;
   (b) ATP;
   (c) NADPH

2. In the first part of the Calvin cycle, one ATP molecule is

   used to activate the 5-carbon compound called (a)_____

   _____. A (b)_____
   molecule is then attached to it, and the resulting
   molecule is immediately split into two 3-carbon molecules

   called (c)_____. Two of
   these 3-carbon molecules are then put together to form

   one (d)_____ molecule.

2. (a) ribulose
   5-phosphate;
   (b) carbon
   dioxide;
   (c) 3-phospho-
   glyceric acid;
   (d) glucose

3. Explain how the Calvin cycle is cyclical.

   _____

   _____

   _____

   _____

   _____

3. Only one of six
   molecules in the
   glyceraldehyde
   3-phosphate pool
   is withdrawn for
   glucose synthe-
   sis. The other
   five are re-
   shuffled to make
   three new mole-
   cules of ribu-
   lose diphosphate
   to begin the
   cycle again.

4. When all the chemical reactions are added up, the

   synthesis of one molecule of glucose requires (a)_____

   carbon dixoide molecules, (b)_____ ATP molecules and

   (c)_____ $NADPH^+$ molecules.

4. (a) 6;
   (b) 18;

5. The efficiency of photosynthesis is fairly high. Approxi-

105

(c) 12

mately _____% of the light energy received by the plant is transformed into sugar.

5. 33

6. Glyceraldehyde 3-phosphate is an intermediate of the _____ pathway and can go directly into all the biosynthetic pathways for amino acids.

6. glycolysis (or glycolytic)

8-10 Some plants use an alternative pathway for CO₂ fixation.

1. The Hatch-Slack pathway of carbon dioxide fixation is used by (a)_____(plants / bacteria) that live in (b)_____(hot and dry / cool and wet) conditions. This pathway is beneficial to organisms that have it, because it allows them to (c)_____ _____.

1. (a) plants;
(b) hot and dry;
(c) continue to photosynthesize in spite of a limited water supply

2. The Hatch-Slack pathway generates (a)_____(C_3 / C_4) compounds first. Malate is then (b)_____ to yield CO_2, which is used to (c)_____ _____.

2. (a) C₄
(b) decarboxy-lated;
(c) operate the Calvin cycle.

3. Photorespiration is _____

_____

_____

3. The process in which the car-boxylase enzyme combines ribu-lose diphosphate with oxygen instead of CO_2 and splits the ribulose diphos-phate into a C_2 and a C_3 compound.

8-11 Most biosynthesis begins with Krebs cycle metabolites.

1. Organic (a)_____ acids with the group C=O are produced by the Krebs cycle. These can be converted to amino acids in the process of (b)_____. The enzymes that catalyze these reactions use a coenzyme derived from (c)_____.

1. (a) keto;
(b) transamina-tion;
(c) vitamin B₆

2. When one is discussing major biosynthetic pathways the term "family" refers to (a)_____ _____. Why is this an example of efficient organization? _____

_____

2. (a) the end products of a biosynthetic pathway beginning with one particular compound; (b) Compounds with similar structures are made together by using common enzymes.

3. _____ is the pathway that "makes new glucose."

8-12 Biosynthetic pathways are generally regulated by feedback inhibition.

3. Gluconeogenesis

1. Metabolic pathways typically have control mechanisms at two levels: (a)_____ that regulate the amounts of all enzymes, and (b)_____ _____ controls that operate on existing enzymes.

1. (a) genetic regulatory systems; (b) feedback

2. In a biosynthetic pathway with several intermediate metabolites and several enzymes, feedback inhibition acts upon which enzyme? (a)_____. In a complex pathway with several branches, (b)_____ _____ is often a control mechanism wherein one enzyme has two binding sites for different products.

2. (a) the first in the pathway; (b) concerted inhibition

8-13 Polymers are synthesized from activated monomers.

1. (a)_____ such as starch and glycogen are made from activated sugar molecules. Starch is made by activating (b)_____, with the addition of an ATP to form adenosine diphosphate glucose, and adding it to a growing chain of sugars.

1. (a) Poly-saccharides; (b) glucose 1-phosphate

2. As polymerizations occur, pyrophosphate molecules are formed. These reactions are not reversed, because pyro-phosphate is split by _____.

2. pyrophos-phatases

107

PRACTICE QUIZ

1. _____ is necessary in both procaryotic and eucaryotic photosynthesis.
    a. A chlorplast
    b. Chlorophyll a
    c. Water
    d. Electromagnetic energy

2. Which of the following statements of a chloroplast is true?
    a. It is surrounded by a double membrane.
    b. The grana is the fluid-filled region in it.
    c. It is found in all photosynthetic organisms.
    d. Each eucaryotic cell has at least one of them.

3. Which of the following is the most common light-absorbing pigment?
    a. xanthophyll
    b. carotenoid
    c. chlorophyll a
    d. chlorophyll b

4. Water is important in plant photosynthesis because it:
    a. is the reducing agent for all photosynthetic reactions.
    b. is the source of atmospheric oxygen.
    c. provides hydrogen ions for glucose production.
    d. serves as an electron acceptor.

5. _____ is the reducing agent used to reduce CO_2 in photosynthesis.
    a. Water
    b. NADH
    c. NADPH
    d. Ferredoxin

6. Which of the following statements about photophosphorylation is true?
    a. Cyclic photophosphorylation creates only NADPH.
    b. Cyclic photophosphorylation creates both ATP and NADPh.
    c. Noncyclic photophosphorylation creates only ATP.
    d. Noncyclic photophosphorylation creates both ATP and NADPH.

7. Beginning with ribulose 5-phosphate, which of the following steps comes first in the Calvin cycle?
    a. Ribulose diphosphate is formed.
    b. 3-phosphoglyceric acid is formed.
    c. Glyceraldehyde 3-phosphate is formed.
    d. NADPH is used as a reducing agent.

8. The Hatch-Slack pathway differs from C_3 photosynthesis in that:

    a. the Hatch-Slack pathway generates 4-carbon compounds to be used a source of energy.
    b. the Calvin cycle is not important in the Hatch-Slack pathway.
    c. all plants in hot, dry places use the Hatch-Slack pathway.
    d. photorespiration is limited in the Hatch-Slack pathway when water is limited.

9. Which of the following is <u>not</u> a possible fate of organic acid metabolites produced by the Krebs cycle?
    a. They may become incorporated into proteins.

b. They may be transaminated.
c. They may be converted into ATP.
d. They may be converted into glucose.

10. _____ is not an activated monomer of a polymer.
   a. ADP-glucose
   b. Pyrophosphate
   c. Amino acyl AMP
   d. ATP

REVIEW QUESTIONS

I. Use the following graph to answer the next four questions.

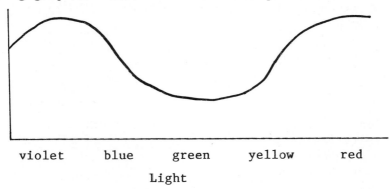

1. This graph represents an (a)_____(action / absorption) spectrum.
    The data for this graph were probably obtained by placing the plant in

    (b)_____ light and measuring the (c)_____

    _____.

2. This plant would probably grow best under which two colors of light?

    (a)_____ and (b)_____.

3. Is it possible from this graph to tell whether the organism used was a

    eucaryote or a procaryote? _____ Why? _____

    _____

4. If only green light were used, the oxygen level near this plant would

    (a)_____(increase / decrease) and the carbon dioxide level would

    (b)_____(increase / decrease), compared to the levels with no
    light shining on the plant.

II. Use the following graph to answer the next five questions. The graph was
based on observations of the number of bubbles produced by an underwater aquarium

109

plant that was exposed to different light intensities.

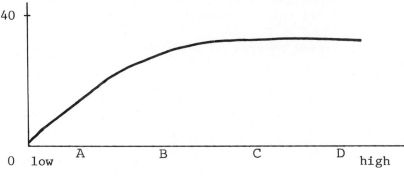

Light intensity

1. The bubbles being produced are probably:
   a. O_2.
   b. CO_2.
   c. H_2.
   d. CO.

2. The release of bubbles indicates the rate of:
   a. respiration.
   b. photosynthesis.
   c. photorespiration.
   d. growth.

3. At high light intensity there is no increase in the rate of bubble production. This is probably because:
   a. too much light has killed the plant.
   b. not enough carbon dixoide is present to sustain photosynthesis.
   c. enzymes for photosynthesis are damaged by light.
   d. glucose is produced in light-independent reactions.

4. As light intensity increases:
   a. carbon dioxide production decreases.
   b. photosynthetic rate remains the same or decreases.
   c. fermentation increases.
   d. glucose production increases.

5. If you wanted the maximum efficiency of photosynthesis in this plant, which light intensity would you use?
   a. A
   b. B
   c. C
   d. D

III. Use the following key to answer the next six questions.

   Key: a. C_3 photosynthesis
         b. C_4 photosynthesis
         c. neither
         d. both

_____ 1. Form of photosynthesis used by plants in hot, dry habitats

_____ 2. Hatch-Slack pathway used

_____ 3. Calvin cycle used

_____ 4. Carbon dioxide used to form glucose

_____ 5. Reduced photorespiration problem

_____ 6. Requires fewer ATP molecules used to synthesize one glucose molecule

IV. In the following imaginary biosynthetic pathway, the letters stand for metabolites and the numbers indicate enzymes.

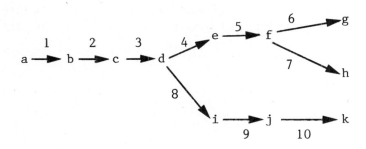

1. g, h, and k could be any of the following except:
   a. amino acids.
   b. bases of nucleotides.
   c. keto acids of the Krebs cycle.
   d. sugars.

2. Suppose g, h, and k are amino acids. In a normal growing cell, what will be their typical fate now that they have been synthesized?

   _____

   _____

3. Which enzyme would be most likely to be subject to feedback inhibition by

   k alone? _____

4. Which enzyme would be most likely to be subject to feedback inhibition by

   both g and h? _____

5. If a single enzyme could be controlled by g, h, and k, which one would it

   be? _____

6. Suppose you found that the cell has two distinct forms of enzyme 4. What would you predict about their sensitivity to various ligands?

111

_____

_____

7. If the cell has only a single form of enzyme 1, what would you predict
    about the mechanism of its b feedback regulation?

_____

_____

V. In the following, the box represents ADP or an equivalent nucelotide (that is,
a nucleotide with a different base; whether the base is adenine or something else
has little effect on the energetic properties of the nucleotide). In each case,
name or describe the polymer that could be made from many molecules of this kind.
Even if you have never heard of such a polymer and can't name it, you can still
describe it.

1. ☐–glucose

2. ☐–amino acid

3. ☐–PO_4

4. ☐–xylose   (Xylose is a sugar.)

5. ☐–isoprene   (Isoprene is shown in Table 4-3.

6. ☐–glucose,   ☐–xylose, plus   ☐–mannose (Mannose is a sugar.)

ANSWERS TO CHAPTER EXERCISES

Practice Quiz

1. d	3. c	5. c	7. a	9. c
2. a	4. c	6. d	8. d	10. b

Review Questions

I. 1. (a) action; (b) different wavelengths of; (c) production of oxygen.
    2. (a) violet, (b) red.
    3. probably eucaryotic, because the only procaryotes that produce oxygen in
        photosynthesis are cyanobacteria (see Chapter 35).
    4. (a) increase; (b) decrease.

II. 1. a   2. b   3. b   4. d   5. c

III. 1. d   3. d   5. b
      2. b   4. d   6. a

IV. 1. c
     2. to be incorporated into proteins

3. enzyme 8
4. enzyme 4
5. enzyme 1
6. One would be inhibited by g, the other by h.
7. Enzyme 1 is probably subject to concerted inhibition, so each of the three end products reduces its activity partially.

V. 1. Starch, glycogen, cellulose, or any other glucose polymer
    2. Protein
    3. Nucleic acids are made from these monomers just by removing pyrophosphates. They could also donate their phosphates to make a polyphosphate.
    4. A polyxylose
    5. A polyisoprene--that is, rubber
    6. A heteropolymer of glucose, xylose, and mannose. (Such polymers are found in gums and other plant products.)

Chapter 9

DNA, RNA, AND PROTEIN SYNTHESIS

WHAT'S IN THIS CHAPTER

This chapter briefly reviews the history and development of those observations and experiments that revealed the structure, function, and significance of DNA and RNA. The relationships among genes, enzymes, DNA, RNA, and protein synthesis are described. Studies employing bacteria, viruses, and radioactive labels were used to determine that DNA is the storage system for information regulating daily and long-term activities of cells and organisms.

Prior to cell division, DNA duplicates itself so that daughter cells receive a copy of the original. This process and some possible errors of duplication are described. DNA is the construction blueprint, but the site of construction (for proteins, the major components of cells) is elsewhere. You will learn how enzymes and various types of RNA act as go-betweens in protein synthesis. This chapter shows you how continuous linear sequences of only 4 DNA bases are used to assemble corresponding linear sequences of 20 different amino acids.

By the end of this chapter you should be able to:

1. Describe   and   (much   more   important)   outline   the   significance   of   the experiments done by Morgan; Beadle and Ephrussi; Beadle and Tatum; Griffith; Avery, MacLeod, and McCarty; Hershey and Chase; Meselson and Stahl; and Nirenberg.

2. Draw, using capital letters for major parts (A = adenine, S = sugar, etc.), a section of DNA structure as proposed by Watson and Crick and draw a model demonstrating DNA replication, transcription, and translation.

3. Name and explain the roles of enzymes involved in replication, transcription, and translation.

4. Explain how the 64 different triplets of bases code for amino acids in a systematic way.

WHAT YOU SHOULD ALREADY KNOW

Before reading this chapter, you should thoroughly understand the fundamental genetic structure of organisms and viruses as outlined in Chapter 3, and you should be generally familiar with amino acid, protein, and nucleotide structure as described in Chapter 4.   Because biochemical manipulations are enzyme-monitored, the structure and function of enzymes should also be reviewed (Chapter 6).

Pre-Test

1. (a)_____, found on chromosomes, consist of the

substance (b)_____.

1. (a) Genes;
    (b) DNA

2. One nucleotide of DNA is composed of a sugar, a phosphate,

and a (a)_____.   There are (b)_____ different bases in DNA.

2. (a) base;
    (b) four

3. The chromosomes are located in the cell's (a)_____

_____.   That part of a chromosome that determines a

particular trait is called a (b)_____.

3. (a) nucleus;
    (b) gene

4. Long chains of amino acids are called (a)_____.

There are (b)_____ (how many?) different amino acids in most proteins.

4. (a) proteins;
    (b) 20

5. Enzymes are (a)_____ molecules that have the

effect of (b)_____ (slowing down / speeding up) chemical reactions in the cell.

5. (a) protein;
    (b) speeding up

6. A _____ is a change in the structure of a gene.

6. mutation

GUIDED REVIEW OF THE CHAPTER

Introduction

1. The _____ carries genetic information that is translated into the structure and operation of the cell.

1. genome

9-1 Genes control the steps in metabolism.

1. Statistically significant results are obtained only with a

_____ sample size.

1. large

2. Morgan studied inheritance in (a)_____, which

115

are excellent subjects for genetic studies because

breeding results can be seen in only (b)_____
days.

2. (a) fruitflies;
(b) 10 to 14

3. Eye tissue from mutant larval fruit flies transplanted to

normal larvae resulted in (a)_____(normal /
mutant) eyes, suggesting that surrounding normal cells

supplied a(an) (b)_____ to complete the normal
biosynthetic pathway.

3. (a) normal;
(b) enzyme or
metabolite

4. True or False: Eye-transplant experiments produced the
following conclusions:
(a) Genes act through biosynthetic pathways catalyzed by
enzymes.
(b) One defective enzyme among a series of normal enzymes
will still usually produce a normal end product.
(c) Defective enzymes result from mutant genes.
(d) Mutant genes can sometimes produce normal enzymes.
(e) The sequence of steps in biosynthetic pathways can be
rearranged by the cell to bypass mutant enzymes.

4. (a) True;
(b) False;
(c) True;
(d) False;
(e) False

9-2 Typical mutants lack only a single enzyme.

1. The "one gene, one (a)_____" hypothesis was

suggested by (b)_____ and (c)_____ as

a result of their work with (d)_____.

1. (a) enzyme;
(b) Beadle;
(c) Tatum;
(d) bread mold
(*Neurospora*)

2. How many genes are necessary to produce a structure made

of four types of polypeptide chains? _____

2. Four

3. In the simplest case, each gene determines the structure

of one (a)_____, which catalyzed (b)_____

(how many?) step(s) in a (c)_____ pathway.

3. (a) enzyme;
(b) one;
(c) metabolic

9-3 The long quest for the genome.

1. Nucleic acid, discovered in (a)_____ (what year?),

was later shown to be of two types: (b)_____ and

(c)_____.

1. (a) 1869;
(b) DNA;
(c) RNA

2. The component of dead S cells responsible for the trans-

formation of R cells into (a)_____ cells was shown by

116

(b)_____, _____, and _____

to be (c)_____.

2. (a) S; (b)
   Avery, Macleod,
   McCarty;
   (c) DNA

3. What is the stuff that genes are made of? _____

3. DNA

9-4 The advent of bacteriophage.

1. Viruses including bacterial virsuses called (a)_____,

   grow only inside (b)_____.

1. (a) phage;
   (b) cells

2. Viruses consist of (a)_____ wrapped around a

   core of (b)_____.

2. (a) protein;
   (b) DNA or RNA

3. Using radioactive (a)_____ and (b)_____,
   Hershey and Chase deomonstrated that, during phage in-

   fection, only the (c)_____ enters the cell.

3. (a) sulfur;
   (b) phosphorus;
   (c) DNA

4. Once phage DNA is inside the cell, the bacterium begins to

   produce more (a)_____, being directed by the

   original piece of injected (b)_____.

4. (a) phage;
   (b) DNA

5. Eventually the bacterium (a)_____, releasing

   many (b)_____, which then repeat the process.

5. (a) lyses;
   (b) phage

6. DNA

6. Phage studies clearly demonstrate that cell activities are

   controlled by _____.

9-5 Two strands of DNA typically make a double helix.

1. A DNA nucleotide consists of three parts. What are they?

   _____, _____,

   _____

1. deoxyribose
   sugars, phos-
   phate and a
   base

2. A deoxyribonucleoside consists of a (a)_____

   plus (b)_____.

2. (a) base;
   deoxyribose

3. (a)_____ and (b)_____ are bases (b)
   consisting of a single ring of C and N atoms and are

   called (c)_____.

3. (a) Thymine;
   (b) cytosine;

4. The other two bases, (a)_____ and (b)_____

117

(c) pyrimidines

_____, are (c)_____ that consist of a (d)_____ _____ ring of C and N atoms.

4. (a) adenine;
   (b) guanine;
   (c) purines;
   (d) double

5. In any DNA sample, the number of A molecules is always equal to the number of (a)_____ molecules; like-wise, C always equals (b)_____.

5. (a) T; (b) G

6. The researchers (a)_____ and (b)_____ discovered that DNA consists of a (c)_____ made of (d)_____ (how many?) polynucleotide strands running in (e)_____ directions to each other.

6. (a) Watson;
   (b) Crick;
   (c) helix;
   (d) two;
   (e) opposite
   (or anti-
   parallel)

7. The DNA molecule resembles a (a)_____ staircase with the (b)_____ units forming the frame and the (c)_____ projecting inward to form the (d)_____.

7. (a) spiral;
   (b) sugar phos-
   phate;
   (c) bases;
   (d) steps

8. The complementary base pairs in a DNA molecule are (a)____ _____, and (b)_____, which are held together by (c)_____ bonds.

8. (a) A-T; (b)
   (c) hydro-
   gen

9. True or False: Purines always pair with purines. C - G ; _____

9. False

10. DNA carries genetic information in its _____ of base pairs.

10. sequence (or
    order)

11. A _____ is any change in the base sequence.

11. mutation

12. Name these mutation types: (a) changed meaning _____ _____; (b) gibberish _____; (c) liology _____ _____; (d) biolbiology _____.

12. (a) missense;
    (b) nonsense;
    (c) substitu-
    tion; (d) dup-
    lication

9-6 *DNA replicates semiconservatively.*

1. True or False: Semiconservative DNA replication means that each strand of the helix becomes half of a new pair of double-stranded molecules. _____

1. True

2. Daughter DNA from a parent helix of heavy nitrogen con-

tains _____ (how much?) heavy nitrogen.

2. half as much

3. _____ are given credit for confirming semiconservative DNA replication.

3. Meselson and Stahl

4. During replication, the DNA helix unwinds, acting as a (a)_____ for a complementary series of (b)_____ to be laid down.

4. (a) template: (b) nucleotides

5. The complement of the DNA sequence A C A T is _____.

5. T G T A

6. Enzymes that effect replication and DNA repair are called _____.

6. DNA polymerases

9-7 *DNA informs RNA and RNA informs protein.*

1. The (a)_____ consists of a series of genes, each one informing a single (b)_____.

1. (a) genome; (b) polypeptide

2. List two structural differences between DNA and RNA.

(a)_____

_____

(b)_____

_____

2. (a) RNA has ribose instead of deoxyribose; (b) RNA has uracil instead of thy-

3. Under the control of the enzyme (a)_____ _____, the DNA helix serves as a (b)_____ for the production of a complementary (c)_____ mine strand.

3. (a) RNA polymerase; (b) template; (c) RNA

4. A DNA sequence A C A T would be (a)_____ into the RNA sequence (b)_____.

4. (a) transcribed; (b) U G U A

5. A codon consists of (a)_____ (how many?) nucleotides of a (b)_____ molecule and codes for one (c)_____.

5. (a) three; (b) or RNA; (c) amino acid

6. How many different combinations of four items (bases) DNA taken three at a time (codons) are there? _____

119

6. 64 (4^3 = 64)

7. both DNA and
   RNA molecules

8. is not

9. (a) repair
   synthesis;
   (b) prevents
   copying at
   wrong time; (c)
   kicks off
   completed RNA
   strands

10. (a) punctuation;
    (b) genes

1. (a) ribosomes;
   (b) RNA;
   (c) protein

2. False
   (only mRNA)

1. (a) three;
   (b) codon;
   (c) m(essenger)

2. amino acids

3. one

7. A codon can be identified in _____

_____(only DNA molecules. / only RNA molecules. /
both DNA and RNA molecues).

8. The same strand _____(is / is not) used as a template
throughout the genome.

9. What three possible functions are there for portions of
strand never transcribed?

(a)_____

(b)_____

(c)_____

10. Transcribing the correct strand in the correct direction

is ensured by (a)_____ signals, which are near

the various (b)_____.

*9-8 Genetic information is carried in an unstable messenger
RNA.*

1. Actual protein assembly occurs on particles called (a)____

_____, which are composed of (b)_____

and (c)_____.

2. True or False: Both rRNA and mRNA are broken down after
use.

9-9 Amino acids are carried to the templates on adaptors.

1. An anticodon of tRNA consists of (a)_____ (how many?)

bases that complement the (b)_____ of (c)_____

_____ RNA.

2. What do transfer RNA molecules transfer? _____

3. How many different kinds of amino acids can one tRNA

carry? _____

4. What makes one tRNA different from another? _____

_____

4. their base sequences, especially their anticodons

5. When codon and anticodon come together on the (a)_____ _____, the (b)_____ of the coupled tRNA moldecules link, producing (c)_____. This process is called (d)_____.

5. (a) ribosome; (b) amino acids; (c) polypeptides; (d) translation (or protein synthesis)

6. The anitcodon for a DNA sequence of C G A is _____.

9-10 The code is systematic and degenerate.

6. C G A

1. The method for cracking the genetic code was developed by (a)_____, who reported that the sequence (b)_____ coded for (c)_____ (which amino acid?).

1. (a) Nirenberg; (b) U U U; (c) phenylalanine

2. A degenerate code means that several (a)_____ can specify the same (b)_____.

2. (a) codons(or triplets); (b) amino acid

3. Which of the three bases of an anticodon is sometimes interchangeable with several others? _____

3. the third

4. Nonsense triplets are actually (a)_____ used to (b)_____ protein synthesis.

4. (a) stop signs; (b) terminate

5. Every gene stars with the codon _____.

5. A U G

9-11 Transcription and translation are coupled in procaryotes.

1. The information for making mRNA, rRNA, and tRNA is in

_____.

1. DNA base sequences

2. True or False: After protein production, mRNA molecules are metabolized for a cellular energy source.

2. False

9-12 The mechanism of information transfer restricts the process of evolution.

1. (a)_____ Law states that information is transferred in one direction: from (b)_____

121

to (c)_____.

1. (a) Crick's;   2. True or False: Large muscles developed by weight lifting
    (b) nucleic   can be inherited by male offspring.
    acid;
    (c) protein

2. False

PRACTICE QUIZ

1. Which conclusion from genetic experiments is not true?
    a. Each gene controls a specific part of a biosynthetic pathway.
    b. Mutations block pathways by producing defective enzymes.
    c. A single mutation will block one step of a pathway.
    d. The sequence of enzymes used in a pathway is variable.

2. The *Neurospora* mutants used by Beadle and Tatum in their studies of nutrient
    growth requriments were:
    a. autotrophs.
    b. auxotrophs.
    c. phototrophs.
    d. prototrophs.

3. Heat-killed S cells and live R cells produced live S cells in mice through the
    process of:
    a. transduction.
    b. transcription.
    c. transformation.
    d. translocation.

4. _____ consists of a double ring of C and N atoms.
    a. Adenine
    b. Cytosine
    c. Thymine
    d. Uracil

5. Which DNA base sequence is complementary to a DNA sequence A G T C ?
    a. U G U C
    b. U C U G
    c. A G T C
    d. T C A G

6. The DNA sequence T A G C would be transcribed as:
    a. A U C G.
    b. T A C G.
    c. U T C G.
    d. T A G C.

7. The anticodon for a DNA sequence C G C would be:
    a. G C G.
    b. C G C.
    c. C U C.
    d. G U G.

122

8. Which of the following "function-location" pairs is <u>not</u> correct in a eucaryote?
    a. replication - nucleus
    b. translation - ribosome
    c. transcription - cytosol
    d. protein synthesis - cytosol

9. A chain of _____ DNA bases is necessary to specify an enzyme that is 60 amino acids long.
    a. 4
    b. 20
    c. 60
    d. 180

10. The structure of RNA:
    a. includes A, C, G, and T as bases.
    b. is usually double - stranded.
    c. contains deoxyribose sugar.
    d. is determined by DNA.

REVIEW QUESTIONS

I. Match the investigators in the left column with the appropriate term(s) in the **right columm.**

_____ 1. Beadle and Ephrussi	a. one gene, one enzyme
_____ 2. Beadle and Tatum	b. DNA structure
_____ 3. Griffith	c. eye pigment mutations
_____ 4. Hershey and Chase	d. genetic code
_____ 5. Meselson and Stahl	e. "nuclein"
_____ 6. Miescher	f. semiconservative replication
_____ 7. Nirenberg	g. the genome is DNA
_____ 8. Watson and Crick	h. transformation

II. Fill in the steps from DNA to assembled protein (see Table 9-2 for the names of the amino acids).

DNA sequence   A G A   G G A G C A

1. mRNA codon   _ _ _   _ _ _ _ _ _

2. tRNA anticodon _ _ _   _ _ _ _ _ _

3. protein   _____ _____ _____

123

III. Fill in the blanks in the following chart.

	DNA	RNA
Sugar present	1.	2.
Bases present	3.	4.
Single-stranded or double-stranded	5.	6.
Site of function in cell	7.	8.

IV. The answer to each of the following questions is a number. Place the correct number in the space provided.

1. C-N rings in quanine _____
2. Different bases in mRNA _____
3. Minimum number of bases that need to be changed to produce a mutation _____
4. Hydrogen bonds between guanine and cytosine _____
5. Hydrogen bonds between adenine and thymine _____
6. Different amino acids in most proteins _____
7. Nucleotides per codon _____
8. Total number of different codons _____
9. Different kinds of RNA involved in protein synthesis _____
10. Number of different kinds of amino acids a specific tRNA can carry _____
11. Bases in each anticodon _____
12. Codons necessary to make a protein 27 amino acids long _____
13. Number of genes required to make one polypeptide chain _____

V. Answer each of the following questions.

1. What is one advantage in having double-stranded genetic material?

_____

_____

2. What ensures that tRNA is formed from the correct starting point on DNA?

_____

3. Why are acquired characteristics, such as loss of a finger, not inherited?

_____

_____

124

4. Why is the genetic code said to be degenerate?

_____

5. What determines, in an evolutionary sense, whether a mutation is beneficial?

_____

_____

_____

_____

ANSWERS TO CHAPTER EXERCISES

Practice Quiz

1. d   3. c   5. d   7. b   9. d
2. b   4. a   6. a   8. c   10. d

Review Questions

I.   1. c   3. h   5. f   7. d
     2. a   4. g   6. e   8. b

II. 1. U C U   C C U   C G U
     2. A G A   G G A   G C A
     3. arginine glycine alanine

III. 1. deoxyribose   3. A, T, C, G   5. usually double   7. nucleus
     2. ribose   4. A, U, C, G   6. usually single   8. cytoplasm

IV. 1. 2   4. 3   7. 3   10. 1   13. 1
     2. 4   5. 2   8. 64   11. 3
     3. 1   6. 20   9. 3   12. 27

V.   1. If one strand is damaged, the remaining strand can be used as a template
        for repair.
     2. There is a base series that signals where to begin.
     3. Information transfer is from DNA to protein and not the reverse. Even
        though a finger may be lost, the information for its structure and
        development remains in the DNA, and only the DNA, in sperm and egg, is
        passed on to the offspring.
     4. Several codons can specify the same amino acid.
     5. Its possessor is better adapted (more fit for the current environment),
        lives through more breeding seasons, and produces more offspring with the
        same beneficial mutation. The success of a mutation is determined by the
        number of fertile offspring its possessor produces.

125

Chapter 10

CYCLES OF GROWTH AND REPRODUCTION

WHAT'S IN THIS CHAPTER

The world we live in is marked by cycles of natural events, such as the cycle of night and day and the regular changes of seasons. Organisms, too, (and individual cells) go through regular cycles of reproduction, as each cell grows and divides or as a larger organism grows, develops, reproduces, and eventually dies. The biological and the physical cycles are often closely tied to one another, and many organisms go through cycles of activity that are correlated with physical cycles.

The most important cycles that mark the lives of organisms are the cell cycle, in which a single cell grows and divides, and the sexual cycle, which entails the fusion of two cells to make a new individual. This chapter examines both cycles. It begins with some information about the structure and replication of chromosomes and then outlines the cell cycle. It goes on to explain the importance of sexual (in contrast to asexual) reproduction. The sexual cycle is then outlined, and you will see that it consists of four phases, or events, that follow one another regularly: a phase when the cells of an organism have only one set of chromosomes; a process of fertilization, in which two such cells combine; a phase in which cells have two sets of chromosomes; and a special kind of cell division, called meiosis, in which the chromosome numbers are reduced again so each cell has one set. In humans it is the sperm and egg cells that have only one set of chromosomes, and the process of fertilization creates a new person all of whose cells have two sets. But in the ovaries or testes of this person, meiosis occurs to again produce new eggs or sperm for another generation.

You will see that one of the most fascinating--and least understood--processes is the development of an individual from a single cell (the fertilized egg) into an adult who consists of many kinds of cells with different structures and functions. This chapter also outlines this process and lays the foundation for a more substantial discussion of it in Chapters 16 and 17.

By the end of this chapter you should be able to:

1. Explain the steps of the cell cycle and the events of each step.

2. Identify the stages and parts of mitosis and meiosis.

3. Draw any stage of cell division, showing the correct number, form, and location of chromosomes.

4. Compare and contrast procaryotic and eucaryotic cell division.

5. Compare the evolution of sexual organisms with that of asexual organisms.

6. Explain and provide examples illustrating haplontic, diplontic, and haplodiplontic life cycles.

WHAT YOU SHOULD ALREADY KNOW

Chapter 3 contains basic information about chromosome structure and how gene function relates to variation and evolution. You should understand this information clearly before beginning Chapter 10. Those portions of Chapter 9 on DNA replication are pertinent for integrating replication with cell division.

Pre-Test

1. Egg cells, sperm cells, and pollen grains, collectively called (a)_____, contain (b)_____(half / twice) as many chromosomes as other body cells.

1. (a) gametes; (b) half

2. The fusion of gametes, called (a)_____, produces a diploid cell called the (b)_____.

2. (a) fertilization or syngamy; (b) zygote

3. Before each cell divison, the (a)_____ is duplicated and one of the exact copies goes to (b)_____(one of the / each) daughter cell(s).

3. (a) DNA; (b) each

4. (a)_____(how many?) of every individual's chromosomes come from each parent via the (b)_____.

4. (a) Half; (b) gametes

5. Sexually reproducing species, therefore, inherit (a)_____ from (b)_____(only one / each) parent.

5. (a) traits or genes; (b) each

6. Recombination of _____ material results in new features in offspring.

6. genetic

GUIDED REVIEW OF THE CHAPTER

Introduction

1. All organisms adjust their lives to natural _____,

127

as shown, for example, by spring flowering and fall migrations.

1. cycles

2. Three environmental signals that organsims use to regulate their cycles are (a)_____, (b)_____, and (c)_____.

2. (a) day length; (b) tides; (c) seasons

3. Carrying out the same cycle at the same time every year, month, or day enhances _____.

3. reproductive success

4. A 24-hour activity cycle is called a _____ rhythm, but for organisms kept in constant conditions, the activity cycle is slightly different from 24 hours.

4. circadian

5. The basic mechanism of these "biological clocks" _____ (is / is not) known.

5. is not

10-1 *All growing cells proceed through a regular cycle.*

1. Division of the cell nucleus is called (a)_____ and is usually followed by cytoplasmic division, called (b)_____.

1. (a) mitosis; (b) cytokinesis

2. Using the proper letters, list in order the periods of the cell cycle: _____, _____, _____, _____.

2. G_1, S, G_2, M

3. Identify each period of the cell cycle by its symbol: (a) DNA replication, _____; (b) preparation for mitosis, _____; (c) chromosome replication, _____; (d) preparation for DNA replication, _____.

3. (a) S; (b) G_2; (c) M; (d) G_1^2

4. Which period of the cell cycle has the greatest variation in length? _____

4. G_1

5. Evidence indicates that the _____ period may be the one regulating frequency of division.

5. G_1

10-2 *Chromosomes are built of DNA-protein complexes.*

1. Procaryotic cells possess (a)_____ (how many?) chromosome(s) in the shape of a long (b)_____.

1. (a) one; (b) loop or circle

2. A (a)_____ pair represents a length of 1,000 nucleotide pairs, and one turn of the helix occurs every

(b)_____ nucleotide pairs.

2. (a) kilobase;
   (b) 10

3. A eucaryotic cell contains 10^3-10^4 times as much DNA as a bacterium in several separate (a)_____; in human cells the DNA molecules total about (b)_____ meters in length.

3. (a) chromo-
   somes
   (b) 1.8

4. Chromatin consists of (a)_____, (b)_____, and (c)_____.

4. (a) DNA;
   (b) protein;
   (c) some RNA

5. The chromatin proteins are of two types: (a)_____ and (b)_____.

5. (a) histones;
   (b) nonhistones

6. (a)_____, consisting of several types of histones, are beads connected to one another by strands of (b)_____.

6. (a) Nucleo-
   somes; (b) DNA

7. Chromosomes become visible (under a light microscope) after DNA replication because of repeated _____.

7. coiling

8. After DNA duplication, the cell possesses (a)_____ copies of each original chromosome and the identical copies are (b)_____.

8. (a) two;
   (b) chromatids

9. A centromere holds _____ together.

9. chromatids

10. True or false: Chromatid pairs contain the same DNA base sequence.

10. True

10-3 Mitosis is a mechanism for dividing chromosomes into two identical sets.

1. Mitosis ensures that each daughter cell has _____ (how many?) complete copy(ies) of the genome.

1. one

2. How many chromatids are there in one chromosome during G_1? (a)_____. During G_2? (b)_____.

2. (a) one;
   (b) two

3. Chromatid pairs attach their centromeres to the _____ fibers at the kinetochore.

3. spindle

4. True or False: (a) Centromere and kinetochore are the same. (b) All spindle fibers connect to chromosomes.

4. (a) False;
   (b) False

5. During which phase of mitosis does: (a) chromatid separation occur? _____; (b) the nuclear membrane

129

begin to reform? _____ ;   (c) the chromatin begin

to compact? _____

5. (a) anaphase;
    (b) telophase;
    (c) prophase

6. In animal cells the spindle forms between the (a)_____

    _____, which eventually become located at (b)_____

    _____(opposite / the same) end(s) of the cell.

6. (a) centrioles;
    (b) opposite

7. During metaphase, all chromosomes lie in the same plane in

    the cell, called the _____ plate.

7. equatorial

8. The results of mitosis are that each (a)_____

    cell gets exactly (b)_____ copy(ies) of each
    chromosome, no matter how many there are.

8. (a) daughter;
    (b) one

10-4 Procaryotic cells go through a similar cell cycle.

1. Procaryotic DNA replication procedes in (a)_____

    directions, eventually producing (b)_____ (how many?)
    complete loops.

1. (a) opposite;
    (b) two

2. What mechanism do procaryotic cells use to separate

    daughter DNA molecules? _____

2. Cell elongation
    pulls them
    apart.

3. How long does it take procaryotes (*E. coli*) to complete

    one round of replication? _____

3. 40 minutes

*10-5 Procaryotic chromosomes replicate in many segments simul-
    taneously.*

1. Eucaryotic chromosomes with (a)_____ times as much
    DNA as *E. coli* complete one replication round in about

    (b)_____ hours.

1. (a) 50;
    (b) 7

2. This is explained by thousands of (a)_____ units

    per chromosome, each about (b)_____ μm long, and

    each replicating in (c)_____ directions at the
    same time.

2. (a) replica-
    tion; (b) 30;
    (c) opposite

3. The speed of complete genome replication depends on the

    number of _____ units operating, thus serving
    as a possible control mechanism for growth.

3. replication

10-6 A cycle of growth implies a cycle of gene regulation.

1. Life cycle sequential changes follow a sequential _____ _____ program.

1. genetic

2. True or False: Baldness could be an example of gene action (or inactivity) later in life's genetic program.

2. True

3. Continuous vegetative cycles of *Bacillus* or *Clostridium* go on until the environment changes, at which time resistant _____ are produced.

3. endospores

4. The (a)_____ for endospore production must be dormant until called into action by (b)_____ conditions.

4. (a) genes;
(b) environ-
mental

5. Differentiation into varied cell types from a single original cell means that (a)_____ sets of genes must be turned on and off in a specific (b)_____.

5. (a) many or
different;
(b) sequence
or pattern

6. True or False: The genes for insulin production in your skin cells will probably never be turned on.

6. True

10-7 It is an advantage for an organism to be a sexual diploid.

1. The genomes of clonally growing species are the same and evolution, which occurs by (a)_____, is relatively (b)_____(slow / fast).

1. (a) mutations;
(b) slow

2. Sexually reproducing species, in comparison to clones, evolve much (a)_____(slower / faster) because genetic (b)_____ produce new features every generation.

2. (a) faster;
(b) recombina-
tions

3. Harmful mutations in sexually reproducing species may not cause harm to the possessor because there are _____ (how many?) copies of each gene.

3. two

4. True or False: Having two copies of each gene means harmful genes can accumulate in a species.

4. True

5. An organism with one copy of the genome per cell is called

131

(a)_____; with two copies it is (b)_____.

5. (a) haploid;
   (b) diploid

6. Sexually diploid organisms recombine different haploid
   sets of _____ offspring, producing new features.

6. chromosomes

7. Use haploid or diploid: Combining two (a)_____
   cells produces one (b)_____ cell, which can
   later undergo meiosis, result in (c)_____ cells.

7. (a) haploid;
   (b) diploid
   (c) haploid

8. Use H for haplontic, D for diplontic, or H-D for haplodiplontic: (a) most animals, _____; (b) the zygote
   undergoes meiosis, _____; (c) most plants, _____; (d) both
   haploid and diploid mitosis in life cycle, _____.

8. (a) D; (b) H;
   (c) H-D; (d) H-D

9. Gametophytes produce (a)_____ and sporophytes
   produce (b)_____.

9. (a) gametes;
   (b) spores

10. Distinguish among the three types of reproduction on the
    basis of the sizes of gametes. (a) all the same size:
    _____; (b) one larger, one smaller: _____
    _____; (c) one small and motile, one large and nonmotile:
    _____.

10. (a) isogamy;
    (b) anisogamy;
    (c) oogamy

11. Label H for haploid or D for diploid: (a) spore, _____;
    (b) sperm, _____; (c) zygote, _____; (d) gametophyte,
    _____; (e) cheek cells, _____; (f) sporophyte, _____.

11. (a) H or D; (b)
    H; (c) D;
    (d) H; (e) D;
    (f) D

*10-8 Meiosis divides a diploid cell into four equivalent
    haploids.*

1. Chromosomes of the same length and centromere position,
   with identical bands, are called _____.

1. homologs

2. A picture of one's metaphase chromosomes is called a
   _____.

2. karyotype

3. Nonidentical homologs are the (a)_____ and (b)_____
   chromosomes.

3. (a) X; (b) Y

4. True or False: Haploid cells resulting from meiosis each

have one member of every homologous pair.

4. True

5. (a) 4; (b) 2

6. True

7. metaphase

8. anaphase

9. chromosomes

10. 4

11. different

12. homologous

13. True

1. (a) spermato-
   genesis;
   (b) 4

2. (a) oogenesis;
   (b) 1

3. cytoplasm

5. Use numbers: A tetrad consists of (a)_____ chromatids representing the (b)_____ chromosomes of one homologous pair.

6. True or False: Synapsis is the pairing of homologs in prophase.

7. Tetrads are in the center of the cell during _____ _____.

8. Chiasmata are evident as _____ begins.

9. At the first anaphase of meiosis, separation occurs between _____, not chromatids as in mitosis.

10. The second meiotic division is a haploid mitosis producing _____(how many?) haploid cells from the original diploid cell.

11. Since gene pairs on homologs can differ, resulting haploid cells can carry _____ genes.

12. Chiasma involves exchange between _____ chromatids.

13. True or False: Genetic variation among individuals is basic to evolution.

10-9 Spermatogenesis and oogenesis entail different patterns of cell division.

1. Meiosis that produces sperm cells is called (a)_____ _____, and it results in (b)_____(how many?) n cells from each diploid cell.

2. Meiosis that produces egg cells is called (a)_____, and it results in (b)_____(how many?) functional n cell(s).

3. At each of the two divisions of oogenesis, almost all of the _____ goes to one daughter cell.

4. Oogenesis produces one large cell and two or three smaller cells called _____ bodies.

133

4. polar

5. embryo
   nutrition

6. 450

7. True

1. hermaphrodites

2. False

3. False

4. variability

5. parthenogenesis

6. True

7. ameiotic

8. meiotic

1. False

5. Why has oogenesis been selected for all the cytoplasm going to the functional egg cell? _____

6. Over a lifetime, human males produce billions of sperm cells, but females mature only about _____ eggs.

7. True or False: The numbers of meiotic products per initial male and female cell are the same in animals as they are in plants.

10-10 Hermaphroditism and parthenogenesis are variations on sexual reproduction.

1. Organisms producing both eggs and sperm cells are called _____.

2. True or False: Most hermaphrodites fertilize themselves.

3. True or False: Humans could be called monoecious.

4. Recombination of one's own gametes limits _____.

5. Production of young without fertilization is called _____.

6. True or False: Eggs of some species begin development after mechanical or chemical stimulation.

7. Eggs produced by mitosis result in _____ parthenogenesis.

8. If an egg combines with one of its polar bodies, it illustrates _____ parthenogenesis.

10-11 Multicellular organisms go through a complex embryological development.

1. True or False: The mechanism of genes turning on and off in a certain sequence is now well understood.

10-12 Some life cycles comprise distinct morphological phases.

1. The different forms in the liver fluke life cycle are created by different (a)_____ of the same (b)_____ expressed at different times.

1. (a) genes;
   (b) genome

PRACTICE QUIZ

1. The circadian rhythm of rats seems to be adjusted to a period of 24 hours by:
   a. genes.
   b. seasons.
   c. tides.
   d. light.

2. DNA synthesis occurs during:
   a. mitosis.
   b. the S period.
   c. the G_1 period.
   d. the G_2 period.

3. Chromatids are joined at their:
   a. nucleosomes.
   b. centromeres.
   c. centrioles.
   d. kinetochores.

4. Chromatid separation in mitosis and meiosis occurs in:
   a. anaphase.
   b. prophase.
   c. telophase.
   d. metaphase.

5. Which of the following best describes the shape of the procaryotic chromosome?
   a. ladder
   b. corkscrew
   c. Y-shaped
   d. circle

6. The advantage of sexual reproduction over asexual reproduction is its:
   a. recombination of genetic material.
   b. slow rate of evolution during favorable times.
   c. control over number of offspring.
   d. elimination of harmful mutations.

7. Which of the following cells is diploid?
   a. secondary spermatocyte
   b. primary polar body
   c. spermatid
   d. oogonium

8. How many chromosomes are there in the gametes of an organism where $2n = 16$?
   a. 2
   b. 4
   c. 8
   d. 16

135

9. During which meiotic stage does synapsis occur?
   a. second prophase
   b. first anaphase
   c. interphase between first and second division
   d. first prophase

REVIEW QUESTIONS

I. Match each event in the right column with the correct phrase from the left column.

_____ 1. after DNA duplication and before mitosis   A. anaphase

_____ 2. chromatids separate   C. cytokinesis

_____ 3. chromatin compacts   D. G_1 phase

_____ 4. chromosomes at center of cell   G. G_2 phase

_____ 5. cytoplasmic division   M. metaphase

_____ 6. DNA duplication   P. prophase

_____ 7. growth, synthesis of cell products   S. S phase

_____ 8. nuclear membrane reforms   T. telophase

II. Consider the drawing to the right and answer the next seven questions.

   1. Name part a. _____

   2. Name part b. _____

   3. Name this stage of mitosis. _____

   4. Name this stage of meiosis. _____

   5. What is the 2n number for this mitotic cell? _____

   6. How many chromatids are in this cell? _____

   7. Which mitotic stage follows this one? _____

III. Compare, in general terms and numbers, procaryotic and eucaryotic cells.

	Procaryotic	Eucaryotic
DNA volume	1.	2.
Average replication time in hours	3.	4.
Replication forks	5.	6.
Number of chromosomes	7.	8.
Mechanisms used to separate daughter DNA cells	9.	10.

IV. What regulates the differentiation of zygote to embryo to fetus to baby to child to juvenile to adult to old person?

_____

_____

V. In the following cell outlines, draw in the correct number, form, and location of chromosomes for a cell whose diploid number is 4 ($2\underline{n} = 4$).

1. second anaphase   2. late first prophase   3. metaphase of mitosis

VI. Answer the following questions.

1. How many different arrangements are there for the paternal and maternal chromosomes of synapsed pairs at the first metaphase of meiosis in humans

($2\underline{n} = 46$)? _____

137

2. How many tetrads are there in a human (2$\underline{n}$ = 46) cell at the first prophase of meiosis? _____

VII. Make a simple drawing illustrating chiasma between homologous nonsister chromatids..

VIII. Label each cell $\underline{n}$ or 2$\underline{n}$.

_____ 1. egg cell   _____ 5. liver cell

_____ 2. spermatogonium   _____ 6. oocyte

_____ 3. polar body   _____ 7. spermatid

_____ 4. primary spermatocyte   _____ 8. secondary spermatocyte

IX. Name (1) an advantage and (2) a disadvantage of being a hermaphrodite.

1. _____

2. _____

X. As a resort owner you are concerned about the unusually large number of itch bugs tormenting your customers, so you spray itchicide to get rid of them. The next season there are very few itch bugs, but the following season they are back in full force. You spray itchicide again, and this time it does no good. What has happened?

_____

_____

ANSWERS TO CHAPTER EXERCISES

Practice Test

1. d	3. b	5. d	7. d	9. d
2. b	4. a	6. a	8. c	10. c

Review Questions

I. 1. G	3. P	5. C	7. D	
2. A	4. M	6. S	8. T	

II. 1. centriole   3. metaphase   5. 4   7. anaphase
     2. spindle fiber   4. second metaphase 6. 8

III. 1. small
      2. many times as much
      3. 1 or less
      4. 7 (4 minutes in *Drosophila*)
      5. 2
      6. thousands
      7. 1
      8. several to hundreds
      9. cell elongation
     10. mitosis

IV. Differentiation is many series of different genes exerting their influence in
     a correct sequence.

V. 1.   2.   3.

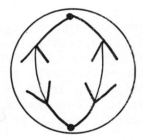   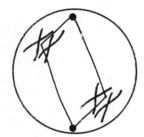   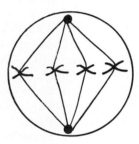

VI. 1. 2^{23}
     2. 23

VII.

VIII. 1. $\dfrac{n}{2n}$ 3. $\dfrac{n}{2n}$ 5. $\dfrac{2n}{2n}$ 7. $\dfrac{n}{n}$
       2.   4.   6.   8.

IX. 1. They can self-fertilize if there is no mate.
     2. Genetic variability is limited.

X. All members of sexually reproducing species are to some degree different from
    each other (variation). A few of the itch bugs of the initial population
    possessed the variation of itchicide resistance and were the only ones left
    after spraying. Two breeding seasons later, the entire population is derived
    from these resistant few, so itchicide is no longer effective.

139

Chapter 11

CELL STRUCTURE I: MEMBRANES AND TRANSPORT MECHANISMS

WHAT'S IN THIS CHAPTER

This chapter initially explains how microscope slides and electron micrographs are prepared. Development of these and other techniques has led to our current under-standing of the cell membrane structure and how a wide variety of materials are transported through these membranes. A detailed analysis of the cell membrane is presented, which is necessary for a thorough understanding of the entry and exit of various substances. Chapter 11 also explains the transport mechanisms that cells use to regulate their inner environment, how cell membranes grow, and how cells hold together to form tissues.

By the end of this chapter you should be able to:

1. Outline the preparation process for light microscope slides, and explain how the light microscope and electron microscope work.

2. Describe physically and chemically the nature and structure of cell membranes and the evidence that provided this information.

3. List all possible mechanisms that cells use for the entry and exit of various substances through the cell membrane.

4. Recognize, differentiate among, and give examples of all transport mechanisms.

5. Predict the directional flow for specific substances into or out of the cell under given circumstances.

6. Explain how cell membranes grow.

7. Name and describe the types of junctions used to hold cells together in tissues.

WHAT YOU SHOULD ALREADY KNOW

A general understanding of cell structure is important for visualizing the processes presented in this chapter; you should review Chapter 3 for this information. Biological molecules (Chapter 4), lipids in particular, must be understood clearly before beginning this chapter. It is most important to understand protein structure and function (especially the basics of enzyme action) as discussed in Chapter 6.

Pre-Test

1. The electron microscope uses a beam of (a)_____

to view objects instead of the (b)_____ beam used in the light microscope.

1. (a) electrons; (b) light.

2. Much greater magnification is possible with the _____ _____ microscope.

2. electron

3. The boundary layer separating the cytoplasm of a cell from the environment is the _____.

3. cell (or plasma) membrane

4. Any substance that enters or leaves a cell must go _____ _____ the cell membrane.

4. through

5. Large molecules move _____(faster / slower) than smaller molecules.

5. slower

6. Lettuce soaking in water becomes crisp because (a)_____ _____ (what substance?) (b)_____(enters / leaves) each lettuce cell.

6. (a) water; (b) enters

7. Onions being sliced in the kitchen can be detected in the bedroom because the onion molecules spread in all directions from the source by the process of _____.

7. diffusion

GUIDED REVIEW OF THE CHAPTER

Introduction

1. Cell membranes are sheets made of (a)_____ and

(b)_____.

1. (a) lipid; (b) protein

11-1 Cell structure is revealed primarily by microscopy.

1. After fixation, biological material is _____ to create contrast.

1. stained

2. Fixing, staining, and sectioning can cause the natural

141

structure of biological materials to be _____.

2. altered (or changed)

3. The resolving power of an instrument is its ability to distinguish (a)_____(how many?) points as (b)_____ (how many?) points.

3. (a) two; (b) two

4. The electron miscroscope uses a beam of (a)_____, which gives it a resolving power about (b)_____ (how many?) times greater than that of light miscroscopy.

4. (a) electrons; (b) 1,000

5. Transmission electron microscopy depends on electrons being stopped by atoms of (a)_____ in the viewed object, producing a (b)_____ _____(black and white / color) photo.

5. (a) heavy metal; (b) black and white

True or False: Artifacts result from treatment procedures and can be difficult to detect.

6. True

11-2 Phospholipids are major components of membranes.

1. Lipids are (a)_____(hydrophilic / hydrophobic), meaning that they (b)_____(will / will not) dissolve in water.

1. (a) hydrophobic; (b) will not

2. Lipids with double bonds in their hydrocarbon chains are said to be _____.

2. unsaturated

3. The major lipids of membranes are the _____.

3. phospholipids

4. What are molecules such as phospholipids called if they have both hydrophobic and hydrophilic portions? _____ _____

4. amphipathic

5. What is the hydrophobic portion of a phospholipid? _____

5. two fatty acid chains

11-3 Osmotic phenomena show that membranes are made of lipids.

1. The movement of molecules through a _____ membrane is called osmosis.

1. semipermeable

2. What is a measure of the tendency of water to diffuse? _____

2. water potential

3. (a) zero;
   (b) negative

4. True

5. True

6. (a) decreased;
   (b) increased

7. (a) hypertonic;
   (b) semi-
      permeable

8. (a) hypotonic;
   (b) turgor

9. True

10. (a) inversely;
    (b) pores

11. (a) slowly;
    (b) charges

12. (a) lipids;
    (b) lipids

3. Pure water at atmospheric pressure has a water potential of (a)_____, but a solution of anything in water has a (b)_____(negative / positive) water potential.

4. True or False: Osmotic potential is a decrease in water potential.

5. True or False: Two different solutions of non-disso- ciating molecules of equal molarity will have the same osmotic potential.

6. Use increased or decreased: Water potential is (a)_____ _____ by adding solute to a solution and is (b)_____ by applying pressure.

7. A cell placed in a(an) (a)_____(isotonic / hypertonic / hypotonic) solution will plasmolyze, because the plasma membrane is (b)_____.

8. A (a)_____(isotonic / hypertonic / hypotonic) solution causes plant cells to swell, producing (b)_____ _____ pressure against the cell wall.

9. True or False: The concentration of solute in cells is equal to that of isotonic solutions for that cell.

10. Small uncharged molecules enter cells at a rate (a)_____ _____(directly / inversely) proportional to their molecular size, suggesting that they may go through (b)_____ in the cell membrane.

11. Charged molecules enter cells (a)_____(quickly / slowly), suggesting that the cell membrane pores are sur- rounded by (b)_____ which repel these molecules.

12. The entry rate of large uncharged molecules into cells is proportional to their solubility in (a)_____, suggesting that the plasma membrane is made of (b)_____ _____.

143

11-4 Membrane lipids form bilayers.

1. The area covered by lipid from one red blood cell (experiment of Gorter and Grendel) was (a)_____ (twice / four times) as much as needed to cover one cell, suggesting that the cell membrane was a (b)_____ of lipid.

1. (a) twice;
   (b) bilayer

2. Amphipathic lipids placed in water associate so that the hydrophilic ends are (a)_____(in / out) of contact with water and the (b)_____ ends are in contact with water.

2. (a) out;
   (b) hydrophobic

3. Freeze-fracture and freeze-etch techniques revealed the lipid bilayer to have globular _____ molecules embedded to various depths.

3. protein

4. True or False: All cells have about the same amount of protein in their lipid bilayer.

4. False

11-5 The membrane is a fluid mosaic of lipid and protein.

1. Singer and Nicolson (1972) proposed the _____ _____ model of membrane structure.

1. fluid-mosaic

2. The hydrophilic-hydrophobic nature of bilayer proteins determines their _____ in the lipid bilayer.

2. position

3. A strongly hydrophobic protein would embed _____ _____(between / superficially on) the lipid bilayers.

3. between

4. True or False: Intrinsic proteins can form multimers within the membrane.

4. True

11-6 A membrane is really fluid.

1. The intermingling of human and mouse heterokaryon membrane proteins demonstrated the _____ nature of the bilayer.

1. fluid

2. Membrane protein mobility is (a)_____ -dependent and, when a membrane is cooled, it reaches a (b)_____ temperature where it changes from a

(c)_____ to a rigid condition.

2. (a) tempera-
ture; (b)
transition;
(c) fluid

3. What two factors concerning phospholipid fatty acid chains
influence membrane fluidity? _____

_____

3. length and
saturation

4. (a)_____(Shorter / Longer) length and

(b)_____(greater / less) saturation produce
the greatest fluidity of the membrane.

4. (a) Shorter;
(b) less

5. True or False: Membrane lipid composition may be
flexible, changing in response to diet and temperature.

5. True

6. Lateral movement of the lipid molecules in a membrane is

_____(faster / slower) than that of the
proteins.

6. faster

11-7 Membranes are asymmetrical.

1. True or False: Asymmetry of the membrane means that the
proteins and lipids of the inner and outer faces are not
the same.

1. True

2. Glycolipids are (a)_____ chains that are
attached to lipids; glycoproteins bear such chains con-

nected to (b)_____.

2. (a) carbohy-
drate;
(b) proteins

3. True or False: End-for-end flips of lipids and proteins
occur commonly in the membrane.

3. False

4. True or False: If translocating proteins of the membrane
flipped end for end they would still move material in the
normal direction for that protein.

4. False

11-8 Membranes grow by intussusception from the inside.

1. Membrane proteins and lipids are made one by one on or in

existing (a)_____ and then wedge their way into

the membrane in a process called (b)_____.

1. (a) membranes;
(b) intussus-
ception

2. Intussusception of membrane proteins is assured by two

intrinsic membrane proteins called _____.

2. ribophorins

145

11-9 Biological structures conserve and inform their own patterns during growth.

1. The general principle of biological organization means that the forms of _____ structures are determined by the form of initial structures.

1. new

2. True or False: Growth by intussusception illustrates the general principle of biological organization.

2. True

11-10 Many substances can diffuse through membranes.

1. The rate of CO_2 or O_2 diffusion through membranes depends on the difference in the (a)_____ of molecules on either side of the membrane; this is called a (b)____ _____ gradient.

1. (a) concentration (b) concentration

2. The larger the concentration difference, the _____ _____(faster / slower) the movement across the membrane.

2. faster

3. True or False: Simple diffusion rates through membranes level off when the concentration is great enough so that all pores are being used for transport.

3. False

11-11 Some substances diffuse by means of a carrier system.

1. The movement of amino acids and sugars across membranes, down a concentration gradient, by a transport protein is called _____ diffusion.

1. facilitated

2. Another name for a transport protein is _____.

2. permease

3. True or False: A permease is specific to the ligand it transports.

3. True

4. True or False: Facilitated and simple diffusion are both saturable.

4. False

5. Facilitated diffusion is saturable because of a limited number of _____.

5. permeases (or transport proteins or carrier proteins)

11-12 Some molecules are pumped against a concentration gradient.

1. Simple and facilitated diffusion move substances (a)_____ (up / down) a concentration gradient; movement against a

concentration gradient is called (b)_____

_____.

1. (a) down;
   (b) active
   transport

2. Active transport requires energy to maintain a _____ (higher / lower) concentration inside the cell than out-side.

2. higher

3. The Na^+-K^+ pump gets its energy from (a)_____

to maintain a (b)_____(high / low) level of K^+ and a

(c)_____(high / low) level of Na^+ inside the cell.

3. (a) ATP;
   (b) high;
   (c) low

4. A substance that is actively transported by hitching a ride on another passively transported substance enters a

cell by a process called _____.

4. cotransport

5. Cotransport of two materials in the same direction is

called _____.

5. symport

6. Antiport is cotransport of (a)_____ (how many?)

substances in (b)_____ directions.

6. (a) two;
   (b) opposite

11-13 Molecules are moved by vectorial protein action.

1. Proteins of the same kind retain the (a)_____ orientation across an asymmetrical membrane, creating a

(b)_____ flow of substrate and ligand molecules

with which they (c)_____.

1. (a) same;
   (b) vectorial;
   (c) interact

2. Some carrier proteins can also carry out a step in

_____ while moving some molecule across a membrane.

2. metabolism

3. A vector is quantity that has a (a)_____ as well

as a (b)_____.

3. (a) direction;
   (b) magnitude

4. True or False: Mitchell's principle of vectorial meta-bolism helps explain the synthesis of ATP in electron transport systems.

4. True

11-14 Materials can be moved across membranes by bulk transport.

1. Movement of large amounts of material across the cell mem-brane is called (a)_____ transport; inward

147

transport is called (b)_____; outward transport is called (c)_____.

1. (a) bulk;
   (b) endocytosis;
   (c) exocytosis

2. In endocytosis, material is enclosed in a vesicle made by pinching off a bit of _____ membrane.

2. plasma

3. Name two substances that are commonly exported by exocytosis. _____

3. hormones, enzymes

4. True or False: Endocytosis of liquid is called phagocytosis.

4. False

11-15 Cells in a tissue may be connected by four types of junctions.

1. Cytoplasmic connections between plant cells are called (a)_____ and function in (b)_____ of material between cells.

1. (a) plasmodesmata;
   (b) exchange

2. _____ hold animal cells together like spot welding, adding structural strength.

2. Desmosomes

3. True or False: Tight junctions are protein rings fusing cells so tightly that fluid can't pass between them.

3. True

4. The animal cell equivalent to plant plasmodesmata are (a)_____, which are (b)_____ between cells for molecular and ion exchange or flow.

4. (a) gap
   junctions
   (b) channels

PRACTICE QUIZ

1. Membrane phospholipids are amphipathic because they are:
   a. hydrophobic on one end.
   b. hydrophilic on one end.
   c. both hydrophobic and hydrophilic.
   d. saturated and unsaturated.

2. Lettuce cells in water swell because water enters by:
   a. osmosis.
   b. diffusion.
   c. facilitated diffusion.
   d. active transport.

3. Plasmolysis is caused by solutions that are _____ to the cytosol.
   a. isotonic
   b. hypertonic
   c. hypotonic
   d. hydrophobic

4. Which of the following statements is <u>not</u> true of the fluid-mosaic model of membrane structure?
   a. The lipid bilayer is interspersed with globular proteins.
   b. Proteins float like icebergs in a sea of lipid.
   c. Hydrophilic proteins bind loosely on the outer surface.
   d. The middle of the lipid bilayer is hydrophilic.

5. The asymmetry of the bilayer:
   a. changes constantly due to end-for-end flips of lipid molecules.
   b. is necessary for transport to occur in the right direction.
   c. is due to uneven proteins because lipids are symmetrical.
   d. is due to its fluid nature.

6. Simple diffusion through a semipermeable membrane depends on:
   a. a concentration gradient.
   b. permeases.
   c. ATP energy sources.
   d. cotransport.

7. Which of the following is <u>not</u> an example of transport against a concentration gradient?
   a. antiport
   b. cotransport
   c. facilitated diffusion
   d. symport

8. Coupling movement to another substance down its concentration gradient is called:
   a. cotransport.
   b. antiport.
   c. endocytosis.
   d. symport.

9. Which term <u>best</u> describes white blood cells eating bacteria?
   a. pinocytosis
   b. endocytosis
   c. bulk transport
   d. phagocytosis

10. Connections between animal cells which resemble spot welds are known as:
    a. desmosomes.
    b. gap junctions.
    c. plasmodesmata.
    d. tight junctions.

REVIEW QUESTIONS

I. Answer each of the following questions.

149

1. Cite in order the steps used to make a microscope slide for a light microscope.

    _____

    _____

2. What are you really seeing when you look at photographs taken through a light microscope and an electron microscope?

    _____

    _____

    _____

3. Why does an electron microscope provide greater resolution than a light microscope?

    _____

    _____

    _____

4. Explain why a phospholipid is amphipathic.

    _____

    _____

II. A 1/2-inch-wide tube contains a sucrose solution, is sealed on the bottom end with a semipermeable membrane, and is placed vertically in a beaker of water.

    1. What happens to the fluid levels?

        _____

        _____

    2. As long as water is added to the reservoir in the beaker, will the level in the tube continue to rise indefinitely? _____

    3. Why?

        _____

        _____

        _____

III. Name the type of solution (isotonic / hypotonic / hypertonic) used to produce each of the following:

_____ 1. Turgor pressure

_____ 2. Plasmolyisis

_____ 3. Cell rupture

_____ 4. No volume change

IV. Answer each of the following questions.

1. List Overton's three general rules about permeation rates, and explain the implication of each regarding the nature of the cell membrane.

    _____

    _____

    _____

    _____

    _____

2. Within the phospholipid bilayer, how are hydrophobic and hydrophilic ends arranged?

    _____

3. What determines the position of intrinsic and peripheral proteins in the fluid-mosaic model of membrane structure?

    _____

    _____

    _____

4. What is the significance of the human-mouse heterokaryon experiments done by Frye and Edidin in 1970?

    _____

    _____

5. What two changes in phospholipid structure can cells make to reduce the transition temperature?

    _____

151

6. What functional reason is there for the asymmetry of the cell membrane?

_____

_____

7. Describe growth by intussusception.

_____

_____

8. What is the General Principle of Biological Organization?

_____

_____

V. Match each of the items in the left column with the letter for the correct descriptive term from the right column.

_____ 1. Amino acids, glucose into   A - active transport
             animal intestinal cells

_____ 2. Cell drinking   F - facilitated diffusion

_____ 3. CO_2, O_2 exchange in the lung P - phagocytosis

_____ 4. NA^+-K^+ exchange pump   R - pinocytosis

_____ 5. Uses permeases   S - simple diffusion

_____ 6. White blood cells eating bacteria   Y - symport

VI. List the four types of cell junctions and give their functions.

1. _____

2. _____

3. _____

4. _____

ANSWERS TO CHAPTER EXERCISES

Practice Quiz

1. c	3. b	5. b	7. c	9. d
2. a	4. d	6. a	8. a	10. a

Review Questions

I. 1. Fixation, dehydration, paraffin replacement, sectioning, paraffin removal, staining, observation.
   2. Light microscope slides show different patterns of stain absorption by different materials, emphasizing contrasts. Electron micrographs likewise show deposition patterns of heavy metals, which serve as stains.
   3. When an object is smaller than the wavelength of the energy being used, it is no longer visible. The wavelengths of electrons are much shorter than the shortest wavelength of visible light.
   4. The fatty acid end of the molecule is hydrophobic and the phosphate end is hydrophilic.

II. 1. The water level will drop in the beaker as the level in the tube rises.
   2. No.
   3. As the tube level rises, it exerts an increasing pressure (weight) on the membrane. When the osmotic pressure in the tube equals the water potential of the beaker water, equilibrium results.

III. 1. hypotonic   3. hypotonic
    2. hypertonic   4. isotonic

IV. 1. Smaller uncharged molecules penetrate faster than larger uncharged molecules; they are moving through pores. Any charged molecule enters slowly; the pores are surrounded by charges which repel. Penetration of uncharged molecules is proportional to their lipid solubility; the membrane is made of lipid.
   2. Hydrophilic ends are external and hydrophobic ends are internal.
   3. The position is determined by the extent of hydrophobic or hydrophilic structure on their surfaces. Peripheral proteins are more hydrophilic and bind loosely on the surface.
   4. The mixing of membrane proteins demonstrated the extreme fluid nature of the membrane.
   5. Transition temperature is reduced by using phospholipids with shorter fatty acid chains and less saturation.
   6. The translocating proteins must be oriented so that they move material in the correct direction.
   7. New phospholipid or protein molecules squeeze their way in between existing molecules much like a wedge driven into wood.
   8. Initial structure, right or wrong, determines the form of newly synthesized structure.

V. 1. Y   3. S   5. F
   2. R   4. A   6. P

VI. 1. Plasmodesmata facilitate exchange of material between cells.
   2. Desmosomes add structural strength and distribute stress.
   3. Tight junction does not allow material to pass between cells, only through them.
   4. Gap junction provides communication channels and offers protection by sealing off injured cells.

153

Chapter 12

CELL STRUCTURE II: THE MAJOR ORGANELLES

WHAT'S IN THIS CHAPTER

Since the perfection of the electron microscope, many new cell parts have been
discovered that were not visible with the light microscope. This chapter examines
these functional subcellular units, called organelles. The role of each organelle
in the overall picture of cellular function is presented. The previous chapter
covered the structure of membranes, and we shall also find these membranes to be
extensive within eucaryotic cells. Cytoplasmic and organelle mobility, along with
mechanisms of internal cellular support, are discussed. Comparisons of eucaryotic
and procaryotic cells are included.

By the end of this chapter you should be able to:

1. Describe the major cell organelles, their functions, and (in most cases) the
    mechanisms used to achieve these functions.

2. Explain experimental procedures leading to determination of the various
    organelles' functions.

3. Relate elements of internal cellular support to movement of cells and
    organelles.

4. Compare and contrast eucaryotic and procaryotic cell organelles.

5. Characterize the molecular nature of the cytoskeleton.

6. Draw the cross section of a centriole and a cilium or flagellum.

7. Explain the relationship between cell size and the ratio of surface area to
    volume.

WHAT YOU SHOULD ALREADY KNOW

The internal cell membranes are much like the outer cell membrane, so a thorough
understanding of membrane structure and function, as presented in Chapter 11, is
essential. A brief review of protein synthesis (Chapter 9), mitochondria (Chapter

7), chloroplasts (Chapter 8), and mitosis (Chapter 10) will be helpful.

Pre-Test

1. The part of the cell that acts as a control center for cellular activities is the _____.

1. nucleus

2. The information for cellular regulation is found in the nucleus on the _____.

2. chromosomes

3. Some protozoans move by lashing many short hairlike structures called (a)_____ in the water, wheras sperm cells move by the action of (b)_____.

3. (a) cilia;
   (b) flagella

4. _____ are pigmented organelles in plant cells that carry on photosynthesis.

4. Chloroplasts

5. ATP is produced by both chloroplasts and by _____, the powerhouses of cells.

5. mitochondria

6. Cells without an organized nucleus are called (a)_____ _____; those with a membrane-bound nucleus are called (b)_____.

6. (a) procaryotic;
   (b) eucaryotic

GUIDED REVIEW OF THE CHAPTER

Introduction to endomembranes and nucleoproteins.

1. A part of a cell with a specific function is called an _____.

1. organelle

12-1 A summary of cell features.

1. Use P for procaryotic and E for eucaryotic: (a)_____ non-circular chromosomes; (b)_____ no nuclear envelope; (c)_____ mitosis; (d)_____ smaller ribosomes; (e)_____ endoplasmic reticulum absent; (f)_____ Golgi membranes present; (g)_____ mitochondria present; (h)_____ plastids absent.

155

1. (a) E; (b) P;
   (c) E; (d) P;
   (e) P; (f) E;
   (g) E; (h) P

12-2 A eucaryotic cell is defined by its nucleus.

1. The largest organelle in eucaryotic cells is the (a)_____

   _____, which is surrounded by (b)_____(how many?)
   membrane(s).

1. (a) nucleus;
   (b) two

2. The (a)_____ in the nuclear membrane are thought
   to control the passage of material into and out of the

   (b)_____.

2. (a) pores;
   (b) nucleus

3. True or False: Any fully developed cell has a constant
   number of pores.

3. False

4. An electrical potential across the nuclear membrane means
   that the membrane probably has control over the flow of

   _____.

4. ions

5. Each of the double membranes of the nuclear envelope is a

   little (a)_____(thicker / thinner) than the
   cell membrane, and they are separated from each other by a

   space of about (b)_____ nm.

5. (a) thinner;
   (b) 10-15

12-3 The nucleolus is the site of ribosome synthesis.

1. True or False: There is a single membrane around the
   nucleolus.

1. False

2. Nucleoli are not visible during (a)_____ (what
   stage of the cell cyle?) but, when visible, they serve as

   factories for (b)_____ synthesis.

2. (a) mitosis;
   (b) ribosome

3. The specific chromosomal region where genes for ribosomal

   RNA are located is called the _____

   _____.

3. nucleolar
   organizer

4. Most diploid cells have (a)_____(how many?)

   nucleoli(us) per cell, and this number shows (b)_____

   _____(little /much) variation among cells.

4. (a) two;
   (b) much

5. The number of nucleoli per cell is influenced by the

   number of _____ needed.

5. ribosomes

6. True or False: In differential centrifugation, heavier
   material stays closer to the top of the tube.

6. False

7. The S value is a (a)_____ constant roughly

   proportional to (b)_____ weight.

7. (a) sedimenta-
   tion;
   (b) molecular

8. True or False: a 40S ribosomal subunit plus a 60S subunit
   equals an 80S particle.

8. True

9. RNA subunits are produced in the (a)_____; RNA

   proteins are produced in the (b)_____; and the

   assembly of subunits and proteins occurs in the (c)_____

   _____.

9. (a) nucleoli;
   (b) cytoplasm;
   (c) nucleoli

10. True or False: The functional RNA subunits are tran-
    scribed individually as small molecules from the nucleo-
    lar organizer region.

10. False

11. True or False: Pulse-chase experiments followed rRNA
    synthesis using radioactive tracers and centrifugations.

11. True

12. _____(Few / Many) rRNA stands are transcribed at one
    time.

12. Many

*12-4 The endoplasmic reticulum is a closed system of mem-
      branes.*

1. Rough endoplasmic reticulum (ER) appears rough in electron

   micrographs because of attached _____.

1. ribosomes

2. If endoplasmic reticulum (ER) does not have attached

   ribosomes, it is called _____ ER.

2. smooth

3. True or False: Nuclear membrane pores communicate directly to the lumen of the ER.

3. False

4. The numerous (a)_____(single / double) mem-

   branes of the ER run (b)_____(parallel /
   perpendicular) to the nuclear and plasma membrane.

4. (a) double;
   (b) parallel

5. True or False: Completed enzymes made on rough ER appear
   first in the ER lumen on the side opposite the ribosomes.

5. True

6. True or False: The "signal" of the signal hypothesis is
   actually an amino acid chain.

6. True

7. The signal hypothesis partially explains protein movement

   from the (a)_____ into the (b)_____.

7. (a) ribosome;
   (b) ER lumen

8. Smooth ER takes the form of (a)_____ or

   (b)_____ and produces nonprotein materials such
   as steroids.

8. (a) tubules;
   (b) vesicles

9. True or False: The relative amounts of rough and smooth
   ER can vary in liver cells depending on need.

9. True

12-5 The Golgi apparatus is a packaging and exporting center.

1. The Golgi apparatus in plant cells is sometimes called a

   _____.

1. dictyosome

2. What two general processes occur in the Golgi apparatus?

   (Both start with the letter "p".) _____

   _____

2. packaging and
   processing

3. Materials enter Golgi apparatus membranes on the

   "(a)_____ face" and emerge packaged and pro-

   cessed on the "(b)_____ face".

3. (a) forming;
   (b) maturation

*12-6 Secretion entails a synthesis and outward flow of
      membranes.*

1. Packaged material is released from secreting cells by

   _____ (what process?).

1. exocytosis

2. True or False; Secretion by exocytosis could explain
   plasma membrane growth.

2. True

3. In the secretion process, membrane flow is from ER to

   (a)_____ to (b)_____
   and into the plasma membrane.

3. (a) Golgi
   complex;
   (b) vesicles

12-7 Lysosomes are bags of digestive enzymes.

1. True or False: Virtually anything can be digested by the
   enzymes in lysosomes.

1. True

2. Primary lysosomes are wrapped in a _____ so
   their enzymes can't digest cellular structures.

2. membrane

3. Vacuoles of endocytotic material (a)_____ with

   primary lysosomes, producing a (b)_____ lysosome
   in which large molecules are digested to small ones.

3. (a) fuse;
   (b) secondary

4. True or False: Digestive products of secondary lysosomes enter the cytosol when the lysosome membrane ruptures.

4. False

5. Waste material in secondary lysosomes is eliminated by _____ (what process?).

5. exocytosis

6. Selected portions of cell can be fused with lysosomes, a process called (a)_____, for the purpose of (b)_____.

6. (a) autophagy;
   (b) reuse or
   recycling

7. True or False: Larger-than-normal numbers of lysosomes would be found in muscle tissue during prolonged starvation.

7. True

12-8 Cells often contain other specialized vesicles.

1. Cosmic electromagnetic radiation produce ions and (a)_____ when they enter a cell. These are any molecules with an electron that is (b)_____(paired / unpaired).

1. (a) free radi-
   cals; (b) un-
   paired

2. Large central vacuoles in plant cells, occupying as much as (a)_____ percent of the cell volume, are used for (b)_____ of various materials.

2. (a) 80-90;
   (b) storage

12-9 Mitochondria and chloroplasts contain their own genetic apparatus.

1. Mitochondria (a)_____(are / are not) connected to the endomembrane system and are numerous in cells with (b)_____(large / small) amounts of cellular activity.

1. (a) are not;
   (b) large

2. Mitochondria keep free (a)_____ ions at a low level in the cell by storing them as (b)_____ phosphate.

2. (a) calcium;
   (b) calcium

3. True or False: Each mitochondrion has a noncircular molecule of double-stranded DNA with histones as its chromosome.

3. False

4. Transcription and translation of mitochondrial DNA occurs (a)_____(outside of / within) each mitochon-

159

drion; growth is by expansion of their (b)_____ and division.

4. (a) within; (b) membranes

5. True or False: All mitochondrial proteins are informed by mitochondrial DNA using the universal code of all procaryotic and eucaryotic genomes.

5. False

6. A plant chromoplast is a plastid bearing _____.

6. pigment

Introduction to the cytoskeleton and cellular motility.

1. True or False: Fully grown cells have definite, unchanging shapes and show little movement.

1. False

2. Three mechanisms that cells use to produce movement are

(a)_____ movement, (b)_____, and

(c)_____ and _____.

2. (a) amoeboid; (b) pseudopods; (c) cilia and flagella

3. The cell cytoskeleton consists of a variety of (a)_____ and (b)_____ stretching throughout the cytoplasm.

3. (a) filaments; (b) tubules

12-10 Some general principles about the cytoskeleton.

1. The cytoskeleton's structural proteins are of two classes:

(a)_____ and (b)_____.

1. (a) myosins; (b) tektins

2. Myosins are (a)_____(long / short) fibrous proteins with a (b)_____(what shape?) end.

2. (a) long; (b) globular

3. Tektins are small (a)_____(what shape?) proteins, which include (b)_____, flagellins, (c)_____, and some membrane proteins.

3. (a) globular; (b) actins; (c) tubulins

4. Helical fibers of myosins and tektins produce movement by

(a)_____ past each other, one of them (b)_____ the other along.

4. (a) sliding; (b) pulling

5. True or False: The energy for movement in eucaryotic cells always comes from ATP.

5. True

6. Movement always seems to be regulated by _____ ions.

6. calcium

7. An exception to generalizations about cell movement are

160

the flagella of (a)_____, which move by rotation

and use a (b)_____ gradient as an energy source.

7. (a) bacteria;
(b) hydrogen-
ion

8. If a microfilament inhibitor stops a cellular process, that process is dependent on the action of _____

_____.

8. microfilaments

12-11 Microfilaments are major effectors of cell movement.

1. Myosin fibers pull on (a)_____ fibers through

activation of (b)_____ found in the globular myosin head.

1. (a) actin;
(b) ATPase

2. ATPase breaks down (a)_____, producing energy,

ADP, and a (b)_____.

2. (a) ATP;
(b) phosphate

3. The actin cytoskeleton breaks down during (a)_____

allowing the cell to assume a (b)_____ shape.

3. (a) mitosis;
(b) rounded

4. Which filaments play a major role in cytokinesis? _____

_____

4. actin filaments

5. During the sliding movement of actin and myosin, the

myosin "(a)_____" along the actin, creating a

slight (b)_____.

5. (a) walks;
(b) pull

6. Three cell processes that use the actin-myosin micro-

filament system to produce motion are (a)_____

_____, (b)_____, and (c)_____

_____.

6. (a) ameboid
action;
(b) cyclosis;
(c) muscle
contraction

12-12 Microtubules shape cells and are used for movement.

1. Microtubules average (a)_____ nm in diameter with a hole

size of 15 nm and are composed of (b)_____ kinds of very

similar (c)_____.

1. (a) 25; (b) 2;
(c) tektins

2. True or False: An α-β dimer is composed of α-tubulin and β-tubulin

161

2. True

3. A microtubule is a (a)_____(what shape?) arrangement of (b)_____(how many?) columns of dimers running parallel to each other.

3. (a) helical;
   (b) 13

4. Name three structures that use microtubules:

   _____

   _____

4. spindle fibers,
   basal bodies,
   centrioles,
   axostyles,
   axopods

12-13 Some microtubule structures are organized by special centers.

1. Name a microtubule-organizing center found in many eucaryotic cells. _____

1. centrioles or
   basal bodies

2. A cross section of a basal body of a flagellum shows _____(how many?) short triplets of microtubules.

2. nine

3. The basal body helps organize microtubules of (a)_____ _____ and (b)_____ and the mitotic spindle.

3. (a) cilia;
   (b) flagella

4. Free microtubules of the mitotic spindle run from a (a)_____ into the (b)_____ of the spindle.

4. (a) pole;
   (b) middle

5. True or False: Chromosome separation and movement are fully explained by the actin-myosin sliding filament theory.

5. False

6. True or False: The mitotic spindle has microtubules with three different termination points.

6. True

7. Centrioles are duplicated from _____.

7. centrioles

12-14 Cilia and flagella are movable bundles of microtubules.

1. A cross section of a cilium or flagellum shows a pattern of (a)_____(how many?) doublets of microtubules arranged in a circle around (b)_____(how many?) central microtubules.

1. (a) nine;
   (b) two

2. Movemnt of kinetids results from doublets (a)_____ past each other, using ATP energy supplied by doublet extensions called (b)_____.

2. (a) sliding;   *12-15 Bacterial flagella are made of flagellin, a different*
   (b) dynein   *tektin.*

                   1. The procaryotic flagellum is made of a tektin called

                       (a)_____ and has the form of a (b)_____ .

1. (a) flagellin; 2. The procaryotic flagellum does not move by sliding
   (b) helix
                       filaments, but by (a)_____ between surrounding

                       (b)_____ and the flagellin core.

2. (a) rotation;
   (b) rings

PRACTICE QUIZ

1. _____ are present in both eucaryotic and procaryotic cells.
    a. Chromosomes
    b. Mitochondria
    c. Ribosomes
    d. Nucleoli

2. Which of the following "structure-location" pairings is correct?
    a. nucleolus - chromosome
    b. smooth ER - nucleus
    c. Golgi complex - plasma membrane
    d. mitochondria - rough ER

3. The pores in the nuclear envelope do not appear to regulate:
    a. passage of material between nucleus and cytoplasm.
    b. mRNA movement between nucleus and cytoplasm.
    c. ion flow between nucleus and cytoplasm.
    d. lysosome migration between nucleus and cytoplasm.

4. Smooth ER is responsible for:
    a. protein synthesis.
    b. nonprotein synthesis.
    c. processing and packaging.
    d. rRNA assembly.

5. Which of the following is not a lysosome function?
    a. polymer conversion to monomers
    b. autophagy
    c. cell destruction
    d. free radical deactivation

6. If a cell lost all its mitochondria, it would:
    a. synthesize new ones using genome instructions.
    b. continue to have normal concentrations of free calcium ions.
    c. be unable to continue active transport mechanism.
    d. produce excess cytochrome oxidase as an energy source.

163

7. Which general principle about the cytoskeleton is accurate?
   a. Myosins include actins, flagellins, and tubulins.
   b. Tektins form long elastic fibers or tubules.
   c. Energy for every mobile system of the cytoskeleton comes from calcium ions.
   d. In all types of eucaryotic cytoskeleton movement, fibers or tubules slide past each other.

8. A primary lysosome becomes a secondary lysosome by:
   a. entering the ER lumen.
   b. emerging from the "maturation face" of the Golgi complex.
   c. fusing with a vacuole.
   d. ridding itself of indigestible residue through exocytosis.

9. "Nine doublets of microtubules with two more singles in the center" describes a cross-sectional view of a:
   a. flagellum
   b. centriole.
   c. basal body.
   d. rod from the retina of the eye.

10. Procaryotic flagellar movement does not work on the sliding filament idea, because:
    a. ATP is not used as an energy source.
    b. its proteins are organized in circular structures.
    c. its tektin is flagellin.
    d. its system of rings is firmly anchored.

REVIEW QUESTIONS

I. Answer each of the following questions.

   1. List five structures that are present (or often present) in eucaryotic cells but are not present in procaryotic cells.

   _____

   _____

   2. Why are cells small?

   _____

   _____

   _____

II. Match each of the items in the left column with the appropriate structure from the right column.

_____ 1. ATP factories   a. basal body

_____ 2. Autophagy   b. Golgi complex

164

_____ 3. "Forming face"   c. lysosomes

_____ 4. Microtubule-organizing center   d. mitochondria

_____ 5. Product packaging   e. nucleolus

_____ 6. Protein synthesis   f. rough ER

_____ 7. Regulates free Ca ion conentration   g. smooth ER

_____ 8. Ribosome synthesis

_____ 9. Semiautonomous

_____ 10. Steroid hormone synthesis

III. Answer each of the following questions.

1. What two methods are used by nuclear envelope pores to regulate passage of material?

_____

2. What is a nucelolus?

_____

3. Briefly describe ribosome synthesis.

_____

_____

_____

4. What is meant by "S value"?

_____

5. How is the physical arrangement between rough ER and nuclear pores conducive to protein synthesis?

_____

6. What are the entry and exit areas of the Golgi complex and what happens to vesicles between entry and exit?

_____

_____

165

7. Describe the sequence of events in the life cycle of a lysosome.

    _____

    _____

    _____

8. Why are free radicals dangerous to cells?

    _____

9. What genetic structure-function aspects of mitochondria are different from
    eucaryotic cells?

    _____

    _____

10. What are myosins and tektins?

    _____

11. Describe the type of action occurring among helical fibers and tubules to
    produce movement.

    _____

    _____

12. List three cell activities in which microfilaments play a role.

    _____

13. How are microtubules constructed?

    _____

    _____

14. What are two major roles of the centrioles, or basal bodie., as
    microtubule-organizing centers?

    _____

    _____

15. What is the basis for ciliary and flagellar motion?

    _____

IV. Draw a cross section of (1) a centriole and (2) a cilium.

ANSWERS TO CHAPTER EXERCISES

Practice Quiz

1. c, d	3. d	5. d	7. d	9. a
2. a	4. b	6. c	8. c	10. b

Review Questions

I. 1. Nuclear envelope, endoplasmic reticulum, Golgi membranes, mitochondria, plastids.
    2. As cells get bigger, volume increases at a greater rate than surface area. A critical size is reached when the surrounding membrane cannot transport material into and out of the cell fast enough to keep up with the demand of a proportionally larger and larger volume.

II. 1. d	3. b	5. b	7. d	9. d
2. c	4. a	6. f	8. e	10. g

III. 1. Opening and closing; electrical potentials attract or repel ions.
      2. A nucleolus is a specific chromosomal region from which ribosomal RNA is transcribed.
      3. Each long piece of transcribed rRNA is cut into the correct subunits, and these are assembled with ribosomal proteins brought in from the cytoplasm. Assembly occurs at the nucleolar organizer site, and completed ribosomes move into the cytoplasm.
      4. It is a sedimentation value roughly proportional to molecular weight.
      5. As mRNA leaves the nucleus, it comes into direct contact with ribosomes.
      6. Vesicles condense on the forming face and emerge, processed and packaged, on the maturation face.
      7. A primary lysosome fuses with an endocytotic vesicle, becoming a secondary lysosome. Vesicle contents are digested and enter the cytosol through the lysosome membrane. Through exocytosis, waste is discharged and the lysosome membrane becomes part of the plasma membrane.
      8. They are very reactive with and damage all kinds of cellular materials.
      9. Mitochondria possess one chromosome of a closed loop of double-stranded DNA without histones, distinctive ribosomes and tRNAs, and a slightly different genetic code.
     10. They are fibrous and globular proteins that form helical fibers or tubules.

167

11. The long fibers run parallel to each other with connections between them. One fiber pulls itself along the other one.
12. Ameboid action, cyclosis, exocytotic and endocytotic membrane movements, muscle contraction.
13. A microtubule is a helical arrangement of 13 columns of dimers (of α- and β-tubulins) running parallel to each other.
14. As a basal body, it organizes the microtubules of cilia and flagella. As a centriole, it organizes the mitotic spindle.
15. The nine doublets, each of subfiber A and subfiber B, slide past each other like actin and myosin.

IV. 1. 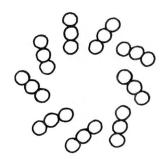   2.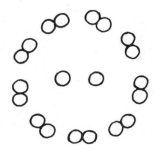

Chapter 13

ELEMENTS OF GENETIC ANALYSIS

WHAT'S IN THIS CHAPTER

Like all scientists, biologists face the problem of finding powerful methods that give them insight into the operations of the systems in which they are interested. For a long time, biologists appeared to have a choice between only two methods: They might try to dissect organisms into their separate chemical components or try to study the properties and behavior of whole, intact organisms. Both methods have serious limitations. The first gives a great deal of information about chemical structure, but it does not provide obvious information about the functioning of intact systems. The second, however, permits only relatively crude manipulations.

The modern paradigm of biology depends to a large extend on the development of a third method that is extremely powerful and has the potential of leading to an understanding of even the most complex biological problems, just as it has already led to insights into the basic properties of organisms and viruses. This is the method of genetic analysis, which is described in this chapter. It depends on finding mutant organisms, which may exhibit very subtle changes in the operation of specific systems, and analyzing the effects of those mutations.

Mutants of easy-to-grow, rapidly reproducing organisms (such as bacteria and fungi) have been the most fruitful material for experimentation. This chapter explains how bacterial mutants are found and how they can be used. It then explains--using phage mutants as an example--how the very structure of the genome itself can be determined through genetic mapping, a method of determining precisely where in the genome each mutation has occurred. A second method, the complementation test, then allows one to determine what the limits of each gene are. Finally, this chapter shows how mutations were used to elucidate the genetic code that specifies how proteins are to be made.

By the end of this chapter you should be able to:

1. Explain the two major philosophies about research methods.

2. State why mutant organisms are used in experiments and how they can be isolated.

3. Discuss the randomness of mutations.

169

4. Describe the molecular basis for mutation.

5. Relate how mutations are used to derive knowledge of the genome and which mutational types are the most useful for this purpose.

6. Construct a simple genetic map based on information from genetic crosses with both point mutations and deletions.

7. Explain how a complementation test can show whether or not two mutations are in the same gene.

8. Reinforce your knowledge of the genetic code by explaining the evidence for its nature.

WHAT YOU SHOULD ALREADY KNOW

A clear understanding of normalcy is basic to an understanding of mutated processes. This chapter assumes you have retained the previous information on genes (Sections 3-5, 3-6, 3-7). If not, review it. The information in Chapter 9 on DNA, RNA, protein synthesis, and the genetic code is so vital that it should be reviewed in detail.

Pre-Test

1. Every organism contains a substructure called its

(a)_____ that carries the (b)_____ information that tells the organism how to operate.

1. (a) genome;
   (b) genetic

2. The genome is divisible into units called (a)_____, each of which codes for a single chain (molecule) of

(b)_____.

2. (a) genes;
   (b) protein

3. _____ are changes in gene structure that result in new features.

3. Mutations

4. Every protein is a polymer made of monomers called

_____.

4. amino acids

5. The genome itself is made of a different kind of polymer called (a) deoxyribo-_____, which is

abbreviated (b)_____.

5. (a) nucleic acid; (b) DNA

6. The monomers of nucleic acid are quite different from those of a protein and are called _____.

6. nucleotides

7. Thus a (a)_____ is a string of amino acids, and a (b)_____ is a string of nucleotides.

170

7. (a) protein;
    (b) nucleic
    acid

8. The <u>sequence</u> of (a)_____ in a protein

    is determined by the <u>sequence</u> of (b)_____ in a
    nucleic acid.

8. (a) amino
    acids;
    (b) nucleotides

9. A mutation might be a change from one (a)_____
    to another in DNA. Such a simple change could result in

    the substitution of one (b)_____ for
    another in the corresponding protein.

9. (a) nucleotide;
    (b) amino acid

10. A string of (a)_____(how many?) nucleotides that informs

    (codes for) one amino acid is called a (b)_____.

10. (a) 3;
    (b) codon

11. Most of the proteins in a cell are _____
    which catalyze specific chemical reactions.

11. enzymes

12. The chemical activity in a cell is typically organized

    into series of reactions called _____

    _____ that are analogous to assembly lines.

12. metabolic
    pathways

13. If a pathway is supposed to be synthesizing a specific
    amino acid, but one of the enzymes in the pathway is de-
    fective, what will be the immediate effect of that defect?

    _____

13. The amino
    acid will
    not be
    made

14. The most obvious reason why an enzyme might be defective

    is that a _____ might have occurred in the
    gene that codes for that enzyme.

14. mutation

GUIDED REVIEW OF THE CHAPTER

Introduction

1. Successful genetic researchers of the past all followed

    one simple dictum; try to understand the _____
    phenomena first.

1. simplest

2. What are some of these simple (living) systems? _____

    _____

2. bacteria,
    phage, yeast,
    algae

171

13-1 Biologists have held two major philosophies about research methods.

1. Comparison experiments ideally should involve _____ (how many?) variable(s).

1. one

2. In identical experiments with a single variable, differing results can only be attributed to _____(how many?) variable(s).

2. one

3. True or False: All experimental procedures can be reduced to a single variable.

3. False

4. Organicism proposes that experiments should involve _____ _____(parts of the / the whole) organism.

4. the whole

5. True or False: Isolated chloroplasts in a petri dish would be the experimental material of a reductionist.

5. True

6. Reductionism has been criticized because tested parts are out of their _____ environment and may there-fore act differently.

6. natural

13-2 Mutant organisms form the basic material of experiments.

1. Mutants possess a small change in their _____, resulting in a change in some feature.

1. genome

2. A comparison of a mutant and a nonmutant is ideal because they differ in _____(how many?) way(s).

2. one

3. Identifying the mutant gene in a mutant-nonmutant comparison reveals the _____ of that gene.

3. function

4. True or False: Conclusions from mutational studies satisfy both organicists and reductionists.

4. True

13-3 Finding bacterial mutants.

1. Bacterial mutants are located through (a)_____ and (b)_____ techniques.

1. (a) selective; (b) differen-tial

2. Which of these two techniques is the easiest? _____ _____

2. selective

3. Using the selective procedure, those (a)_____(few/ many) that are (b)_____ are selected.

172

3. (a) few;
   (b) different

4. True

5. sensitive

6. (a) wild;
   (b) +

7. (a) mutant;
   (b) cannot;
   (c) lactose

8. (a) pink;
   (b) mutation

9. (a) absence;
   (b) lactose

10. True

11. (a) lacZ
    (b) factor

12. cell
    membrane

13. True

4. True or False: In the differential technique, bacteria are placed on a specific media plus dye, and mutants distinguish themselves through color reactions to their chemical components.

5. The symbol Str^{s} indicates a bacterial strain that is _____(resistant / sensitive) to streptomycin.

6. A nonmutant is also called a (a)_____ type and is indicated by a (b)_____ sign.

7. The symbol lac^{-} designates a (a)_____(mutant/ nonmutant) that (b)_____(can / cannot) metabolize (c)_____.

8. On EMB agar, a lac^{-} colony is (a)_____(what color?), but rarely dark colonies appear on lac^{-} plates, indicating that a (b)_____ occurred from lac^{-} to lac^{+}.

9. Enzyme assay of lac^{-} bacteria normally shows the (a)_____ _____(absence / presence) of β-galactosidase, which is necessary for growth on (b)_____ media.

10. True or False: A $lacZ$ mutant lacks the β-galactosidase enzyme; a $lacY$ mutant has the enzyme but can't use it.

11. $LacZ$ and $lacY$ bacteria grown on radioactive lactose revealed that (a)_____ bacteria incorporate the lactose, indicating that at least one other (b)_____ is involved in lactose metabolism.

12. The $lacY$ cells β-galactosidase is useless to them because they cannot get lactose across their _____ _____.

13. True or False: The inability to transport lactose into the cell is proof that a factor for this purpose normally exists.

13-4 Mutations are not specific reactions to the environment.

1. True or False: Mutations occur as a specific reaction to a need.

173

1. False

2. Beneficial and detrimental mutations occur (a)_____ (randomly / nonrandomly), totally (b)_____ (dependent / independent) of current environmental conditions.

2. (a) randomly; (b) independent

3. True or False: In stable populations the mutation rate is zero.

3. False

4. Two environmental sources of mutations are _____ and _____.

4. mutagens and radiation

13-5 *Mutations are alterations in nucleic acid structure.*

1. Chemical mutagens either directly (a)_____ a nucleotide or cause a change to occur during (b)_____ _____.

1. (a) change; (b) replication

2. Nitrous acid can cause DNA polymerase to insert _____ instead of thymine during replication.

2. cytosine

3. 5-bromouracil converts a T-A base pairing to (a)_____ after (b)_____(how many?) replication cycles.

3. (a) C-G; (b) two

4. True or False: Carcinogens are also mutagens.

4. True

5. True or False: The breakdown products of some harmless substances are carcinogens.

5. True

13-6 *Auxotrophic mutants are used to elucidate metabolic pathways.*

1. A mutant that cannot synthesize one or more of its own components is called _____.

1. auxotrophic

2. To isolate mutants that can't synthesize substance X, a culture is first exposed to a (a)_____ and then grown with the antibiotic penicillin in a medium (b)_____(with / without) substance X.

2. (a) mutagen; (b) without

3. Because penicillin kills only growing cells, the cells that are killed in this procedure are the (a)_____ _____, whereas many of the survivors are the (b)_____ that cannot grow without substance X.

174

3. (a) proto-
    trophs;
    (b) auxotrophs

4. True or False: X mutants cannot grow on nutrient medium containing substance X.

4. False

5. The one-gene, one-enzyme theory developed by Beadle and Tatum tells us that mutant X will be defective in one

   (a)_____ required in the (b)_____

   _____ for the synthesis of X.

5. (a) enzyme;
    (b) metabolic
    pathway

6. Isolated cultures of mutant X will accumulate the metabolite (we'll call it W) just (a)_____(before / after) the metabolite block created by the mutation.

6. before

7. True or False: The accumulated substance W in X mutants is present in quantities large enough for identification.

7. True

8. We now know that substance (a)_____ is the precursor

   to substance (b)_____.

8. (a) W;
    (b) X

9. Different mutants accumulate (a)_____ materials

   and can (b)_____-feed one another.

9. (a) different
    (b) cross

10. If mutant A feeds mutant B, the metabolite block in A is

    (a)_____(after / before) the block in B.   B

    (b)_____(can / cannot) cross-feed A.

10. (a) after;
     (b) cannot

11. If a mutant grows on a substance, its mutational block is

    _____(after / before) that substance.

11. before

13-7 Mutants can be used to analyze complex systems.

1. Movement responses to chemicals are called (a)_____

   _____ and the sensing device is called a (b)_____

   _____.

1. (a) chemotaxis;
    (b) chemosensor

2. True or False: Chemotaxis experiments in *E. coli* mutants show that there are different chemosensors that detect different sugars.

2. True

3. If a single *E. coli* mutant fails to respond to a series of related compounds, this indicates that there is(are)

   _____(one / several) chemosensor(s) for the compounds.

3. one

4. Bacterial sensing and transport of galactose is controlled

175

by _____ (a single / several) factor(s).

4. a single

5. The bacterial galactose chemosensor can stimulate (a)_____ or (b)_____ .

5. (a) transport;
   (b) chemotaxis

6. True or False: Patterns of mutations affecting bacterial chemotaxis have revealed the number of different chemo-reception systems, their specificity, and chemosensing-transport relationships.

6. True

13-8 The most useful mutations are conditional lethals.

1. (a)_____ (Genotype / Phenotype) determines (b)_____ (genotype / phenotype).

1. (a) Genotype;
   (b) phenotype

2. True or False: The genotypes of some phage can be determined by observing thier plaque phenotype.

2. True

3. A lethal mutation causes (a)_____ ; a conditional lethal causes (b)_____ only under certain circumstances.

3. (a) death;
   (b) death

4. Auxotrophic mutations _____ (are / are not) conditional lethals.

4. are

5. The *ts* and *cs* phage mutants' protein stability is _____ _____-dependent.

5. temperature

6. Host-dependent phage mutants will grow in specific _____ strains.

6. bacterial

7. True or False: Host-dependency is not a type of conditional lethal.

7. False

13-9 A set of mutations defines a genetic map of the genome.

1. A genetic map shows the sizes and (a)_____ of all genes, the control elements, and a (b)_____ for each gene.

1. (a) positions;
   (b) function

2. Mutations used to map and define genes are called _____ _____.

2. markers

3. A change in one nucleotide pair is a (a)_____ mutation; its place on the genetic map is called its (b)_____ .

3. (a) point;
   (b) site

4. locus

5. relative

6. (a) the same;
   (b) as a
   package

7. False

8. (a) *ri*
   (b) *tu*

9. (a) crossover;
   (b) recombinant

10. (a) random;
    (b) distance

11. (a) recombi-
    nants;
    (b) offspring

12. farther apart

13. True

14. (a) single
    (b) *mi* and *r*

4. A gene's location on the map is its _____.

5. A gene map shows only the position of one mutation or gene

   _____ relative to that of another, and it
   may be distorted.

6. Linked genes are on (a)_____(the same /
   different) chromosome(s), and their features are inherited

   (b)_____(as a package / independently).

7. True or False: The closer together two markers are, the
   easier it is for them to be separated and inherited
   independently.

8. Expected results of a *r* and *tu* mutant cross would be

   (a)_____ and (b)_____ offspring.

9. But the *r* x *tu* cross also shows a few plaques with both

   mutations and a few wild types due to (a)_____

   that results in these new (b)_____ types.

10. Crossover is a (a)_____(random / nonrandom)
    process, and the probability of separating two markers is

    proportional to the (b)_____ between them.

11. The frequency of recombination (*R*) is the total number of

    (a)_____ divided by the total number of

    (b)_____, expressed as a percentage or a
    decimal.

12. The larger the *R* value, the _____
    (closer together / farther apart) are the two markers.

13. True or False: Recombinants from the cross *tu mi r* x + +
    + will have a mix of mutant and wild-type features.

14. The recombinants *tu mi* + and + + *r* show a (a)_____

    (double / single) crossover between (b)_____

    and _____.

15. The recombinants *tu* + *r* and + *mi* + show a double crossover

    between (a)_____ and _____ and

    between (b)_____ and _____.

177

15. (a) *tu* and *mi*;
    (b) *mi* and *r*

16. As linked genes get farther apart, the *R* value becomes

    (a)_____(more / less) reliable due to greater

    frequency of (b)_____(single / double / multiple) crossover.

16. (a) less;
    (b) multiple

17. *R* values are useless when they approach (a)_____ percent, and considered reliable when they are less than

    about (b)_____ percent.

17. (a) 50;
    (b) 20

18. The *R* value of 10 percent equals _____(how many?) map units.

18. 10

19. Map units _____(are / are not) real physical units between genes.

19. are not

20. If R_{ab} = 19, R_{ac} = 4, and R_{bc} = 15, marker (a)_____

    (*a* / *b* / *c*) is between (b)_____ and _____, and the

    marker closest to *a* is (c)_____(*b* / *c*).

20. (a) *c*;
    (b) *a* and *b*;
    (c) *c*

13-10 The sequence of three markers can always be determined unambiguously.

1. True or False: The distance between markers is more important than the sequence of markers.

1. False

2. The rarest recombinants from a *tu mi r* and + + + cross are

    _____ and _____.

2. *tu* + *r*,
   + *mi* +

3. The frequency of a particular class of recombinants

    _____(decreases / increases) as the number of crossovers required to create it increases.

3. decreases

4. How many crossovers are necessary to get (a) $a^+b^+c^+$ and

    (b) ab^+c^+ from a cross of abc^+ and a^+b^+c ? (a)_____;

    (b)_____.

4. (a) one;
   (b) two

13-11 Mutations can be mapped rapidly by using deletions.

1. The smallest possible *R* value among 100 offspring would be

    _____.

1. 1/100 or
   0.01

2. Benzer found that *r* mutants grow only in strain (a)_____ of *E. coli* but that any wild-type recombinants will grow

    in strain (b)_____, permitting the detection of very

small numbers of recombinants.

2. (a) B; (b) K

3. True or False: Deletion mutations can mutate back to wild type.

3. False

4. Deletions cover _____ (one / more than one) point mutation site.

4. more than one

5. Crosses of nonoverlapping deletion mutations _____ (can / cannot) produce wild-type recombinants.

5. can

6. A point mutation crossed with a known deletion _____ (does / does not) produce wild type if the point mutation is in the deleted area.

6. does not

7. The smallest R value for T4 phage studies by Benzer was

(a)_____, and all of them added together showed

the genome to consist of about (b)_____ map units.

7. (a) 0.01;
    (b) 2,000

8. Therefore, any mutations mapped at 0.01 map units apart

are probably _____.

8. neighbors

9. Dividing the total number of base pairs of the T4 phage genome by the total number of map units revealed about

_____ (how many?) base pairs per map unit.

9. 100

13-12 Genes are defined by complementation tests.

1. Two mutants _____ each other if each supplies a missing factor for the other.

1. complement

2. True or False: The *trans* position is one in which two mutations are in different genomes.

2. True

3. The _____ position means that both mutations are on one genome.

3. *cis*

4. Growth of *cis*-positioned mutations with wild type means

that mutant genes _____ (do / do not) block wild-type genes.

4. do not

5. True or False: Benzer's mutations formed two complementation groups.

5. True

6. A mutation in a complementation group _____ (will / will not) complement another in the same group.

6. will not

7. A complementation group is also called a _____.

7. criston

179

13-13 The messenger is read by threes without commas.

1. The reading-frame mechanism proposed by Crick *et al.* marks

   off (a)_____ (how many?) bases at a time (b)_____
   (with / without) commas between bases.

1. (a) three;
   (b) without

2. Does a frameshift mutation always involve the loss or gain

   of only one base pair? _____

2. no - it
   could be
   any number

3. A one-base deletion closely followed by a one-base addi-

   tion shifts the reading frame to (a)_____
   (normal / an even worse) condition.   This addition is

   called a (b)_____ mutation.

3. (a) normal;
   (b) suppressor

4. The addition of 1, 4 or 7 bases has the same reading-frame

   effect as a deletion of (a)_____, (b)_____, or (c)_____
   (how many?) bases, respectively.   All shift the reading

   frame one base to the (d)_____ (left / right) and

   are called (e)_____ mutations.

4. (a) 2; (b) 5
   (c) 8;
   (d) left;
   (e) L

5. R mutations shift the reading frame one base to the right

   and are caused by (a)___, ___, or ___ base deletions or by

   (b)___, ___, or ___ base additions.

5. (a) 1, 4, or 7;
   (b) 2, 5, or 8;

6. Any L mutation should produce wild-type offspring if

   combined with any _____ mutation.

6. R

7. True or False: Three nearby L or R mutations should
   produce wild type if the code is read in triplets.

7. True

13-14 A gene is really colinear with its protein product.

1. Yanofsky's tryptophan auxotrophs showed a series of

   (a)_____ (how many?) genes responsible for (b)_____ (how
   many?) enzymes in the pathway to tryptophan.

1. (a) 5;
   (b) 4

2. The sites of specific mutations (in Yanofsky's work)

   correlated perfectly with (a)_____
   replacements   in   the   protein,   demonstrating   the

   (b)_____ between gene and protein.

2. (a) amino acid;

3. True or False: If two different mutations affect the same

(b) colinearity   amino acid position, they must be in the same codon.

3. True

PRACTICE QUIZ

1. Studies of mutant organisms satisfy both organicists and reductionists because:
   a. both consider bacteria and phage to be simple organisms.
   b. they require that the organism be broken up into its components.
   c. a small part in the whole organism is studied.
   d. genes work as well in glassware as they do in the organism.

2. One culture plate of lac^- mutants shows a single dark colony near one edge after a few days. Which is the best explanation for this dark colony?
   a. Recombinant genomes produced a wild type.

   b. A lac^- mutated to lac^+.
   c. Accumulated waste product stained the culture media.

   d. Cross-feeding produced lac^+ phenotype.

3. If a giraffe's long neck was the result of a mutation, it obviously occurred:
   a. by chance.
   b. in response to taller trees (food source).
   c. to place the eyes higher up to watch for predators.
   d. nonrandomly for protection and food gathering.

4. The most basic cause of observed mutations is:
   a. environmental need.
   b. defective proteins.
   c. transcription and translocation abnormalities.
   d. DNA changes.

5. If a mutant colony grows on compound W:
   a. its mutational block is before W.
   b. nonrandom mutations allow it to use W.
   c. cross-feeding allows it to use W.
   d. its pathway does not involve W.

6. A conditional lethal is deadly to the possessor:
   a. when its chemosensor can't sense the lethal substance.
   b. if it can't mutate some cells for cross-feeding.
   c. under certain specific conditions.
   d. only if suppressor mutations don't occur.

7. If R_{ab} = 18, R_{ac} = 9, and R_{bc} = 9, the order of these markers would be:

   a. a b c.
   b. a c b.
   c. c a b.
   d. c b a.

8. Which result of cross between a + c and + b + phage indicates a double crossover?
   a. a + c
   b. a + +

181

c. + + c

d. + + +

9. To produce a wild type, a deletion of efgh (of the normal abcdefghijklmnop) must be crossed with a deletion of:
   a. bcde.
   b. lmno.
   c. efgh.
   d. hijk.

10. A frameshift and a suppressor mutation occurred in a base sequence to produce 123123121231231233123. How many amino acids of this chain of seven will be the original specified amino acids?
    a. 1
    b. 3
    c. 4
    d. 7

REVIEW QUESTIONS

I. Answer each of the following questions.

1. In any experimental investigation, why is it important to keep the number of variables to one, if possible?

   _____

   _____

2. Outline the organicist philosophy and the reductionist philosophy about research methods.

   _____

   _____

   _____

3. How do mutant organisms satisfy both philosophies?

   _____

4. How are mutant bacteria located?

   _____

   _____

   _____

5. What do these symbols mean? (a) + _____; (b) *lac*⁻

_____; (c) *lacY* _____

_____.

6. What does a mutant's defect demonstrate about a particular function?

   _____

7. What relationship, if any, exists between mutations, back mutations, and
   environmental need?

   _____

   _____

   _____

8. What relationship exists between mutations and environmental stimuli?

   _____

9. How do mutagens cause mutations?

   _____

   _____

II. The following chart shows growth patterns for mutants 1, 2, 3, 4, and 5 on
intermediates A, B, C, and D leading to product E. Use this chart to answer the
next three questions.

	A	B	C	D
1	+	+	+	+
2	+	0	+	+
3	+	0	0	0
4	+	0	+	0
5	0	0	0	0

1. What is the pathway sequence to E? _____

2. Excluding mutant 1 (because we aren't sure what it might accumulate),

   which mutant can cross-feed the other three? _____

3. Which mutants will die if isolated and grown on substance D?

   _____

183

III. Answer each of the following questions.

1. What have bacterial mutants revealed about galactose chemotaxis and translocation?

_____

_____

_____

2. Why are *ts* and *cs* phage mutants called conditional lethals?

_____

_____

3. What is a genetic map?

_____

_____

4. What is the difference between a site and a locus?

_____

_____

5. How is the frequency of recombination (R) calcuated, and what does this R value tell us?

_____

_____

_____

IV. The results of a phage cross are as follows:

+ + + 480;   e f g 470;   e + + 12;   + f g 8;   + + g 16;   e f + 14

1. What were the parental types? _____ and _____

2. How many e-f recombinants are there? _____

3. Which of the recombinants, if any, result from double crossover?

_____

4. What are R_{ef} and R_{fg} values? R_{ef} = _____; R_{fg} = _____

5. How far is e from f, f from g, and e from g, expressed in map units?

   e to f, _____; f to g, _____; e to g, _____

6. What is the linear arrangement of e f g from these results? _____

V. Answer each of the following questions.

1. An a b c x + + + phage cross is carried out. Label each offspring 1, 2, or 0 for single crossover, double crossover, or zero crossover: (a) a b c

   _____; (b) + b c _____; (c) + + c _____; (d) + b + _____;

   (e) a + + _____.

2. List all possible results of the a b c x + + + cross.

   _____

3. Why are deletions more valuable as markers than point mutations?

   _____

   _____

4. Which deletion crosses can produce a wild type? (Use + if wild type can be produced, 0 if it can't.)

   (a) abcdegh x abcdgh _____

   (b) abghijk x abcdejk _____

   (c) adefgh x abcdgh _____

   (d) abcklmnopqr x abcdefghijkgrs _____

5. Label each complementation test *cis* or *trans*: (a) $a^- b^+ + a^+ b^-$ _____;

   (b) $a^- b^- + a^+ b^+$ _____

6. What is the difference between R and L frame-shift mutations?

   _____

   _____

7. What proof is there that genes are colinear with amino acid sequences?

   _____

   _____

185

VI. The following triplet series has a frameshift deletion and a suppressor addition.

1 2 3 1 3 1 2 3 1 2 3 3 1 2 3 1 2 3 1 2 3

1. Indicate with a vertical line where the deletion occurred, and circle the addition.

2. How many amino acids does this segment code for? _____

3. Which of the amino acids in the series resulting from this code will still be the originally specified amino acids? _____

ANSWERS TO CHAPTER EXERCISES

Practice Quiz

1. c	3. a	5. a	7. b	9. b
2. b	4. d	6. c	8. d	10. b

Review Questions

I. 1. Any observed differences can then be attributed to only the single variable.
   2. The reductionist says we can understand the whole organism by studying isolated parts. The organicist says we must study the organism intact to gain genuine overall understanding, and that biological methods must be used.
   3. One mutant factor is studed in a whole, functioning organism.
   4. Mutant bacteria are located either by picking out colonies that appear different on special indicator media, or by selecting mutants that can grow under special conditions.
   5. (a) Wild type; (b) cannot metabolize lactose; (c) can make β-galacto-side, but can't grow on lactose.
   6. The defect is proof of the existence of the function that is defective.
   7. Mutations occur at measurable rates, and mutants can back-mutate, also at a measurable rate. Mutations are random events that are not associated with environmental needs.
   8. Radiation and chemical mutagens cause mutations.
   9. Mutagens cause nucleotide alternations directly, or they produce errors during replication.

II. 1. B-D-C-A   2. 2   3. 3, 4, and 5

III. 1. Some can't sense galactosé, but can transport it; others can sense it but can't transport it. A third group can't sense or transport and has a single defect, indicating a connection of some type between sensing and transport.
    2. Their existence depends on the continuing condition of low (*ts*) and high (*cs*) temperatures to keep their proteins from unfolding into useless shapes.
    3. A map of the genome showing such features as the gene sizes and positions, control elements, and (ideally) all of their functions.
    4. A site is the position of a mutation. A locus is the position of a gene.

5. Frequency of recombination is a percent or decimal obtained by dividing the number of recombinants by the total number of offspring. The larger the R value, up to 0.5, the farther apart on the chromosome are the two sites involved in that cross.

IV. 1. + + + and efg
     2. 8 + 12 = 20
     3. None indicated, although a second e f crossover between e + + and + f g would produce + + + and e f g.
     4. R_{ef} = 20/1000 = 0.02, R_{fg} = 30/1000 = 0.03
     5. e to f = 2 map units, f to g = 3 map units, e to g = 5 map units
     6. e f g

V. 1. (a) 0; (b) 1; (c) 1; (d) 2; (e) 1.
    2. abc, +++, a++, +bc, ab+, ++c, a+c, +b+
    3. Point mutations can back mutate to wild type. Deletions do not back mutate.
    4. (a) 0; (b) 0; (c) +; (d) +
    5. (a) *trans*; (b) *cis*
    6. L mutations shift the reading frame to the left, whereas R mutations shift the reading frame to the right.
    7. The sequence of mutations in a gene has been compared with the sequence of amino acid changes in the protein coded by that gene.

VI. 1. 1 2 3 1/3 1 2 3 1 2 3 ③ 1 2 3 1 2 3 1 2 3
     2. 7
     3. 1, 5, 6 and 7

187

Chapter 14

FUNDAMENTALS OF MOLECULAR GENETICS

WHAT'S IN THIS CHAPTER

In this chapter you will learn about the genetic apparatus in bacteria and viruses and how it operates. In particular, you will learn how bacteria exchange genes through conjugation and transduction and become acquainted with current ideas about what "turns on" certain segments of a DNA strand. Bacterial genes often work in well-orchestrated blocks, especially those genes involved in particular metabolic pathways, and their mode of operation and regulation is an area of active research. In genetic engineering, pieces of DNA from any organism can be spliced into bacterial plasmids and the plasmids inserted into bacteria. As you will see, this technique is important in the study of genes and for the production of mass quantities of proteins. The experiments outlined in this chapter helped develop the fundamentals of molecular genetics, and the pattern of genetic regulation described here may have broad application.

By the end of this chapter you should be able to:

1. Define the word <u>auxotroph</u> and outline the role auxotrophs have played in the study of molecular genetics.

2. Describe a typical bacterial chromosome.

3. Differentiate among conjugation, transformation, and transduction.

4. Explain the difference between a virulent and a noninfectious virus.

5. Explain how the terms <u>episome</u>, <u>replicon</u>, and <u>plasmid</u> are related.

6. Explain the importance of plasmids to the evolution of antibiotic-resistant bacteria and to studies in genetic engineering.

7. Define <u>operon</u>.

8. Describe two different methods of genetic regulation in bacteria.

9. Explain the importance of nonsense codons.

10. Explain how genes can overlap one another.

WHAT YOU SHOULD ALREADY KNOW

One of the fundamental aspects of biology is the genetic apparatus which is made up, in part, of nucleic acids. In this chapter we will focus on the nucleic acids of bacteria and viruses to help establish the fundamentals of molecular genetics. You should already understand the relationship between DNA, RNA, and protein synthesis (Chapter 9) and be familiar with the principles of genetic analysis (Chapter 13).

Pre-Test

1. (a)_____ informs RNA, and RNA informs (b)_____.

1. (a) DNA;
   (b) protein

2. A mutant is _____

   _____

   _____.

2. an organism in
   which a small
   change in the
   genome pro-
   duces a corre-
   sponding change
   in some feature
   of growth,
   structure, or
   metabolism
   because of
   an altered pro-
   tein or RNA.

3. True or False: If we want to develop a strain of bacterium X that is resistant to antibiotic Y, all we have to
   do is place bacterium X cells in a dilute solution of
   antibiotic Y. This will cause mutants to develop that are
   resistant to the antibiotic.

3. False

4. A recombinant type bacterial cell is _____

   _____

   _____.

4. a cell that re-
   sults from the
   recombination
   of parental
   genomes. The
   resultant cell
   carries genetic
   information
   from both
   parent cells.

GUIDED REVIEW OF THE CHAPTER

14-1 Bacteria have a pseudosexual mechanism.

1. A mutant cell that cannot make one of its essential

189

components is called an _____.

1. auxotroph

2. The process in which bacteria exchange DNA directly from cell to cell is called (a)_____. Experimenters can demonstrate that this DNA exchange is not the result of transformation by (b)_____

_____

_____.

2. (a) conjugation; (b) separating cells by a fine filter that allows DNA, but not bacteria, to pass from one side to the other. If no recombination occurs, cell contact is required for DNA exchange.

3. In conjugation, the partners are not equal. If the (a)_____ cell is killed, no recombination occurs. If the (b)_____ cell is killed, recombination still occurs.

14-2 Donor genes are transferred in a definite sequence.

3. (a) recipient; (b) donor

1. With ordinary F^+ and F^- bacterial cells, recombination occurs at a (a)_____(high / low) frequency. The Hfr strain produces (b)_____

_____.

1. (a) low; (b) a high frequency of recombination

2. Jacob and Wollman's experiments using Hfr bacterial strains helped establish a genetic map of the bacteria. Their hypothesis of conjugation was that _____

_____

_____

_____.

2. in conjugation the donor is moving a piece of its DNA into the recipient cell gene by gene in

3. The shape of a bacterial chromosome is (a)_____. The shape was determined before this chromosome was seen with a microscope because (b)_____

_____.

a regular se-
quence, a pro-
cess that can
be interrupted
at any time

14-3 Some viruses replicate in a noninfectious form.

3. (a) circular;
   (b) donor cells
   transfer their
   genes in dif-
   ferent se-
   quences, but
   all sequences
   can be com-
   bined into a
   single circular
   sequence

1. Bacteria that have the capacity to lyse and liberate phage

   are said to be (a)_____. A phage that can

   establish lysogeny is called (b)_____.

1. (a) lysogenic;
   (b) temperate

2. A phage that adsorbs to a bacterium and causes only the
   synthesis of new phage and the death of the bacterium is

   called a (a)_____ phage. This process, which

   results in lysis of the bacterial cell, is the (b)_____
   cycle.

2. (a) virulent;
   (b) lytic

3. The noninfectious form of phage is called the (a)_____

   _____. The phage genome is (b)_____(single /

   double) stranded with (c)_____(single / double)
   stranded cohesive ends that allow the DNA to form a
   circle. Even after the phage genome is integrated into
   the bacterial chromosome, no infection occurs because

   (d)_____

   _____.

3. (a) prophage;
   (b) double; (c)
   single; (d) the
   phage genes are
   not expressed
   due to the
   action of con-
   trol mechanisms

14-4 A new class of genetic elements.

1. The transmitted infectious agent that converts F$^-$ cells to

   F$^+$ cells is called the (a)_____. In F$^+$ cells

   this agent replicates (b)_____

   _____(autonomously / with the entire bac-
   terial chromosome). In Hfr cells, this agent replicates

   (c)_____(auto-
   nomously / with the entire bacterial chromosome).

1. (a) F factor;
   (b) autono-
   mously;

2. Temperature phages and F factors are members of a class of

   genetic elements called (a)_____. These genetic

(c) with the entire bacterial chromosome

elements can exist in either of two conditions with respect to the bacterial chromosome: (b)_____ _____ or _____.

2. (a) episomes; (b) attached to the chromosome or not attached

3. Many episomes can transmit themselves from cell to cell, either by (a)_____ or by (b)_____.

3. (a) becoming free virus particles; (b) promoting conjugation with another cell

14-5 *Viruses can promote genetic exchange.*

1. Genetic exchange between two bacterial cells can occur in three different ways. (a)_____ occurs when cells are in contact; (b)_____ occurs when free DNA is transferred from cell to cell; and (c)_____ occurs when a phage carries some of the host DNA into other bacterial cells.

1. (a) Conjugation; (b) transformation; (c) transduction

2. There are two kinds of transduction. One kind involves a phage that can carry any bacterial genes from one cell to another and is called (a)_____ transduction. Another kind involves a phage that can carry only a few bacterial genes and is called (b)_____ transduction.

2. (a) generalized; (b) specialized

3. "Pseudophages" carry no (a)_____ DNA, only (b)_____ DNA.

3. (a) phage; (b) bacterial

4. A phage is defective if _____ _____

4. it does not carry all of its own genes upon leaving a host cell

14-6 *The concept of an independently replicating unit.*

1. A replicon is _____ _____ _____

1. an independently replicating piece of DNA or RNA that

2. Three examples of a replicon are a (a)_____ _____, a (b)_____,

can regulate its own replication

and an (c)_____.

2. (a) bacterial chromosome; (b) phage genome; (c) F factor

3. A random fragment of bacterial DNA carried into another cell is not a replicon because _____

_____.

3. it lacks the proper control elements

14-7 *Plasmids are extrachromosomal genetic elements.*

1. Extrachromosomal genetic elements called (a)_____ are (b)_____(attached / not attached) to the bacterial chromosome.

1. (a) plasmids; (b) not attached

2. A whole bacterial chromosome is about (a)_____(400 / 4,000) kbp, whereas a plasmid is between (b)_____ kbp.

2. (a) 4,000; (b) 20 and 100

3. Bacteria causing dysentery in Japan were found to be resistant to several antibiotics. These bacteria were found to harbor plasmids called _____ that carry resistance to several different antibiotics at once.

3. R factors

4. Plasmids that carry resistance to heavy metals have been selected in places where _____

_____ is found.

4. heavy indus-trial pollution of water

5. A (a)_____ is any agent that can cause a disease. Some bacteria can cause disease only when they are (b)_____, such as the agents of diph-theria, botulism, or scarlet fever.

5. (a) pathogen; (b) lysogenized

14-8 *Insertion elements hop around on the DNA.*

1. (a)_____ are extra pieces of DNA that can move from place to place and insert themselves into bacterial DNA. They generally cause mutations because they (b)_____

_____.

1. (a) Insertion sequences; (b) insert themselves in

2. _____ are plasmidlike elements that carry specific genes for drug resistance.

193

the middle of
a gene

2. Transposons

3. it may inte-
grate fertility
factors or con-
fer the ability
to exchange
genetic
material with
another cell

1. (a) nuclease;
(b) exonu-
clease;
(c) endonu-
clease

2. An isolated
gene from a
plant or animal
that codes for
a practical
hormone or pro-
tein can be
inserted into
the bacterial
DNA, which will
then make large
amounts of the
protein cheaply.

3. If a gene that
produced a
toxin was in-
serted into a
bacterial cell
and the cell
escaped from
the laboratory,
there could be
unregulated
production of
the toxin

3. An advantage to a bacterium of an insertion sequence is

that _____

_____.

14-9 New genes can be tailored into plasmids.

1. A (a)_____ is an enzyme that hydrolyzes

nucleic acids into nucleotides. An (b)_____
is one such enzyme that chews the DNA from an end while an

(c)_____ cuts between two internal
nucleotides.

2. From a human perspective, give one practical application
of genetic engineering.

_____

_____

_____

_____.

3. Name one fear that was initially expressed about recom-
binant-DNA studies.

_____

_____

_____

_____.

4. List two precautions taken by biologists working with
recombinant DNA to maintain high safety standards.

(a)_____

_____

(b)_____

_____

194

4. (a) physical methods of containment, including sterilization and restrictions on air flow; (b) use of bacteria so debilitated by mutations that they could not live outside of stringent laboratory conditions

14-10 Bacterial genes are highly organized into functional clusters.

1. In bacteria, genes with (a)_____ functions tend to cluster together. This was unexpected, because proteins can (b)_____

_____ .

1. (a) related; (b) move freely about and go to their proper place of function in the cell

2. An example of genes clustering together in bacteria is

_____

_____ .

14-11 The expression of bacterial genes is tightly regulated.

2. the systems for synthesis of the amino acids histidine or tryptophan, or for catabolism of lactose or galactose

1. *E. coli* growing in a medium that does not contain lactose

makes (a)_____(small / large) amounts of β-galactosi-

dase. Lactose is an (b)_____, a material that causes the rate of β-galactosidase synthesis to rise

in a phenomenon called (c)_____ .

1. (a) small; (b) inducer; (c) enzyme induction

2. A _____ mutant is a bacterial cell that cannot regulate its production of enzymes such as β-galactosidase and permease.

2. constitutive

3. A repressible enzyme is one that _____

_____

_____ .

3. can be repressed to a low level by high concentrations of product

4. (a)_____(Anabolic / Catabolic) enzymes in bacteria are generally inducible by their substrates,

whereas (b)_____(anabolic / catabolic) enzymes are repressible by their end products.

4. (a) Catabolic; (b) anabolic

14-12 Genes are regulated in blocks.

1. An (a)_____ is a block of genes that are all

195

transcribed together. This block may be repressed by a

(b)_____ that binds to an

(c)_____ site and stops (d)_____.

1. (a) operon;
(b) repressor
protein; (c)
operator; (d)
transcription

2. The repressor is an allosteric protein that is paratactic

to an (a)_____ and to an

(b)_____.

2. (a) operator
site;
(b) inducer

3. The site where the RNA polymerases begin to synthesize

mRNA is known as the (a)_____.
One kind of control of RNA synthesis is exerted by a

protein called a (b)_____,
which forces the RNA polymerase to start only at
promotors.

3. (a) promotor
site; (b) sigma
factor

14-13 Operons may be regulated by positive control systems.

1. In both positive and negative regulatory systems, a

(a)_____ of genes is regulated together and

the regulation is effected by one (b)_____
that recognizes a single important ligand and responds to

its (c)_____.

1. (a) block;
(b) protein;
(c) concen-
tration

2. An activator protein binds at the (a)_____

site on the DNA and initiates (b)_____.

2. (a) initiator;
(b) transcrip-
tion

*14-14 Operons may also be regulated by broader control
mechanisms.*

1. _____ are signal ligands that regulate
cellular processes simultaneously as a broad response to a
critical situation.

1. Alarmones

2. cAMP and ppGpp are both (a)_____ made from

energetic (b)_____. cAMP is made in re-

sponse to the lack of (c)_____, whereas

ppGpp is made in response to the inhibition of (d)_____

_____.

2. (a) alarmones;
(b) nucleo-

tides; (c)
glucose;
(d) protein
synthesis

14-16 The genome contains distinct punctuation signals.

1. 61 of 64 triplets code for amino acids, but the remaining

    3 are _____ .

1. stop signals

2. Special proteins called (a)_____
    recognize termination signals on the messenger RNA. These

    proteins stop protein synthesis by (b)_____

    _____ .

2. (a) release
factors; (b)
clipping the
last tRNA and
releasing the
protein from
the ribosome

14-17 Some genes can overlap.

1. If two genes are coded for by the same region of DNA, one
    must be shifted relative to the other by at least

    (a)_____ . In such a situation,

    each nucleotide belongs to (b)_____ codons simul-

    taneously and one mutation would affect (c)_____
    proteins at the same time.

1. (a) one nucleo-
tide; (b) two;
(c) two

PRACTICE QUIZ

1. Which of the following statements about auxotrophs and prototrophs is true?
    a. All recombinants are prototrophs.
    b. A bacterium that is thr$^+$ leu$^+$ met$^+$ is auxotrophic.
    c. An auxotroph cannot make one of its essential components.
    d. An auxotroph is any bacterium with a pseudosexual mechanism.

2. Which of the following statements about bacterial chromosomes is true?
    a. They are located inside a nuclear membrane.
    b. They are made up of RNA.
    c. A bacterium has as many chromosomes as does a human body cell.
    d. They have the same shape as do plasmids.

3. Which of the following processes does <u>not</u> involve contact between two cells?
    a. transformation
    b. transduction
    c. conjugation
    d. repression

4. Which of the following occurs in the lytic cycle?
    a. Viral DNA is integrated into the bacterial chromosome.
    b. New bacterial cells are produced with viral DNA inside.
    c. New virus particles are formed inside the bacterial cell.
    d. Viral DNA is injected into a bacterial nucleus.

5. Which of the following statements is true?
   a. All plasmids are replicons.
   b. All replicons are episomes.
   c. All plasmids are episomes.
   d. All replicons are R factors.

6. Which of the following is directly responsible for the production of antibiotic-resistant gonorrhea bacteria?
   a. an increase in human sexual activity
   b. R factors
   c. an increase in the use of antibiotics
   d. heavy metal pollution in water

7. Which of the following statements is true of an operon?
   a. It is a set of genes regulated as a unit by a single operator.
   b. Several different kinds of messenger RNA are produced by each operon.
   c. All operons are repressed when a repressor protein binds to an inducer.
   d. Most research on operons has been conducted with garden peas and fruit flies.

8. Which of the following is not a signal ligand that regulates cellular processes as a response to a critical situation?
   a. an alarmone
   b. an activator protein
   c. ppGpp
   d. cAMP

9. Which of the following statements about nonsense codons is true?
   a. Nonsense codons are two nucleotides long.
   b. Nonsense codons code for unusual amino acids.
   c. Approximately 50% of all triplets are nonsense codons.
   d. Nonsense codons act as stop signals for protein synthesis.

10. Which of the following statements about codons and genes is true?
    a. One codon may code for two different amino acids.
    b One gene may code for two different proteins.
    c. One DNA nucleotide could, in principle, be part of three different genes.
    d. One chromosome codes for the production of one enzyme.

REVIEW QUESTIONS

I. One ml of a pure culture of bacterium X was thinly spread on four different media in four different petri dishes. Here are the results.

Petri Dish	Medium (Agar +)	Number of Bacterial Colonies on Agar after 24 Hours
1	sugar	1
2	sugar + amino acid A	1,000
3	amino acid A + vitamin A	0
4	sugar + vitamin A	2

For each of the following items, answer true (T) or false (F).

_____   1. Sugar is necessary for the growth of bacterium X.

_____ 2. Amino acid A is necessary for the growth of bacterium X.

_____ 3. Bacterium X is an auxotroph.

_____ 4. Vitamin A is necessary for the growth of bacterium X.

_____ 5. Bacterium X has the genes that control the production of amino acid A.

II. Use the following key to answer the next five questions.

    Key: a. transformation
          b. transduction
          c. conjugation
          d. a and b
          e. a, b, and c

_____ 1. Involves contact between two bacterial cells

_____ 2. Involves exchange of DNA between two cells

_____ 3. Involves a phage

_____ 4. Helped to determine the shape of the bacterial chromosome

_____ 5. Involves free DNA picked up by a bacterial cell

III. A pure culture of a particular bacterium is susceptible to antibiotic X. After exposure to antibiotic X, bacterial cells from the culture are found to be resistant to the antibiotic. Did the antibiotic induce the formation of cells that were resistant to the antibiotic? Explain

_____

_____

ANSWERS TO CHAPTER EXERCISES

Practice Quiz

1. c	3. c	5. a	7. a	9. d
2. d	4. c	6. b	8. b	10. c

Review Questions

I. 1. T	2. T	3. T	4. F	5. F
II. 1. c	2. e	3. b	4. c	5. a

III. No. A susceptible bacterial cell may have a gene that mutated to a form that made a bacterial cell resistant to the antibiotic. When it reproduces, this resistant cell passes the resistance gene to other cells. Thus, when placed in the antibiotic, a few cells survive.

Chapter 15

PATTERNS OF MENDELIAN HEREDITY

WHAT'S IN THIS CHAPTER

The science of genetics started with Mendel, an Austrian monk, who formulated rules governing inheritance. His rules, and examples illustrating them, are the basis of Chapter 15.

If you've ever wondered how brown-eyed parents can have blue-eyed childen, this chapter will answer that question. Basic inheritance patterns involving one pair, more than one pair, linked genes, and nonlinked genes are covered. Organisms whose genes are known can be crossed with unknowns to determine what these unknowns are and what the probable results will be. Multiple effects of genes and multiple genes are explained. Normal and abnormal patterns of sex determination are analyzed, along with sex-linked characteristics. Finally, some genetic anomalies and some aspects of the impact of genetic knowledge are discussed.

By the end of this chapter you should be able to:

1. Explain how meiosis is the basis for inheritance patterns.

2. Discuss probability as it relates to genetic events.

3. Explain how to determine unknown genotypes using testcrosses.

4. State and give examples of Mendel's Laws.

5. Provide examples of genes showing multiple effects, multiple alleles, and linkage.

6. Explain sex determination and sex linkage.

7. Describe several genetic anomalies and cite their causes.

8. Solve genetic problems on any of these topics.

WHAT YOU SHOULD ALREADY KNOW

This chapter assumes a knowledge of what genes and chromosomes are and the relationship between them (see Sections 3-5 and 3-6). You must thoroughly understand meiosis (Sections 10-8 and 10-9) to develop an appreciation of its basis in heredity. Be sure to review it. The genetic mapping techniques (Section 13-9) will be helpful.

Pre-Test

1. Suppose a cell has 7 chromosomes and is going to divide by _mitosis_. How many chromosomes will each daughter cell have? _____

1. 7

2. A special kind of cell division occurs only in diploid cells and produces (a)_____ cells; it is called (b)_____.

2. (a) haploid;
   (b) meiosis

3. If a diploid cell containing 10 chromosomes divides by meiosis, how many chromosomes will each daughter cell get? _____

3. 5

4. When a meiotically dividing cell reaches the stage where its chromosomes can be seen clearly, will these chromosomes look more like (a) ⌒⌒ or (b) ⤬ ? _____

4. b

5. The two halves of the chromosome shown in part (b) of Question 4 are called _____.

5. chromatids

6. The point where the two chromatids are joined is called the _____.

6. centromere

7. A diploid cell got to be diploid because at some time earlier it had two parents, each of which contributed one _____ set of chromosomes.

7. haploid

8. A diploid organism containing 10 chromosomes had 2 parents, each of which contributed (a)_____(how many?) chromosomes. Therefore, it has (b)_____(how many?) of chromosome 1, (c)_____ of chromosome 2, and so on.

8. (a) 5; (b) 2;
   (c) 2

9. The two chromosomes of each kind that are essentially

identical are called _____.

9. homologs

10. During the earliest stages of meiosis, homologous chromo-

somes _____.

10. pair with
each other

11. When these pairs are divided during the first meiotic

division, the chromatids of each chromosome _____
(do / do not) separate from each other at their
centromere.

11. do not

12. What things <u>do</u> separate from each other at this division?

_____

12. the homologs
in each pair

13. After the first meiotic division, how many chromosomes
(<u>not</u> chromatids) are in each daughter cell if there were

10 to begin with? _____

13. 5

14. These five chromosomes have (a)_____ chromatids

<u>each</u>, for a total of (b)_____.

14. (a) 2; (b) 10

15. In each chromosome, the chromatids _____(do / do not)
separate from each other in the second meiotic division.

15. do

16. Suppose that, in a cell about to go through meiosis, one
of the number-3 chromosomes has a copy of a gene that is
slightly different from that on the homologous chromosome.

After meiosis is complete, (a)_____(how many?) of

the (b)_____(how many?) haploid cells will contain
the different copy of the gene.

16. (a) 2; (b) 4

17. Flipping a coin has (a)_____(how many?) possible
outcomes. The probably of getting heads on any toss is

(b)_____.

17. (a) 2;
(b) 1/2

18. A yellow plant and a blue plant produce all blue off-

spring. This shows that blue is _____ to yellow.

18. dominant

GUIDED REVIEW OF THE CHAPTER

Introduction

1. Checking an unborn fetus for genetic diseases is done

through a process called _____.

1. amniocentesis

1. Red-flowered and white-flowered zinnias produced (a)_____ _____-flowered F$_1$ offspring, indicating a mix of distinct (b)_____ factors.

1. (a) pink;
   (b) hereditary

2. Remixing distinct hereditary factors in a pink F$_1$ x pink F$_1$ cross should produce red, pink, and white in a _____ ratio.

2. 1:2:1

3. In the foregoing cross, is it possible to get all red-flowering plants? _____

3. yes (but very unlikely)

4. Mendelian heredity depends on two events; chromosome (a)_____ in meiosis and the way (b)_____ gametes combine.

4. (a) segregation; (b) different;

5. True or False: Both events cited in Question 4 occur at random.

5. True

6. A diploid cell has _____(how many?) of each kind of chromosome.

6. 2

7. Homologous chromosomes are linear series of (a)_____, each series governing (b)_____(different / the same) traits from(as) the other series.

7. (a) genes;
   (b) the same

8. Slightly different genes of homologous chromosomes that govern the same trait are called _____.

8. alleles

9. The alleles of a homozygote are _____(the same / different).

9. the same

10. The RW zinnia is said to be (a)_____ (heterozygous / homozygous) and will show a flower color of (b)_____.

10. (a) heterozygous;
    (b) pink

11. At meiosis the RW plant segregates alleles so that the ratio of R to W in the gametes will be _____.

11. 1:1

12. True or False: Statement 11 illustrates Mendel's Law.

12. True

203

15-2 The chance of two things happening together is the pro-
duct of the chances that they will happen independently.

1. Ten percent of Americans are left-handed. The probability that the next person you shake hands will will be left-handed is (a)_____(decimal); the probability that she or he will be right-handed is (b)_____(decimal).

1. (a) 0.1;
   (b) 0.9

2. The probability that the next person you shake hands with will be left-handed and the second one will <u>not</u> be is _____(decimal).

2. 0.09
   (0.1 x 0.9)

3. The probability of two RW (= pink) zinnias producing two white-flowering plants is _____(decimal).

3. 0.0625
   (0.25 x 0.25)

15-3 Some genes exhibit dominance.

1. Only purple-flowering pea plants result from a purple x white cross. Purple is (a)_____ to white; white is (b)_____ to purple.

1. (a) dominant;
   (b) recessive

2. Crossing heterozygous purple-flowered pea plants produces purple-flowered and white-flowered offspring in a _____ ratio.

2. 3:1

3. The white-flowered pea plant is (a)_____ (heterozygous / homozygous) and its genotype is expressed as (b)_____(PP / Pp / pp).

3. (a) homozygous;
   (b) pp

4. True or False: The genotype of an organism showing a dominant phenotype can be determined by looking at it.

4. False

5. (a) How many different gametes can heterozygous purple-flowered pea plants produce? _____ (b) What are they? _____

5. (a) 2
   (b) P and p

6. True or False: Two individuals with dominant phenotypes are always heterozygous if they produce at least one offspring with a recessive phenotype.

6. True

7. True or False: In Sweden, blue eyes must be dominant to brown eyes because there are proportionately more blue eyed people there than in other countries.

7. False

8. A purple cat and a green cat produce a litter of all green

kittens. Which cat is homozygous recessive? (a)_____

_____   Which cat(s) is(are) heterozygous?

(b)_____

8. (a) the green
   cat; (b) the
   kittens

15-4 Genotypes can be determined with testcrosses.

1. A testcross is always a cross between an unknown genotype

   and a (a)_____(heterozygous / homozygous)

   (b)_____(dominant / recessive) individual.

1. (a) homozygous;
   (b) recessive

2. If all offspring of a testcross are of the dominant

   phenotype, the tested parent is (a)_____

   (heterozygous / homozygous) (b)_____(dominant/
   recessive).

2. (a) homozygous;
   (b) dominant

3. True or False: Testcrosses reveal genotypes of unknowns.

3. True

*15-5 Two genes may be inherited quite independently of each
     other.*

1. True or False: Mendel's traits of flower color, seed
   texture, and height were all inherited independently of
   each other.

1. True

2. Independently inherited traits, such as seed texture and

   height, _____(are / are not) on the same pair of
   homologous chromosomes.

2. are not

3. The genotype for an individual who is homozygous dominant

   for two nonlinked traits would be _____(use
   the letters A, a, B, b).

3. A/A B/B

4. True or False: Nonlinked genes act independently of each
   other in meiosis.

4. True

5. Heterozygous alleles (homologs) arrange themselves

   (a)_____(randomly / nonrandomly) and

   (b)_____(dependently / independently)
   on(of) other homologs at the first metaphase of meiosis.

5. (a) randomly;
   (b) indepen-
   dently

6. True or False: Question 5 is a statement of Mendel's
   Second Law of Independent Segregation.

6. True

7. How many different gametes does each of the following

205

genotypes   produce?   (a)   A/A   B/B   _____;

(b) A/a B/B _____; (c) a/a B/b _____;

(d) A/a B/b _____.

7. (a) 1; (b) 2;
    (c) 2; (d) 4

8. What proportion of gametes from A/A B/b will contain A and

    B? _____

8. 1/2

9. Crossing two individuals who are heterozygous for two

    nonlinked genes produces a (a)_____ ratio of
    phenotypes. The largest resulting phenotype group is made

    up of the (b)_____(how many?) showing (c)_____
    (both / one / no) dominant trait(s).

9. (a) 9:3:3:1;
    (b) 9;
    (c) both

10. The probability of getting an A/? B/? offspring from an

    A/a B/b x a/a B/b cross is _____.

10. 3/8

11. In Question 10, the probability of getting an A in the

    offspring is (a)_____; the probability of getting

    a B is (b)_____.

11. (a) 1/2;
    (b) 3/4

12. How many different gametes can an A/a B/b D/d genotype

    produce? _____

12. 8

13. True or False: In determining the number of different
    gametes from a given genotype, we make the number of
    heterozygous gene pairs the exponent of 2.

13. True

14. What is the probability that two dark-eyed people who are
    heterozygous for eye color (B/b) will have two children

    who are both blue-eyed (b/b)? _____

14. 1/16

15-6 Many genes have multiple effects.

1. Most genes act through a series of _____(one
    or a few / many) steps to produce the phenotypic result.

1. many

2. True or False: Many complex traits are produced by a
    single gene.

2. False

3. Most genes are _____, having multiple effects.

3. pleiotropic

4. True or False: A pleiotropic mutation can confer both
    advantages and disadvantages on its possessor.

4. True

15-7 Any gene can have more than two alleles.

1. Multiple alleles are more than _____(how many?) forms of a gene for a specific trait, as with human blood types.

1. 2

2. In human blood types, alleles (a)_____ and _____ are dominant to (b)_____ but codominant to each other.

2. (a) I^A and I^B; (b) i^O

3. What are all the possible genotypes for type A blood? _____

3. $I^A I^A$ and $I^A i^O$

4. A type O child has type A parents. How is this possible? _____

4. $I^A i^O$ x $I^A i^O$ = $i^O i^O$

15-8 Many genes are inherited as linkage groups.

1. Linked genes are those on _____(the same / different) chromosome(s).

1. the same

2. True or False: Characteristics that consistently appear together are probably linked.

2. True

3. Linked genes can become unlinked through the process of _____ formation and crossover.

3. chiasma

4. The probability of a crossover between two genes _____(increases / decreases) with the distance between them.

4. increases

5. A 1 percent recombination equals _____(how many?) map unit(s).

5. one

6. Two factors that complicate frequencies of recombination are (a)_____ and (b)_____ _____.

6. (a) inter-ference; (b) double crossover

7. A recombination frequency of 11 percent between two markers places them _____ map units apart.

7. 11

8. Small recombination frequencies between two genes indicate that the two probably _____(are / are not) linked.

8. are

9. A three-factor cross of linked genes reveals the

207

_____ of the genes.

9. sequence

10. True or False: The linked three-factor cross reveals the middle gene to be the one opposite the other two in the double crossover recombinants.

10. True

11. True or False: A double crossover frequency is used twice for map distances, once for a and b and again for b and c.

11. True

12. Which are the linked genes in Exercise 15-17 in your text?

_____

12. D and F

13. Which gene is in the middle position in Exercise 15-18?

_____

13. z

15-9 Sex may be determined by special chromosomes.

1. The sex of an animal is determined by a special _____ chromosome.

1. sex

2. The sex that makes only one kind of gamete is said to be

(a)_____; the other, which makes two

kinds of gametes, is (b)_____.

2. (a) homo-gametic;
(b) hetero-gametic

3. The sex of offspring is determined by gametes from the

_____ sex.

3. heterogametic

4. Humans possess 22 pairs of (a)_____ and one

pair of (b)_____ chromosomes.

4. (a) autosomes;
(b) sex

5. Human males have the sex chromosomes (a)_____ and

_____; females possess two (b)_____
chromosomes.

5. (a) X and Y;
(b) X

6. True or False: Sex determination in all other animals is like that in humans.

6. False

7. What is the sex of a ZW fish? _____

7. female

8. What is the sex of each of the following fruit flies?

(a) 3A 3X _____; (b) 2A XY _____;

(c) 2A 2X _____

8. (a) female;
(b) male;
(c) female

15-10 Genes on sex chromosomes show a distinctive pattern of inheritance.

1. Genes of the X chromosomes are called X-linked or

   (a)_____-linked because they are inherited

   with the (b)_____-determining genes.

1. (a) sex;
   (b) sex

2. True or False: Human males are heterozygous for sex-linked traits.

2. False

3. True or False: Human males always express sex-linked traits.

3. True

4. Sex-linked recessives in heterozygous human females are

   _____(always / never) expressed.

4. never

5. A human male inherits sex-linked traits from his _____

   _____(mother / father / parents).

5. mother

6. A human female heterozygous for a sex-linked recessive is

   called a (a)_____, and she will pass this gene

   to (b)_____(what proportion?) of her male off-

   spring and to (c)_____(what proportion?) of

   her female offspring.

6. (a) carrier;
   (b) 1/2;
   (c) 1/2

7. True or False: Human males are carriers for a few, very rare sex-linked traits.

7. False

8. In pedigree charts, a square represents a _____.

8. male

9. Give the genotype of: (a) a colorblind female _____;

   (b) a carrier female _____; (c) a colorblind male

   _____.

9. (a) X^bX^b;
   (b) X^BX^b;
   (c) X^bY

15-11 Chromosomes sometimes fail to separate in meiosis.

1. Failure of chromosomes to separate during meiosis is

   called (a)_____; it produces gametes with

   (b)_____(normal / abnormal) chromosome numbers.

1. (a) nondis-
   junction;
   (b) abnormal

2. A (a)_____ (picture of chromosomes) of

   Down's syndrome shows an extra number (b)_____
   chromosome.

209

2. (a) karyotype;   3. True or False: Most **trisomies** are fatal, but abnormal sex
    (b) 21   chromosome numbers are not.

3. True   4. The Lyon hypothesis suggests that one of the two X chromo-

                        somes of every cell in females is _____.

4. inactive   5. The inactive X chromosomes in female cells are called sex

                        chromatin, or _____ bodies, after their discoverer.

5. Barr   6. True or False: Tortoiseshell in cats and Turner's syn-
                        drome in humans are evidence supporting Lyon's hypothesis.

6. True   7. A human female of XO genotype has (a)_____

                        syndrome and lacks (b)_____.

7. (a) Turner's;   8. Men with one or more extra X's show (a)_____
    (b) Barr bodies

                        (no / the presence of) Barr bodies and have (b)_____

                        _____ syndrome.

8. (a) the pre-   9. True or False: The aggressive, violent behavior of some
    sence of; (b)   men is always traced to extra Y chromosomes.
    Klinefelter's

9. False   10. True or False: XYY males, XO females, and XXY females
                        would produce some gametes with normal chromosome numbers
                        if gametogenesis occurred.

10. True

                 15-12 Information about genetics has moral consequences.

               1. Sickle-cell heterozygotes are carriers, and _____
                        (what proportion?) of their children will have sickle-cell
                        gene.

1. half   2. True or False: Lethal sex-linked dominants must be
                        obtained by mutation.

2. True   3. True or False: The easiest way to find out whether you
                        are heterozygous for genetic diseases is to have a lot of
                        children.

3. False

PRACTICE QUIZ

Questions 1, 2, and 3 are based on the following cross. Pure-breeding red-flowered
four o'clocks are crossed with pure-breeding white-flowered four o'clocks. All the
F_1 are pink-flowered plants.

1. Which plants are heterozygous?
    a. red-flowered
    b. white-flowered
    c. pink-flowered
    d. both red-flowered and white-flowered

2. Which of Mendel's laws does this cross illustrate?
    a. Mendel's First Law
    b. Mendel's Second Law
    c. neither of Mendel's Laws
    d. both of Mendel's Laws

3. What is the proability that a F_1 x F_1 cross would produce three plants, all heterozygous?
    a. 1/2
    b. 1/4
    c. 1/8
    d. 1/64

Questions 4 and 5 are based on the following cross. Long hair (H) and large teeth (T) are dominant to short hair (h) and small teeth (t). A test cross is conducted on an animal with dominant traits. All F_1 have long hair, and half have large teeth.

4. What is the genotype of the tested animal?
    a. Hh Tt
    b. HH Tt
    c. Hh TT
    d. HH TT

5. What proportion of the F_1 are heterozygous for both traits?
    a. 1/4
    b. 1/2
    c. 3/4
    d. all of them

6. What proportion of the gametes from the Aa Bb Dd Ee genotype will contain only one dominant gene?
    a. 1/4
    b. 5/16
    c. 3/8
    d. 11/16

7. A type A female has a type B child. Which answer lists all possible blood type genotypes of the father?

    a. $I^A I^B$, $I^B I^B$, $I^B i^O$

    b. $I^A I^B$, $I^B I^B$, $I^A I^A$

    c. $I^A I^B$, $I^B i^O$, $I^A i^O$

    d. $I^A i^O$, $I^B I^B$, $I^A I^A$

8. An AaBbDd x aabbdd cross is done as a linkage test. It produces ABD 485, ABd 53, Abd 51, abd 428, abD 39, aBD 41, aBd 513, and AbD 415. Which genes are

211

linked?
a. A and B
b. B and D
c. A and D
d. all three

9. Genes A, B, and D are linked. An aaBbDd x aabbdd cross produces ABD 1299, abd 1267, aBD 234, Abd 240, AbD 80, aBd 81, ABd 4, and abD 3. Which gene is in the middle?
a. A
b. B
c. D
d. The results indicate that these genes are not linked.

10. Which of the following is a male?
a. XX grasshopper
b. ZW goldfish
c. ZO chicken
d. AAXY fruit fly

REVIEW QUESTIONS

I. Answer each of the following questions.

1. Using capital A's and small a's, provide a genotype that is (a) heterozygous

_____, one that is (b) homozygous dominant _____, and one that

is (c) homozygous recessive _____.

2. a. What gametes can an AaBb genotype produce? _____
   b. Using the heterozygous nonlinked allele pairs A and a, B and b, draw all possible homolog arrangements as they would appear in the first metaphase of meiosis.

(c) How does this illustrate Mendel's First Law?

_____

II. Make the appropriate calculations to solve each of the following "genetics problems."

1. Tall plants x short plants produce F_1 that are all tall. What is the phenotypic ratio of tall to short in the F_2 $(= F_1 \times F_1)$? _____

2. Black pigeons x white pigeons produce F_1 that are all grey. What is the phenotypic ratio of black to grey to white in the F_2 ($= F_1 \times F_1$)?

_____

3. Sixty percent of all cameras in Overshoe, North Dakota, are Japanese. The people of Overshoe are 90 percent German and 20 percent left-handed. Someone takes your picture while you're vacationing in Overshoe. What is the probability that the photographer used a Japanese camera, was German, and was

right-handed? _____

4. Betty and Bob have two girls. What is the probability that their next child

will be another girl? _____

5. Purple flowers are dominant to yellow flowers. Pete likes purple flowers and Yvonne likes yellow flowers. Each wants to grow a flower bed of his or her preferred color, so they begin by collecting seeds from purple-flowering or yellow-flowering plants they find at random in roadside ditches.

   a. Who will have the easiest time establishing a pure-breeding bed of all

      purple or all yellow flowers? _____

   b. Why? _____

      _____

6. How does a test cross reveal genotypes? _____

   _____

7. a. What ratio of phenotypes results from crossing two individuals who are

      each heterozygous for two nonlinked traits? _____

   b. How many dominant traits does each group of the ratio possess?

      _____

8. How do Questions 3, 4, and 9 illustrate Mendel's Second Law?

   _____

   _____

9. What ratio of phenotypes results from AaBb x AABb? _____

10. List all gametes that the AaBbDD genotype can produce. _____

    _____

213

11. How many different gametes does the AaBbDdEEGg genotype produce? _____

12. Free ear lobes and curly hair are dominant to attached ear lobes and straight hair. A curly-haired man with free ear lobes, whose mother had straight hair and attached ear lobes, marries a woman with curly hair and attached ear lobes. Her father had straight hair and attached ear lobes. What is the probability that their first child will have curly hair, attached ear lobes,

    and be a boy? _____

13. What are all the possible blood phenotypes that an $I^A I^B$ x $I^A i^O$ marriage could

    produce? _____

III. Answer each of the following questions.

1. What is the difference between chiasma formation and crossover? _____

   _____

   _____

2. What causes crossover interference? _____

   _____

3. How is linkage inferred from recombination frequency? _____

   _____

4. In three-factor crosses with linked genes, how is it determined which gene is

   in the middle? _____

   _____

5. Fill in the blanks in the following chart.

	Male Sex Chromosomes	Female Sex Chromosomes
Human	a. _____	b. _____
Bug	c. _____	d. _____
Trout	e. _____	f. _____
Chicken	g. _____	h. _____
Fruit Fly	i. _____	j. _____

6. Normal vision (N) and normal blood clotting (H) are dominant to colorblindness (n) and hemophilia (h). Both are sex-linked on the X chromosome. A colorblind male with normal blood clotting marries a female normal for both traits, but whose father was colorblind and had normal blood clotting and whose mother had hemophilia and was homozygous for normal vision.

   a. What proportion of their daughters will be colorblind? _____

   b. What proportion of their sons will have hemophilia? _____

   c. What is the genotype of the normal female? _____

7. How do Barr bodies document the Lyon hypothesis? _____

   _____

8. Why does Down's syndrome affect either sex? _____

   _____

9. Fill in the blanks in the following chart.

	Sex Affected	Genotype of Victim	Barr Bodies (+ or −)
Turner's Syndrome	a. _____	b. _____	c. _____
Klinefelter's Syndrome	d. _____	e. _____	f. _____
Supermales	g. _____	h. _____	i. _____

10. What causes trisomy? _____

ANSWERS TO CHAPTER EXERCISES

Practice Quiz

1. c	3. c	5. b	7. a	9. c
2. a	4. b	6. a	8. c	10. d

Review Questions

I. 1. a. Aa,   b. AA   c. aa
    2. a. AB, Ab, aB, ab
        b.

OR

c. Alleles A and a, B and b, segregate from each other during meiosis, so that half the gametes carry one allele of each pair and half carry the other.

II. 1. 3 tall : 1 short
 2. 1:2:1
 3. .6 x .9 x .8 = .432 = 43.2%
 4. 1/2
 5. a. Yvonne
    b. Yellow is homozygous recessive; but purple can be heterozygous, resulting in yellow flowers in future generations.
 6. If all F_1 are the dominant phenotype, the tested individual is homozygous dominant. If any recessive traits show up in the F_1, the tested individual is heterozygous.
 7. (a) 9:3:1;   (b) 9 – two; 3 – one; 3 – the other one; 1 – none
 8. The genes for various characteristics segregate independently from each other during meiosis.
 9. 3:1
 10. ABD, aBD, AbD, abD
 11. 16
 12. 3/8 x 1/2 = 3/16
 13. types A, B, and AB

III. 1. In a chiasma, homologs are held tightly together. Crossover occurs when pieces of homologs break, exchange, and reattach.
 2. One crossover often suppresses another nearby.
 3. Linked genes show much lower recombination frequencies than nonlinked genes.
 4. In the double crossovers, the gene separated from the other two is the middle gene.
 5. a. XY   b. XX   c. XO   d. XX   e. ZZ
    f. ZW   g. ZZ   h. ZO   i. AAXY   j. AAXX
 6. a. 1/2   b. 1/2   c. $X^{nH}X^{Nh}$
 7. An inactivated X chromosome in female cells appears as a Barr body.
 8. It does not involve the sex chromosomes.
 9. a. female   b. XO   c. –   d. male   e. XXY, XXXY
    f. +   g. male   h. XYY   i. –
 10. nondisjunction

Chapter 16

DEVELOPMENTAL BIOLOGY I:
MORPHOGENESIS AND THE CONTROL OF GROWTH

WHAT'S IN THIS CHAPTER

This chapter presents an overview of developmental processes in animals from the zygote stage to the development of the three germ layers: ectoderm, endoderm, and mesoderm. The development of a representative echinoderm, the sea urchin, is used to illustrate the meaning of basic terms such as cleavage, blastomere, blastula, gastrula, blastocoel, animal pole, vegetal pole, archenteron, and blastopore. The latter background terminology provides a basis for comparison of development of vertebrates, in which the amniotic egg and extraembryonic membranes provide for development in animals that live in an environment of air.

Basic mechanisms that shape tissues and organs as morphogenesis progresses are explained by means of controlled planes of cell divisions, which can produce filaments, sheets, or masses and, by means of adhesiveness between cells, can account for layered structures.

Controlled growth of tissue masses is explained in terms of contact inhibition of movement and mitosis, which involves membrane surface receptors and the production of glycoproteins called chalones. In addition, the role of mitogens (substances that stimulate mitosis) is examined, along with their regulatory action on concentrations of cyclic AMP.

By the end of this chapter you should be able to:

1. Explain how developmental patterns differ among vertebrates up to the formation of the three germ layers.

2. Define the terms differentiation and morphogenesis and relate them to development.

3. List the three germ layers and give examples of tissues that are derived from them.

4. Define the terms zygote, blastula, blastocoel, gastrula, archenteron, blastodisc, primitive streak, blastopore, chorion, and amnion.

5. Describe blastula formation, gastrulation, and neurulation.

217

6. Explain what is meant by animal pole and vegetal pole, and give embryonic derivatives of each.

7. Discuss the significance of the amniotic egg. List the groups in which it is found and describe its structure.

8. List four factors that are involved in the shaping of sheets of tissue.

9. Explain what is meant by plane of division and cell adhesiveness and what these two factors have to do with the shape into which a tissue grows.

10. Explain the factors that are responsible for recognition between cells, where they exist, what they are made of chemically, and what various substances may affect them.

11. Define and relate the terms contact inhibition, contact inhibition of mitosis, chalone, mitogen, glycoprotein, lectins, and concanavalin A.

12. Explain the action of hormones on tissue growth.

WHAT YOU SHOULD ALREADY KNOW

You need to know basic ideas of developmental biology (Chapter 10). You need to know the concept of life cycles in organisms and some basic mechanisms of gene action and regulation. You should know basic cell structure, structural properties of cell membranes, and fundamentals of mitosis. In addition, you need to know the structural and functional importance of proteins and carbohydrates and the significance of antigens.

Pre-Test

1. If the mother cell has 22 chromosomes and undergoes mitosis, each daughter cell will have _____(how many?) chromosomes.

1. 22

2. A certain length of DNA that serves as a unit of function in determining the amino acid sequence of a protein is called a (a)_____. The process whereby information is transferred from DNA to RNA is called (b)_____.

2. (a) gene; (b) transcription

3. The process whereby a message in DNA eventually directs the synthesis of a protein is called _____.

3. translation

4. An outer coating found on the membrane of most animal cells is the (a)_____. This substance consists of the chemical components (b)_____ and _____.

218

4. (a) glycocalyx;
(b) protein and
carbohydrates

5. A molecule on a cell membrane that would be recognized as foreign in another organism is called an _____ (antigen / antibody).

5. antigen

6. Every somatic cell in an organism will have _____ (the same / different) genes.

6. the same

7. What does the term gene regulation mean in the development of a multicellular organism?

_____

_____

7. In a particular cell, some genes are active in protein synthesis while others are not.

8. Eucaryotic chromosomes contain regions in which some genes are actively transcribed. Such regions are called _____ (euchromatin / heterochromatin).

8. euchromatin

GUIDED REVIEW OF THE CHAPTER

Introduction

1. The two important areas of developmental biology are

(a)_____ and (b)_____.

1. (a) differen-
tiation; (b)
morphogenesis

16-1 Fertilization activates the egg and initiates development.

1. Development normally begins with formation of a _____.

1. zygote

2. The part of the sperm that contains enzymes that break down the external layers of the ovum is the _____.

2. acrosome

3. The first action in the ovum after sperm entrance is activation of the _____ granules just below the vitelline membrane.

3. cortical

4. True or False: Only one sperm can enter the ovum in all groups of vertebrates.

4. False

16-2 Animal embryos are shaped by massive movements of cells.

1. The three germ layers of the embryo from which all other

219

tissues are derived are (a)_____, (b)_____

_____, and (c)_____.

1. (a) ectoderm;
   (b) endoderm;
   (c) mesoderm

2. Using the following numbered terms, designate the part of the sea urchin embryo that gives rise to the structures listed.

   1. vegetal pole cells
   2. archenteron
   3. animal pole cells.

   (a) embryonic skeleton _____

   (b) archenteron _____

   (c) "ancient gut" _____

   (d) blastopore _____

   (e) future mouth _____

2. (a) 1; (b) 1;
   (c) 2; (d) 2;
   (e) 3

3. From which germ layer does each of the following develop?

   (a) intestinal tract lining _____

   (b) muscles _____

   (c) skin _____

   (d) bone _____

   (e) notocord _____

3. (a) endoderm;
   (b) mesoderm;
   (c) ectoderm
   (d) mesoderm;
   (e) mesoderm

4. Individual cells resulting from cleavage of the zygote are

   called _____.

4. blastomeres

5. Cells that form the skeleton of the sea urchin come from

   the embryonic _____(animal / vegetal) pole.

5. vegetal

6. The process of gastrulation results in the formation of a

   cavity called the _____.

6. archenteron

7. The opening of the archenteron in the embryo is called the

   _____.

7. blastopore

8. The term for embryonic tissue movements that result in the basic structure of the central nervous system is

   _____.

8. neurulation

16-3 Higher vertebrates develop extraembryonic membrane systems.

1. The first mechanism to evolve in animal development to preserve an aqueous environment for the embryo was the

(a)_____. The group of animals in which

this evolved was the (b)_____.

1. (a) amniotic egg;
   (b) reptiles

2. Match each of the following developmental characteristics with the particular animal group that exhibits it.

   1. amphibians
   2. reptiles
   3. birds
   4. mammals

   (a) placenta present _____

   (b) amnion and chorion present _____

   (c) little yolk, but chorion and amnion present _____

   (d) no extraembryonic membranes _____

2. (a) 4;
   (b) 2, 3, 4;
   (c) 4; (d) 1

3. In bird development, the equivalent of the blastula is the

   _____.

3. blastodisc

4. Frog embryos require _____(little / much) stored food.

4. little

5. The blastodisc in bird embryos splits into two layers, the

   (a)_____ and the (b)_____.

5. (a) epiblast;
   (b) hypoblast

6. The neural tube develops from _____(ectoderm / endoderm / mesoderm).

6. ectoderm

7. The "breathing organ" of the embryo is a membrane well

   supplied with blood vessels, the _____ membrane.

7. chorioallantoic

8. The system of membranes found in the amniotic egg would

   form the (a)_____ in mammals. The role of the

   latter is (b)_____.

8. (a) placenta;
   (b) exchange of gases, nutrients, and wastes

16-4 Patterns of cell division determine the form of many tissues.

1. The two major features of cells that determine the shape

221

into which a tissue grows are (a)_____

_____ and (b)_____.

1. (a) plane of
   division; (b)
   adhesiveness

2. If cells keep their axis of division oriented in the same
   direction for each division, the resulting structure will

   have the shape of a(an) (a)_____. In the
   formation of a surface sheet such as an epithelium,

   division is in (b)_____(one / two) axis(es).

2. (a) filament;
   (b) two

16-5 *Differential adhesion can determine the arrangement of
     some tissues.*

1. Differential adhesion of cells to form aggregates of like
   cells depends on recognition. Substances that are re-

   sponsible for this recognition are (a)_____

   and (b)_____ that exist on the (c)_____

   _____ of the cell.

1. (a) proteins;
   (b) carbohy-
   drates;
   (c) plasma
   membrane (or
   surface)

2. The fact that sponge cells can be separated and will
   re-form into the original structure demonstrates the

   (a)_____ Principle. An investigator
   who demonstrated this principle with chick embryos was

   (b)_____.

2. (a) Self-
   Assembly;
   (b) Moscona

3. The antigens that form the basis of the ABO blood groups

   in humans are chemically _____(proteins /
   oligosaccharides).

3. oligosac-
   charides

16-6 *Sheets of tissues may be shaped by several factors.*

1. The shaping of a particular sheet of tissue has to do with

   at least three factors relating to cells, (a)_____

   _____, (b)_____, and

   (c)_____, plus the environmental

   influence of (d)_____ material
   produced by and found between the cells.

1. (a) cell move-
   ment; (b) cell
   shape; (c) cell
   growth; (d)
   extracellular

16-7 *Contact inhibition restricts the growth and movement of
     cells.*

1. Restricted growth of cells in development is due to the

fact that, when cells become packed together, mitosis slows and then stops. This phenomenon is called (a)_____ _____. A naturally occurring substance that inhibits mitosis is called a(an) (b)_____, which chemically is a(an) (c)_____. A substance that has the opposite effect and stimulates mitosis is called a(an) (d)_____.

1. (a) contact inhibition of mitosis; (b) chalone; (c) glycoprotein; (d) mitogen

2. Embryonic cells have (a)_____(great / little) contact inhibition. Abnormal cells such as tumor cells are (b)_____(similar / dissimilar) in this respect.

2. (a) little (b) similar

3. An example of a lectin, or phytohemagglutinin, is (a)_____. The substance is a (b)_____ _____(mitogen / mitosis inhibitor).

3. (a) concan-avalin A; (b) mitogen

4. True or False: An epidermal chalone may be effective against liver tissue, and vice versa.

4. False

5. True or False: A cut or other injury to the skin can release epidermal cells from contact inhibition.

5. True

6. True or False: Epidermal cells that have been transformed by wart viruses are more sensitive to inhibitory influences from surrounding cells.

6. False

16-8 Specific proteins regulate the growth of some tissues.

1. The _____ make up an important group of ligands in animal tissues that regulate growth by altering the intracellular concentration of cAMP and cGMP. Cells that are growing and undergoing mitosis have (b)_____ (low / high) concentrations of cAMP. The enzyme that catalyzes the formation of cAMP would be (c)_____ (activated / inhibited) by lectins.

1. (a) hormones; (b) low; (c) inhibited

2. Nerve growth factor (NGF) _____(is / is not) a mitogen.

2. is not

223

1. The first structure formed in the development of a diploid organism is the:
    a. gastrula.
    b. blastula.
    c. zygote.
    d. neurula.

2. The process in which a certain cell type develops properties different from those of other cell types is called:
    a. morphogenesis.
    b. gene regulation.
    c. embryology.
    d. differentiation.

3. Which of the following is not a germ layer?
    a. mesoderm
    b. blastoderm
    c. endoderm
    d. ectoderm

4. Which of the following gives the proper sequence of events in development?
    a. blastula, gastrula, zygote, neurulation
    b. zygote, neurulation, gastrula, blastula
    c. zygote, blastula, gastrula, neurulation
    d. gastrula, neurulation, zygote, blastula

5. Invagination of cells from the vegetal pole in the sea urchin forms the:
    a. archenteron.
    b. blastopore.
    c. primitive streak.
    d. blastodisc.

6. The process of tissue movement that forms the basis of the development of the brain and spinal cord is:
    a. neural tube.
    b. neural plate.
    c. neural crest.
    d. neurulation.

7. Which of the following is(are) not derived from mesoderm?
    a. cartilage
    b. brain
    c. bones
    d. muscle

8. Embryos of _____ do not have extraembryonic membranes.
    a. frogs
    b. reptiles
    c. mammals
    d. birds

9. In mammals, the embryo proper develops from the:
    a. trophoblast.
    b. chorion.
    c. inner cell mass.
    d. amnion.

10. In morphogenesis of tissues, cells that keep their division axis oriented in the same direction:
   a. are characteristic of mammal tissue morphogenesis.
   b. will form a tissue mass.
   c. will form a sheet such as epithelium.
   d. will form a filamentous structure.

11. Chemical structures responsible for cell adhesions in tissue morphogenesis are:
   a. lipid.
   b. nucleic acids.
   c. protein and oligosaccharides.
   d. antibodies.

12. A substance that is produced by multicellular organisms and induces cell division is called a:
   a. mitogen.
   b. chalone.
   c. glycoprotein.
   d. lectin.

13. Contact inhibition does not involve:
   a. inhibition of cell movement or migration.
   b. chalone production.
   c. inhibition of mitosis.
   d. lectin production.

14. Which of the following statements about contact inhibition is true?
   a. Tumor cells are subject to a high degree of contact inhibition.
   b. Embryonic cells are subject to little or no contact inhibition.
   c. Normal skin cells have poor contact inhibition mechanisms.
   d. In trauma to skin, contact inhibition is increased.

15. Which of the following statements is not true of lectins?
   a. Concanavalin A is an example of a lectin.
   b. They are phytohemagglutinins.
   c. They have different specificities.
   d. They are oligosaccharides.

16. Which of the following statements is not true of concanavalin A?
   a. It is paratactic to glucose and mannose residues in oligosaccharides.
   b. It is a protein.
   c. It agglutinates normal cells.
   d. It is a mitogen.

17. Cyclic AMP:
   a. synthesis is stimulated by concanavalin A.
   b. at high concentrations will stimulate mitosis.
   c. is synthesized as a result of activation of the enzyme adenylate cyclase.
   d. levels are low in cells that are contact inhibited.

REVIEW QUESTIONS

I. The members of each of the following groups of terms have a functional relationship to each other. Make a statement that outlines that relationship.

225

1. Mitogens, chalones, mitosis, contact inhibition

_____

_____

_____

2. Chalones, lectins, glycoproteins, concanavalin A

_____

_____

_____

3. Embryology, differentiation, morphogenesis, gene regulation

_____

_____

_____

4. Blastomeres, cleavage, blastula

_____

_____

_____

5. Brain and spinal cord, neural tube, neural plate, neurulation

_____

_____

_____

6. Cyclic AMP, tissue growth, concanavalin A, adenylate cyclase

_____

_____

_____

II. Arrange the following events in the proper sequence to reflect the order of their occurrence in embryonic development. _____

                    a. 2,4,8, etc. cell stages
                    b. gastrula
                    c. neural tube formation
                    d. zygote
                    e. neural plate formation
                    f. blastula
                    g. formation of three germ layers
                    h. somite formation

III. Reptiles, birds, and mammals embryos have extraembryonic membranes associated with the embryo. The developmental patterns are similar. One difference, however, is the amount of yolk in the eggs. Comment on the developmental difference associated with the amount of yolk.

_____

_____

_____

_____

ANSWERS TO CHAPTER EXERCISES

Practice Quiz

1. c	5. a	9. c	13. d
2. d	6. d	10. d	14. b
3. b	7. b	11. c	15. d
4. c	8. a	12. a	16. c
			17. c

Review Questions

I. 1. Mitogens stimulate mitosis; when growth is complete, chalones are produced that inhibit further growth.

    2. Chalones are glycoproteins that have a role in growth inhibition; lectins, of which concanavalin A is an example, are mitogens.

    3. Embryology is the study of development of the embryo from zygote formation to birth. The process is dependent on gene regulation, which determines differentiation of tissues and development of form, or morphogenesis.

    4. Cleavage of the zygote produces individual cells called blastomeres; with repeated cleavage the blastula is formed.

    5. Neurulation is the process of formation of the embryonic brain and spinal cord. It begins with formation of the neural plate, from which the neural tube pinches off.

227

6. Concanavalin A inhibits adenylate cyclate, which decreases cyclic AMP with the result that growth is stimulated.

II. d, a, f, b, g, e, c, h

III. Much yolk is needed in bird and reptile eggs, because this is the only source of food. A large amount of yolk is not needed in mammalian eggs, because nutrients for the embryo will be obtained from the mother through the placenta.

Chapter 17

DEVELOPMENTAL BIOLOGY II: DIFFERENTIATION

WHAT'S IN THIS CHAPTER

Chapter 17 considers major questions relating to differentiation. Two important factors are examined: localized differences already present in eggs and the interactions between cells in the developing embryo. The text also highlights the results of experiments ranging from those involving oocytes to those involving more advanced stages of development and their contribution to existing knowledge about differentiation.

You are first shown that embryonic cells can become determined at various times and that the distribution of material in the cortical portion of the egg of some species determines the fate of cells. In addition, the fate of cells becomes more determined with successive divisions in the developmental process. However, some cells (such as blood cell precursor cells) remain relatively undifferentiated in the adult until they divide to produce the fully differentiated blood cells.

Because all cells in an animal originate from one cell, they should all have the same number of chromosomes and genes, yet they are specialized for certain functions. You naturally will ask why, then, or how different cells do only certain things if the genetic machinery is the same in all the cells. Information contained in the chapter provides a bit of the answer, with explanations of activation and repression of gene activity. In addition, a partial explanation for the role of the "extra" DNA is given, along with coverage of gene regulation in the process of differentiation.

By the end of this chapter you should be able to:

1. Distinguish between mosaic and regulative types of development and explain experiments that were performed to demonstrate the difference.

2. Explain the importance of the egg cortex in development and how this was demonstrated.

3. Explain what is meant by a cell becoming "determined" as development progresses and the significance of its being determined insofar as mRNA and the proteins synthesized are concerned.

4. Describe the concept of stem cells and the value of some cells remaining stem

229

cells when development is completed.

5. Explain how the genomes of unspecialized and specialized cells may be the same, and cite experiments showing that there is no loss of genome with differentiation.

6. Define embryonic induction and relate it to the gray crescent, dorsal lip of the blastopore, chordamesoderm, and neural plate.

7. Distinguish between instructive and permissive induction and cite examples of each.

8. Explain the clock mechanism of differentiation, citing examples and experiments that demonstrated the phenomenon.

9. Discuss the relationship between the size of the genome and the actual amount of DNA that functions in protein synthesis, and suggest possible functional reasons for the excess.

10. Distinguish between heterochromatin and euchromatin, and relate them to gene action and RNA trancription.

11. Define lampbrush and polytene chromosomes and relate them to RNA transcription.

12. Relate the terms transcriptional unit, premessenger RNA, intron, exon, coding sequence, and intervening sequence.

13. Explain what is involved in the regulation of gene action by steroid hormones.

14. Explain what is meant by "jumping genes" and cite experiments to indicate their existence.

15. Summarize major factors that are known or believed to be important in the control of development and gene regulation.

WHAT YOU SHOULD ALREADY KNOW

You should know the contents of Chapter 16 and all material that is a prerequisite for that chapter. (Return to the background review for that chapter to test your knowledge of prerequisite material).

Pre-Test

1. Morphogenesis and differentiation depend on the turning

    on and off of (a)_____. These functional units

    are nucleotide sequences in (b)_____ molecules.
    Transfer of a message from DNA to RNA is called

    (c)_____, whereas the use of that
    message to create a sequence of amino acids for protein

    synthesis is called (d)_____.

1. (a) genes;
   (b) DNA; (c)
   transcription;
   (d) transla-
   tion

2. The shaping of tissues in morphogenesis involves three factors relating to cells. These are cell (a)_____, (b)_____, (c)_____.

2. (a) movement;
   (b) shape;
   (c) growth

3. State in one sentence the relationship between genes and chromosomes. _____

   _____

3. Genes are
   units of DNA
   in chromo-
   somes

4. Where in the eucaryotic cell do the following carry out their function?

   (a) DNA _____

   (b) mRNA _____

   (c) steroid hormones _____

4. (a) nucleus;
   (b) cytoplasm;
   (c) chromo-
   somes (genes)

GUIDED REVIEW OF THE CHAPTER

17-1 Determination may occur at different times during development.

1. The egg of *Nereis* is said to show mosaic development in that each blastomere is destined to become a specific part of an organ. Give the fate of each of the following parts in terms of germ layer.

   (a) macromeres _____

   (b) top 3/4 micromeres _____

   (c) bottom 1/4 micromeres _____

1. (a) endoderm;
   (b) ectoderm;
   (c) mesoderm

2. In the sea squirt *Styela*, what structures are derived from these particular pigmented parts of the egg?

   (a) light gray cytoplasm _____

   (b) clear cytoplasm in animal half _____

   _____

   (c) yellow-crescent cytoplasm _____

   _____

231

2. (a) notocord,
    neural tube;
    (b) ectoderm;
    sense organs;
    (c) muscles of
    larval tail

3. The type of development characteristic of vertebrates, where the fate of individual embryonic cells is not determined early, is called a _____ (regulative/ mosaic) development. In such development, cells destined to become tissue X are called (b)_____ X cells.

3. (a) regulative;
    (b) presumptive

4. Development in which the fate of each cell is determined early is said to be _____.

4. mosaic

5. Mice that develop from blastomeres from mice of two different colors are mixed to create mice that have two different phenotypes. They are called _____ mice.

5. allophenic

17-2 *The structure of the egg cortex may partially determine development.*

1. Cite two experiments which demonstrated that the highly structured cortex of an egg may help to determine differentiation.

    (a)_____

    (b)_____

1. (a) centrifu-
    gation of sea
    urchin eggs;
    (b) coiling
    inheritance
    in snails

2. True or False: Freshwater snails, *Limnaea*, inherit the direction of coiling.

2. True

3. The coiling of *Limnaea* may be to the left, (a)_____ _____, or to the right, (b)_____. Coiling direction is determined by the parent that produces the (c)_____(egg / sperm).

3. (a) sinistrally;
    (b) dextrally;
    (c) egg

17-3 *Cells become progressively determined as they divide.*

1. In development, as blastomeres divide they become (a)_____(more / less) restricted in their potential. This is well illustrated in the development of vertebrate (b)_____ cells. When a cell reaches the point where it can express only a certain

phenotype, it is said to be (c)_____.

1. (a) more;
   (b) blood;
   (c) determined

2. When a hematopoietic stem cell becomes a "committed" cell, it is referred to as a _____ cell as opposed to a stem cell.

2. blast

3. The specific protein that stimulates formation of red blood cells is called _____.

3. erythropoietin

17-4 Some cells remain stem cells indefinitely.

1. Give an example of a plant and animal stem cell that divides to produce one cell that will differentiate. Then give an example of another stem cell.

   (a) _____

   (b) _____

1. (a) epidermal;
   (b) meristem

2. Three specialized differentiated cells that have lost the power to divide are (a)_____ cells, (b)_____ cells, and (c)_____ cells.

2. (a) nerve;
   (b) blood;
   (c) upper epidermal

3. An example of an organ that contains specialized, differentiated cells which divide little or not at all, but still possess the capacity to divide, is the (a)_____. The absence of a specific (b)_____ permits this.

3. (a) liver;
   (b) chalone

17-5 Differentiation does not generally entail loss of DNA.

1. What experiment first demonstrated that, as cells become differentiated and specialized, they do not, in general, lose any of their genomes?

   _____

   _____

   _____

1. Inserting the nucleus of a late embryo frog cell into a frog egg whose nucleus

2. True or False: Plasma cells that function in the production of antibodies have some loss of DNA.

233

is removed.
Result: Eggs
develop to
late embryo.

2. True

3. Transplanting a nucleus of one cell into another
enucleated cell is called _____.

3. cloning

17-6 *Some tissues can induce the differentiation of other tissues.*

1. The dorsal lip of the blastopore in the amphibian embryo
develops from the (a)_____ region
of the zygote. Cells derived from the dorsal lip induce
the central portion of dorsal ectoderm to form the
(b)_____. Experimentation in-
dicates that the inducer is (c)_____(RNA /
DNA / protein).

1. (a) gray
crescent; (b)
neural tube;
(c) protein

2. True or False: In the newt, the dorsal lip material is
called the organizer because of its ability to direct the
growth pattern of the embryo.

2. True

3. The embryonic tissue resulting from dorsal lip cells in
the newt is first called _____.

3. chordamesoderm

17-7 *Inductive interactions may be instructive or permissive.*

1. The embryonic eye cup is a(an) (a)_____
(instructive / permissive) inducer. It induces the over-
lying epithelium to develop into the (b)_____.
A target tissue that is capable of reacting in the proper
manner to an inducing tissue is said to be (c)_____.

1. (a) instruc-
tive; (b) lens;
(c) competent

2. An inducer that supports development of a tissue which has
already been determined is said to be _____.

2. permissive

3. True or False: A pancreas will develop from pancreas
primordium only if pancreatic mesenchyme is used.

3. False

17-8 *Some differentiating tissues appear to be regulated by a clock mechanism.*

1. An example of a "clocklike" mechanism involved in develop-

ment is the formation of (a)_____. What

has this mechanism to do with gene regulation? (b) _____

_____

1. (a) limb bones; 2. Which two germ layers are involved in formation of limb
   (b) Genes
   appear to be   structures? (a)_____ and (b)_____
   turned on in
   sequence as the
   tissue ages.

2. (a) ectoderm;   3. True or False: An explanation of the clock mechanism is
   (b) mesoderm   that one gene produces a substance which turns on a second
               gene, and so on.

3. True

17-9 Eucaryotic cells have "too much" DNA.

   1. In eucaryotic cells, the most likely function of the

      excess DNA is _____.

1. regulatory   2. True or False: It is generally believed that excess DNA
               in the cell is used only to form chromosome structure.

2. False

17-10 Chromosome structure may regulate gene transcription.

   1. Chromosome regions that are compact and therefore visible

      when most of the chromosome is not are _____
      (heterochromatin / euchromatin).

1. heterochromatin 2. Heterochromatin is _____(active / not
                 active) in transcribing RNA.

2. not active   3. Chromosomes that consist of highly condensed regions
            separating many thin chromatin loops are called

      (a)_____. The part of the chromosome from

      which RNA is transcribed is the (b)_____
      (condensed part / loop).

3. (a) lampbrush; 4. Chromosomes that contain many strands of DNA formed by
   (b) loop
              replication without separation are called (a)_____
      chromosomes. A major place where these are found is in

      (b)_____.

4. (a) polytene;
   (b) salivary
   glands

235

17-11 The structure of eucaryotic transcription units is complex.

1. Interspersed among their coding sequences, eucaryotic genes have intervening segments of DNA that do not supply information for protein structure. These sequences are also referred to as (a)_____. The DNA sequences in the gene that actually provide information for amino acid sequences are called the (b)_____.

1. (a) introns;
   (b) exons

2. Pre-messenger RNA is a copy of (a)_____
   _____(introns / exons / both introns and exons). The pre-mRNA has a tail of nucleotides containing the base (b)_____. What is one proposed function of this tail?

   (c)_____

2. (a) both introns and exons;
   (b) adenine;
   (c) exit through nuclear membrane

3. Though the exact reason for the existence of introns is not known, list two possible functions.

   (a)_____

   _____

   (b)_____

   _____

3. (a) multiple functions of same gene, depending on which introns are excised;
   (b) role in evolution, which depends on variety possible through intron-exon structure

4. True or False: Mammalian hemoglobin molecules are protomers.

4. False

5. True or False: Human hemoglobin molecules have been cloned and sequenced.

5. True

6. True or False: Pseudogenes are never expressed.

6. True

17-12 Some genes are directly regulated by steroids.

1. Steroid hormones (a)_____(do / do not) act through cyclic AMP and cyclic GMP mechanisms. A well-known steroid hormone in insect larvae is (b)_____

   _____. An effect of the hormone is to induce specific protein synthesis. Its effects are manifested through what effect on salivary gland chromosomes?

   (c)_____

1. (a) do not;
   (b) ecdysome;
   (c) puffing

17-13 Some genetic elements "jump" from one place to another.

1. A genetic element that can move around from place to place in a genome and exert an effect on genes is called a

   (a)_____. The element under control

   of the latter is called a (b)_____.

1. (a) regulator;
   (b) receptor

PRACTICE QUIZ

1. Which of the following statements is <u>not</u> true of spiral cleavage of *Nereis*?
   a. The animal pole consists of micromeres.
   b. The vegetal pole consists of cells that develop into endoderm.
   c. The egg shows mosaic development.
   d. The blastomeres retain the ability to become any germ layer late in development.

2. Development of the frog:
   a. is the regulative type.
   b. shows that the fate of blastomeres is set early in development.
   c. demonstrates mosaic development.
   d. is such that, if the location of presumptive epidermis is changed early, it will still develop into epidermis.

3. Studies on centrifugation of the sea urchin egg:
   a. were performred by Beatrice Mintz.
   b. showed the importance of the egg cortex.
   c. demonstrated the early establishment of the fate of blastomeres.
   d. showed that mild centrifugation would result in abnormal development.

4. Which of the following statements is <u>nct</u> true of coiling in the snail *Limnaea*?
   a. They coil dextrally or sinistrally.
   b. A dominant gene results in dextral coiling.
   c. Offspring have the coiling pattern of the parent that produces the sperm.
   d. Coiling direction is determined by a nuclear gene.

5. As the cells in a developing embryo progressively divide:
   a. they become more determined.
   b. some of the genetic information is lost.
   c. the cells can be relocated throughout development and will still develop
      into the same cell type as those surrounding them.
   d. the cells begin to produce the same types of protein.

6. Three of the following cell types, when they divide, produce one cell that
   becomes differentiated plus another stem cell. Which type does not?
   a. lower epidermal cells
   b. cambium cells
   c. hemopoietic cells
   d. red blood cells

7. Which of the following is the most acceptable explanation for the relationship
   between the genome and the specialization of a cell?
   a. There is a loss of genes or DNA as a cell becomes specialized.
   b. All genes in a specialized cell are active at one time or another.
   c. The genome of the specialized cell is larger than the genome before
      specialization.
   d. Specialized cells have complete genomes, but some genes are not used.

8. Three of the following investigators showed that differentiation is not
   usually accompanied by a loss of DNA. Which one did not?
   a. King
   b. Gurdon
   c. Mintz
   d. Briggs

9. Which of the following statements is not true of the dorsal lip of the
   blastopore in amphibian embryos?
   a. It is called an organizer.
   b. The gray crescent region develops from it.
   c. The tissue can induce formation of the neural plate.
   d. The cells form a tissue called chordamesoderm.

10. Embryonic induction:
    a. was demonstrated by Ulrich Cleaver.
    b. apparently occurs as a result of the action of specific proteins.
    c. is thought to occur through direct contact interaction of cell surfaces.
    d. will not occur if chordamesoderm is separated from ectoderm by a filter.

11. Experimentation with vertebrate limb buds demonstrated:
    a. a "clock mechanism" of differentiation.
    b. embryonic instructive induction.
    c. that some cells remain relatively undifferentiated.
    d. a loss of genome as cells become more specialized.

12. Which of the following statements is true of heterochromatin?
    a. RNA is actively transcribed on it.
    b. It may activate genes.
    c. An example is the Barr body.
    d. DNA is less compact in heterochromatin than in euchromatin.

13. Chromosome puffs:
    a. are heterochromatin.
    b. are regions of active RNA transcription.

c. are regions where chromomeres are located.
d. contain inactive DNA.

14. Pre-messenger RNA consists of:
    a. introns but not exons.
    b. exons but not introns.
    c. neither exons nor introns.
    d. both exons and introns.

15. Introns:
    a. are not found in eucaryotic genes.
    b. are functional mRNA transcripts.
    c. are spliced out of transcriptional units.
    d. do not exist in the same transcriptional unit with exons.

16. Which of the following statements is not true of human hemoglobin molecules?
    a. The genes have been cloned.
    b. The genes have been sequenced.
    c. Each molecule is one promoter.
    d. They are not the same in embryos and adults.

17. An insect hormone that controls molting is:
    a. ecdysone.
    b. epinephrine.
    c. cortisone.
    d. aldosterone.

18. Steroids do not:
    a. act directly on genes.
    b. increase levels of cAMP or cGMP.
    c. pass through plasma membranes.
    d. belong to the class of lipids.

REVIEW QUESTIONS

I. Column I is a list of important experimental tools and procedures. Column II is a list of important principles that apply to the field of development and gene regulation. Match each principle with the experiment that led to its discovery.

Column I

A. Pigmented areas in sea squirt oocytes
B. Centrifugation of sea urchin eggs
C. Allophenic mice
D. Transplantation of nuclei from undifferentiated cells into enucleated eggs
E. *Nereis* cleavage

F. Mesenchyme taken from various places to see effect on endodermal tubes
G. Dissociator and activator elements
H. Transplantation of dorsal lip material in amphibians
I. Lampbrush chromosomes in oocytes
J. Cloning and sequencing of human hemoglobin gene
K. Limb bud development

Column II

_____ 1. The fate of some blastomeres is set early in development.

_____ 2. Genes may be arranged on chromosomes in order of expression.

_____ 3. The fates of regions of cytoplasm determined.

_____ 4. RNA is transcribed from noncompacted "loop" areas in chromosomes.

_____ 5. Differentiation does not entail loss of DNA.

_____ 6. The structure of the cortex of an egg may determine development.

_____ 7. Embryonic induction.

_____ 8. As the zygote divides, blastomeres become more restricted in what they can become.

_____ 9. Clock mechanism of differentiation.

_____ 10. Permissive induction occurs in pancreatic development.

_____ 11. Genetic elements that regulate genes may "jump" from one place to another on their genome.

II. Distinguish between the members of each of the following pairs of terms.

1. Mosaic and regulative development: _____

_____

_____

2. Dextral and sinistral coiling: _____

_____

_____

3. Embryonic induction and gene induction: _____

_____

_____

4. Instructive and permissive induction: _____

_____

_____

5. Heterochromatin and euchromatin: _____

_____

6. Introns and exons: _____

_____

_____

III. What is the distinctive difference between each of the following pairs of terms?

1. Stem cell and blast cell: _____

_____

_____

2. Meristem and cambium: _____

_____

_____

3. Including tissue and competent target tissue: _____

_____

_____

4. Chromomeres and lampbrush chromoscmes: _____

_____

_____

ANSWERS TO CHAPTER EXERCISES

Practice Quiz

1. d	7. d	13. b	
2. a	8. c	14. d	
3. b	9. b	15. c	
4. c	10. b	16. c	
5. a	11. a	17. a	
6. d	12. c	18. b	

Review Questions

I. 1. E	4. I	7. H	10. F
2. J	5. D	8. C	11. G
3. A	6. B	9. K	

II. 1. mosaic - fate of blastomeres determined early
regulative - fate not determined so early

2. dextral - to the right
sinistral - to the left

3. embryonic - involves induction by tissue
gene - involves induction of genes by specific ligands

4. instructive - specific directions come from the inducing tissue
permissive - specific instructions come from a tissue other than the inducing tissue

5. heterochromatin - compact, not actively transcribed
euchromatin - not tightly coiled, actively transcribed

6. introns - intervening noncoding segments of DNA in a gene
exons - coding sequences in a gene

III. 1. A blast cell is further along in differentiation.

2. Cambium is an example of meristem cells.

3. A target tissue must be competent in order to receive proper instruction from an inducing tissue.

4. Chromomeres are parts of lampbrush chromosomes.

Chapter 18

THE ORGANIZATION OF PLANTS AND ANIMALS

WHAT'S IN THIS CHAPTER

This chapter introduces you to functioning plants and animals and lays the
foundation for the next several chapters. This is a general introduction about
plant and animal physiology and anatomy, including the function and form of tissues
and organs. A comparison will be made between plants and animals, including their
structure, growth patterns, and the physical limitations that help to determine
their biological architecture. You will learn about some common problems that
plants and animals face and the differences between plants and animals. The most
important differences, as you will see, are related to nutrition and movement.

By the end of this chapter you should be able to:

1. Distinguish between a thallus and the body of a vascular plant.

2. Compare xylem and phloem.

3. Contrast the growth pattern of plants and animals.

4. Name one important similarity and one major difference between a plant's and
   an animal's metabolic activities.

5. List the major parts of an animal's digestive system.

6. Explain the significance of cephalization.

7. Compare the structures of support in a plant and in an animal.

8. Describe the importance of surface/volume ratio to living organisms, and name
   two structures whose shape is determined by it.

9. Describe the importance of mass/area ratio, and cite one example of its effect
   on structure.

10. Define poikilothermic and homeothermic, and relate metabolic rate to an
    organism's size.

11. Name three types of tissues that are common to both plants and animals and one that is unique to each.

12. Describe the two fluid compartments in plants and in animals.

WHAT YOU SHOULD ALREADY KNOW

This chapter deals with common features in the organization of plants and animals. Many of these differences have been dealt with in previous chapters and will be referred to again here. Keep in mind that all living organisms share certain characteristics, so similarities between plants and animals should not be looked on as oddities. On the other hand, their different "life styles" have selected for structures of different form and function.

Pre-Test

1. A _____ is a group of cells with a common structure and function.

1. tissue

2. Plants are (a)_____, organisms that capture light energy and produce high-energy organic compounds.

   Animals are (b)_____, organisms that consume organic molecules of other organisms.

2. (a) photo-
   trophs;
   (b) chemotrophs

3. One major difference between plants and animals is that plants _____(are not motile / have no movement).

3. are not
   motile

4. All living organisms are related by (a)_____ (what continuing process?). The basic unit of every organism is the (b)_____. The genetic material of all organisms is (c)_____. Most of the weight of organisms is (d)_____(what substance?), and the three most common elements in biological molecules are (e)_____, (f)_____, and (g)_____.

4. (a) evolution;
   (b) cell; (c)
   DNA; (d) water;
   (e) carbon;
   (f) hydrogen;
   (g) oxygen

GUIDED REVIEW OF THE CHAPTER

Introduction

1. The study of how organisms function is _____.

1. physiology

2. Plants are (a)_____; that is, they make their own food using sunlight. Animals are (b)_____; that is, they depend on the compounds in the bodies of other organisms. Animals are also (c)_____, meaning that they engulf pieces of food and digest them in an internal tube.

2. (a) photo-
   trophic; (b)
   chemotrophic;
   (c) holotrophic

18-1 The life of the green plant.

1. Some giant kelp may reach a length of (a)_____(20 / 200) meters. Algae do not have specialized body parts but have a body structure called a (b)_____.

1. (a) 200;
   (b) thallus

2. An organism's weight is mostly (a)_____. The (b)_____ of a plant cell prevents the cell from bursting when a high internal pressure, or (c)_____, develops.

2. (a) water;
   (b) wall; (c)
   turgor pressure

3. A cell with a high turgor pressure is said to be (a)_____. A loss of turgor pressure causes a plant to lose its shape, or to (b)_____.

3. (a) turgid;
   (b) wilt

4. Terrestrial algae and mosses are restricted to being small, low-growing plants mostly living in shady areas, because (a)_____. Mosses have simple, rootlike extensions called (b)_____.

4. (a) they must
   remain moist;
   (b) rhizoids

5. The two parts of a vascular plant's specialized system for transporting fluids, called the (a)_____ system, are the (b)_____, which carries dissolved organic materials, and the (c)_____, which carries water.

245

5. (a) vascular;
   (b) phloem;
   (c) xylem

6. Most of the xylem in a tree forms the _____ (what substance?).

6. wood

7. Although animals are confined to a certain size, plants grow _____ and are not confined.

7. indeterminately

8. Various gases pass through small openings in a leaf called (a)_____. Around these openings are specialized (b)_____ cells that can change the size of the opening. Through these openings, water vapor may leave the leaf in a process called (c)_____. For photosynthesis to take place, (d)_____ _____ gas must enter the leaf through the same openings.

8. (a) stomates;
   (b) guard; (c)
   transpiration;
   (d) carbon
   dioxide

18-2 The life of an animal.

1. If a motto could be assigned to a plant, it might be "one direction is (a)_____(as good as / better than) another." For an animal, the motto might be "one direction is (b)_____(as good as / better than) another."

1. (a) as good as;
   (b) better than

2. The head end of an animal is the first part to encounter new objects. The head is equipped with a (a)_____, the opening into which food enters, and with (b)_____ _____ that detect light, sound, and chemicals. The (c)_____ is also located in the head, which directs the behavior of the entire organism. The concentration of all these structures in the head is known as (d)_____.

2. (a) mouth; (b)
   sense organs;
   (c) brain; (d)
   cephalization

3. Indigestible food passes through the (a)_____ in the form of solid waste called (b)_____. The tube between this opening and the mouth is called the (c)_____ canal.

3. (a) anus; (b)
   feces; (c)
   alimentary

4. Waste materials are (a)_____(excreted / secreted); hormones are (b)_____(excreted / secreted).

246

4. (a) excreted;
   (b) secreted

5. All muscles work by _____ (contracting /
   expanding).

5. contracting

6. In animals, the vascular system is made up of a pump

   called the (a)_____, or cardium, and a

   tubular system called the (b)_____, or
   cardiovascular, system.

6. (a) heart;
   (b) circulatory

7. The system or rigid structures against which muscles can

   push and pull is called the (a)_____. The

   simplest of such structures consists of (b)_____
   confined to a tight bag in such organisms as worms.

7. (a) skeleton;
   (b) water

8. There are two different solid skeletons, an (a)_____

   _____ outside an organism's body, which also serves

   a protective function, and an (b)_____ on
   the inside that serves a support function.

8. (a) exo-
   skeleton; (b)
   endoskeleton

9. Many structures and organisms show a mirrored or (a)_____

   _____ symmetry around a midline. Organisms with

   such symmetry have a top, or (b)_____, surface

   and a bottom, or (c)_____, surface.

9. (a) bilateral;
   (b) dorsal;
   (c) ventral

18-3 Some animals have become more like plants.

1. There are many animals that live a (a)_____,
   or nonmotile, existence on the ocean floor. They exhibit

   (b)_____ symmetry and suck or snatch in food
   that passes near them. An example of a large group of

   such organisms is (c)_____.

1. (a) sessile;
   (b) radial; (c)
   coelenterates
   or echinoderms

2. Most animals are (a)_____(motile / nonmotile)

   and (b)_____(radially / bilaterally)
   symmetrical.

2. (a) motile;
   (b) bilaterally

*18-4 Surface/volume ratios determine many architectural fea-
   tures of organisms.*

1. The smaller a structure is, the _____(larger /
   smaller) is its ratio of surface area to volume.

1. larger

2. Materials move into and out of a structure at rates

247

proportional to the _____ of the structure.

2. surface area

3. The circulatory system of an animal is an example of a (a)_____ structure, one that continually subdivides into smaller and smaller branches. In the plant world a similar example is that of a (b)_____

_____.

3. (a) ramifying; (b) root system

4. Three examples of adaptations dictated by the principle of surface/volume ratios are the (a)_____

_____ in the lung, the (b)_____

in the intestines, and the (c)_____

_____ of leaves.

4. (a) tubules and alveoli; (b) villi; (c) thin, flat shape

5. Cacti are adapted to live in very (a)_____ conditions. One of the adaptations that allows them to live in such conditions is their (b)_____

_____, reducing water loss in transpiration.

5. (a) dry; (b) barrel-shaped bodies with no broad leaves

18-5 *Biological architecture is often determined by mass/area restrictions.*

1. The main supporting material for a plant is (a)_____

_____, whereas the main supporting material for a human is (b)_____.

1. (a) xylem; (b) bone

2. The strength of a structure increases with its _____

_____ area.

2. cross-sectional

3. The strength of a muscle is determined by its (a)_____

_____ area, but the mass it pulls on increases with the (b)_____ of a dimension.

3. (a) cross-sectional; (b) cube

4. Compared to its own height, which animal can jump a greater distance, a flea or a horse? _____

4. flea

18-6 Metabolic rate is closely related to an organism's size.

1. A major reason why every organism is adapted to live within a particular temperature range is that its _____ are adapted to work best at certain temperatures.

1. enzymes

2. Terrestrial habitats have _____(extreme / small) shifts in temperature compared to aquatic habitats.

2. extreme

3. Primitive land vertebrates are (a)_____, which means that they obtain much of their heat from outside. They are also (b)_____, or cold-blooded, which means that their temperature is determined by (c)_____ _____.

3. (a) ectothermic; (b) poikilothermic; (c) the temperature of the environment

4. A poikilothermic animal may have behavioral adaptations to temperature, such as _____ _____.

4. selecting sunny places to sit

5. Birds and mammals are (a)_____, organisms that get their heat primarily through their metabolism. They use this heat to remain (b)_____, or warm-blooded, which means that (c)_____ _____ _____.

5. (a) endothermic; (b) homeothermic; (c) their body temperature remains relatively constant no matter what the temperature of the environment

6. An example of a homeotherm's insulation is (a)_____ _____, which helps conserve (b)_____ _____. If a mammal's body temperature rises too high, it may start to (c)_____, which will lower the body temperature as water evaporates from the skin surface.

6. (a) fat layers, feathers, or hair; (b) body heat; (c) pant or sweat

7. The Q_{10} of an organism is _____ _____ _____

249

7. the ratio of an organism's metabolism at one temperature compared to a temperature 10°C lower

8. for every increase of 10°C, the metabolic rate of the organism doubles

9. (a) basal metabolic rate, the rate of metabolism that is needed just to keep an animal alive; (b) 1,800 kcal/ day; (c) 1,700 kcal/day

10. it has a small surface/volume ratio

11. the BMR for small animals is incredibly high, and it would be diffi- cult for such an organism to obtain enough food to keep itself alive

12. Organisms living in colder climates tend to have more compact forms and

8. The Q_{10} of most organisms is approximately 2, which means that _____ _____.

9. The BMR is (a)_____ _____. For an adult male human, the BMR is approximately (b) _____; for an adult female, the BMR is approximately (c)_____.

10. A large endotherm has a mass that produces considerable amounts of heat, but it does not lose much heat because _____ _____.

11. It is unlikely that there would be smaller endotherms than shrews and hummingbirds, because _____ _____ _____ _____.

12. State Allen's rule. _____ _____ _____

13. Why do animals in colder climates conform to this rule? _____ _____

shorter ex-
tremities than
those living in
warmer areas

13. The small sur-
face/volume
ratio conserves
heat better.

1. a group of
similar cells
that function
together

2. (a) a large
substructure
made of several
kinds of tissue
working to-
gether, with a
specific struc-
ture and func-
tion; (b)root,
stem, leaf,
or flower

3. (a) epithelial;
(b) connective;
(c) parenchyma

4. (a) boundaries;
(b) one; (c)
endothelium

5. They are often
rectangular
cells that make
up the substance
of large masses
such as the
liver or the
middle layers
of a leaf.

6. (a) support,
bind, or con-
nect; (b) bone,

18-7 Multicellular organisms are built of tissues and organs.

1. A tissue is _____

_____.

2. An organ is (a)_____

_____.

An example of a plant organ is a (b)_____.

3. The three tissues common to both plants and animals are

(a)_____, (b)_____, and

(c)_____.

4. Epithelial tissue forms the (a)_____ of

structures and is often (b)_____ cell layer(s)
thick. An epithelium that rolls into the inner surface of

a structure is called an (c)_____.

5. Outline the structure and function of parenchyma cells.

_____

_____

_____

6. The function of connective tissue is to (a)_____
other tissues. An example of such a tissue from an animal

is (b)_____ and an example from a plant is

(c)_____.

7. In an animal the nervous system and digestive system are

both (a)_____ systems, made up of organs,

shell, or carti-
lage; (c) fibers
or xylem

7. (a) organ; (b)
do not have

1. interstitial

2. (a) blood
cells;
(b) plasma

3. (a) intracel-
lular; (b)
extracellular

4. (a) symplast;
(b) apoplast

5. (a) intercel-
lular gas space;
(b) oxygen; (c)
carbon dioxide

vascular elements, and associated nerves. Plants
(b)_____(have / do not have) similar systems.

18-8 A multicellular organism has two fluid compartments.

1. The channels and spaces between animal cells are filled
with _____ fluid.

2. The blood of a circulatory system consists of two
components: (a)_____ and
(b)_____.

3. An animal's volume is divided into two major fluid compartments, the (a)_____ fluid, or cytosol,
and the (b)_____ fluid.

4. The entire series of interconnected plant cells is the
(a)_____ (symplast / apoplast); the fibrous
walls of all cells make up the (b)_____(symplast
/ apoplast).

5. The air-filled channels that run between all the cells in
a plant are the (a)_____
system. It allows free flow of (b)_____
throughout the plant to support respiration and of
(c)_____ to supply the needs of
photosynthesizing cells.

PRACTICE QUIZ

1. A thallus will have:
   a. roots.
   b. parenchyma.
   c. phloem.
   d. leaves.

2. Which of the following statements about xylem and phloem is true?
   a. Wood is mostly phloem.

b. Phloem carries water from the vascular system of a plant.

c. Xylem and phloem make up the vascular system of a plant.

d. Xylem carries sugars from the leaves to the roots.

3. Which of the following statements about the growth of plants and animals is true?

a. Each plant species has a predictable number of leaves.

b. A plant is confined to a certain size.

c. Because animal growth is determinate, the environment plays no role in an animal's size.

d. A plant continues to add new tissues to itself as long as it is alive.

4. Which of the following gases flows through stomates in the least amount?

a. hydrogen gas

b. carbon dioxide

c. water vapor

d. oxgen gas

5. Which of the following is(are) part of the digestive tract of an animal?

a. feces

b. mouth

c. coelom

d. cardium

6. Plants do not show cephalization because:

a. they have no sense organs.

b. they have no digestive tract.

c. they are not bilaterally symmetrical.

d. they do not move in one direction.

7. Which of the following structures in animals serves a funtion similar to that of wood?

a. cardium

b. digestive tube

c. endoskeleton

d. sense organ

8. Which of the following structures has a shape that is not dictated by surface/volume considerations?

a. leg bones

b. root system

c. tubules in a lung

d. leaves

9. A poikilothermic organism:

a. is endothermic.

b. is warm-blooded.

c. maintains a relatively constant body temperature.

d. has a body temperature that is largely determined by the environment.

10. Which of the following tissues is not common to both plants and animals?

a. parenchyma

b phloem

c. epithelium

d. connective tissue

253

REVIEW QUESTIONS

I. Use the following key to characterize the structures listed in the next eight items.

            Key: a. tissue
                  b. organ
                  c. organ system
                  d. none of the above

_____ 1. parencyhma

_____ 2. thallus

_____ 3. rhizoid

_____ 4. phloem

_____ 5. stomate

_____ 6. digestive system

_____ 7. leaf

_____ 8. heart

II. Match each plant structure on the left with the animal structure on the right that has the most similar function.

_____ 1. phloem   a. artery

_____ 2. wood   b. endoskeleton

_____ 3. leaf epidermis   c. extracellular fluid space

_____ 4. intercellular gas space   d. skin
            system

III. Imagine a cell with a cube shape. Suppose that the cell requires 1 molecule of substance X for every cubic micrometer each minute for its survival.

Also suppose that substance X can enter the cell over all of the cell's surface area at the rate of 1 molecule per square micrometer of surface area per minute. What is the largest cell that can be supported under these conditions? That is, at what point will there _not_ be enough substance X entering the cell to keep it alive? Explain your reasoning.

_____

_____

_____

_____

IV. Use the following key to answer the next ten questions.

Key: a. characteristic of animals only
      b. characteristic of plants only
      c. characteristic of both plants and animals
      d. characteristic of neither plants nor animals

_____ 1. contains connective tissue

_____ 2. has sense organs

_____ 3. shows cephalization

_____ 4. conducts cellular respiration only during the day

_____ 5. is phototropic

_____ 6. has indeterminate growth

_____ 7. water evaporates from the body

_____ 8. shows bilateral symmetry

_____ 9. is ectothermic

_____ 10. has organ systems

ANSWERS TO CHAPTER EXECISES

Practice Quiz

1. b	3. d	5. b	7. c	9. d
2. c	4. a	6. d	8. a	10. b

Review Questions

I. 1. a   2. d   3. b   4. a   5. d   6. c   7. b   8. b

II. 1. a   2. b   3. d   4. c

III. A cube 6 micrometers on each side will have a surface area of 216 square micrometers. This same cube will have a volume of 216 cubic micrometers. Thus the needs of the cell, in terms of substance X, will balance the supply in a cell of this size. A cell any larger than this will not be able to supply enough of substance X to keep the cell alive.

IV. 1. c   2. a   3. a   4. d   5. b   6. b   7. c   8. c   9. c   10. a

Chapter 19

PLANT BIOLOGY I:
GENERAL STRUCTURE AND PHYSIOLOGY

WHAT'S IN THIS CHAPTER

In the last chapter you were introduced to some of the problems that plants and animals both face, and you learned about some of the adaptations that organisms use to cope with their environments. Although plants and animals share many characteristics, there are distinctive features of both. In this chapter we will focus on the unique aspects of plant structure and physiology. The plant kingdom includes a wide variety of organisms with different approaches to life on land and in the water. Chapter 19 focuses on plants with an internal vascular system for conduction of water and nutrients.

By the end of the chapter you should be able to:

1. List three distinctive features of a plant cell.

2. Name three different plastids and give a function for each.

3. Describe the importance of lignin, suberin, and cutin to a plant.

4. Compare the structure and function of xylem and phloem.

5. Give two major differences between monocots and dicots.

6. Explain the significance of the vascular tissue arrangement in roots and stems as it relates to plant support.

7. Name a storage root.

8. Describe the importance of nitrogen fixation to plants and animals, and outline the relationship between bacteria and vascular plants involved in nitrogen fixation.

9. Name the meristems responsible for primary and secondary growth and explain how they differ.

10. Name and describe two specialized stems.

11. Describe the relationship between guard cells and stomate size.

12. Explain how organic materials are moved through the phloem.

13. Describe the movement of water into and through a plant.

14. List two plant adaptations for coping with water shortage and two plant adaptations for coping with high salt concentration.

WHAT YOU SHOULD ALREADY KNOW

In Chapter 18 you were introduced to the general organization of plants and animals, to the typical life of a green plant, and to the tissues that help a green plant live in the water or on the land. You should thus be familar with the most common tissues that make up a plant, with the morphological structures that are made of these tissues, and with the most significant differences between plants and animals. Because so much of a plant's life is involved in obtaining and using energy, and because most adaptation that plants exhibit are related to their metabolism, you should be familiar with basic metabolic requirements, This includes the processes of photosynthesis (Chapter 8) and respiration (Chapter 7) and the molecules coming into and going out of a plant.

Pre-Test

1. Most of the weight of a plant is (a)_____. Nonvascular plants such as mosses absorb through simple rootlike extensions called (b)_____, whereas vascular plants absorb through their roots and send minerals up through the (c)_____.

1. (a) water;
   (b) rhizoids;
   (c) xylem

2. For photosynthesis to continue, (a)_____ _____(gas) must be supplied to a plant and (b)_____(gas) removed. For respiration to continue, (c)_____ must be supplied and (d)_____ removed.

2. (a) carbon dioxide;
   (b) oxygen;
   (c) oxygen;
   (d) carbon dioxide.

3. Plants lose water in a process called (a)_____ _____, as water vapor moves through the (b)_____ _____ of the leaves.

3. (a) transpiration;
   (b) stomates

4. (a)_____ and (b)_____ make up the vascular tissues of a plant, which (c)_____ (are / are not) found in animals.

4. (a) Xylem;
   (b) phloem;
   (c) are not

257

19-1 Plant cells have some distinctive features.

1. Plant cell walls are made primarily of (a)_____.

   Two plant cells share a (b)_____
   made primarily of pectin.

1. (a) cellulose;
   (b) middle
   lamella

2. Some plant cell walls are toughened with (a)_____,
   a hydrophobic polymer. This polymer is highly resistant

   to decay because (b)_____

   _____.

2. (a) lignin;
   (b) few organ-
   isms produce
   ligninases

3. The cytoplasm of mature plant cells contains one or more

   (a)_____ that may take up 90% of the cell's

   volume. These structures may contain (b)_____.

3. (a) vacuoles;
   (b) water,
   wastes, or
   pigments

4. There are several kinds of plant plastids, including the

   (a)_____ wherein photosynthesis takes

   place, the (b)_____, which are filled
   with pigments and give color to some fruits and flowers,

   and (c)_____, which are colorless and
   may snythesize starch.

4. (a) chloro-
   plasts; (b)
   chromoplasts;
   (c) leuco-
   plasts

19-2 Plants are constructed of some distinctive tissues.

1. The most abundant tissue in plants is (a)_____.

   A type of this tissue is (b)_____, which

   contains chloroplasts. (c)_____ is a
   supporting tissue with thick, heavily lignified walls, an

   example of which is the (d)_____ that humans
   use to make ropes and textiles.

1. (a) paren-
   chyma; (b)
   chlorenchyma;
   (c) Schleren-
   chyma; (d)
   fibers

2. (a)_____ tissue is a kind of epithelium
   on stem, leaf, and root surfaces. This tissue is covered

   with a layer of (b)_____ made of cutin or
   suberin in wax. This layer creates a barrier against

   (c)_____ invading the plant or (d)_____
   leaving a plant.

2. (a) Epidermal;
   (b) cuticle;
   (c) bacteria;

3. (a)_____ tissue forms the outer bark of trees.

   The cells of this tissue secrete (b)_____ for

258

(d) water

waterproofing and protection.

3. (a) Cork;
   (b) suberin

4. (a)_____ is the plant tissue that conducts water and dissolved substances. The two major kinds of elements in the tissue are (b)_____, which are broad tubes, and (c)_____, which are long, tapered cells.

4. (a) Xylem;
   (b) vessels;
   (c) tracheids

5. (a)_____ is the plant tissue that conducts organic compounds manufactured in the leaves. This tissue is made up of (b)_____, which are made of several cells fitting end to end, with continuous cytoplasm.

5. (a) Phloem;
   (b) sieve tubes

6. (a)_____ tissue is made up of small undifferentiated cells. The function of this tissue is (b)_____, and it is found at the (c)_____ of roots and stems.

6. (a) Meristematic;
   (b) cell division or growth;
   (c) tips

19-3 There are two types of flowering plants, each with different organizations.

1. All the flowering plants can be divided into two large groups, the (a)_____, with only one (b)_____ or seed leaf, and the (c)_____, with two seed leaves.

1. (a) monocots;
   (b) cotyledon;
   (c) dicots

2. The cotyledon is packed with _____ _____.

2. food for the developing young plant

3. Two examples of monocots are (a)_____ and (b)_____.

3. (a and b) wheat, barley, rye, cattails, orchids

4. The embryonic shoot, the (a)_____, grows upward; the embryonic root, the (b)_____, grows downward.

4. (a) epicotyl;
   (b) hypocotyl

19-4 Roots are built on a core of strong vascular tissue.

1. A function of roots is _____.

1. anchorage or conduction

2. The center of a root is called the (a)_____

259

_____ or (b)_____. Surrounding this center is the (c)_____, which is made of parenchymal cells.

2. (a) vascular bundle;
    (b) stele;
    (c) cortex

3. There are three stages in the growth of each root cell. The youngest cells are small and (a)_____ rapidly. Older cells are (b)_____, while even older cells are (c)_____ into different kinds of mature cells.

3. (a) dividing;
    (b) elongating;
    (c) differen-
    tiating

4. What is a root cap and what function does it serve? _____

    _____

    _____.

4. A root cap is a cuplike cover that protects the root tip from damage as it pushes through the soil.

5. The undifferentiated cells of the apical meristem are divided into three groups: the (a)_____ cells on the outside that will become epidermal tissue, the (b)_____ that will become root cortex, and in the center the (c)_____, from which xylem and phloem develop.

5. (a) protoderm;
    (b) ground meristem;
    (c) procambium

6. In the (a)_____ zone, root cells grow wider and longer. In the (b)_____ zone, root cells become recognizable mature cells.

6. (a) elongation;
    (b) maturation

7. Epidermal cells in the maturation zone of the root develop extensions called (a)_____ that may increase the surface area (b)_____ times.

7. (a) root hairs;
    (b) 10-20

19-5 Some roots store food.

1. An example of a storage root is (a)_____. Storage roots store the (b)_____ that are produced from photosynthesis.

1. (a) yam or sweet potato;
    (b) starches

19-6 Some roots can fix nitrogen.

1. Nitrogen gas (a)_____ can / cannot) be used directly by plants and animals. Nitrogen fixation is carried out by procaryotes with a (b)_____

enzyme system. This system adds three pairs of hydrogens to the nitrogen molecule to make two (c)_____ molecules. These molecules are then converted into (d)_____ that are used by the plant.

1. (a) cannot;
    (b) nitro-
    genase; (c)
    ammonia; (d)
    amino acids

2. The most important nitrogen fixers are (a)_____ _____ that have a (b)_____ association with plants like (c)_____.

2. (a) *Rhizobium*
    bacteria; (b)
    mutualistic;
    (c) legumes

3. Nitrogenase is very sensitive to molecular (a)_____, which inactivates the enzymes, but the Rhizobium bacterial nodules produce (b)_____, which binds the interfering molecules.

3. (a) oxygen; (b)
    leghemoglobin

19-7 Stems grow from apical meristems, much as roots do.

1. The embryonic _____(root / shoot) emerges first from the germinating seed.

1. root

2. Groups of meristematic cells that are sources of lateral outgrowths are called (a)_____, and the length of the stem between two of these groups is called an (b)_____.

2. (a) nodes;
    (b) internode

3. Leaves develop from meristematic tissue called _____ _____.

3. leaf primordia

*19-8 The arrangement of vascular bundles gives the stem maxi-
    mum strength.*

1. Xylem and phloem are combined in the stem to form (a)_____ bundles with the (b)_____ (xylem / phloem) toward the inside.

1. (a) vascular;
    (b) xylem

2. A stem increases its strength by the arrangement of (a)_____, which are arranged (b)_____ in dicot stems and (c)_____ _____ in monocot stems.

2. (a) vascular

261

bundles; (b)
in a ring;
(c) scattered
throughout
the stem

19-9 Dicot stems and roots increase in diameter through secondary growth.

1. Plant growth in length is called (a)_____ growth, whereas growth in diameter is called (b)_____ _____ growth; the latter is due to division of cells in the (c)_____.

1. (a) primary;
   (b) secondary;
   (c) vascular
   cambium

2. Wood is made up of (a)_____ cells. The growth pattern of woody tissues forms (b)_____, each of which repre- sents one year's growth with larger cells formed in the (c)_____(early / late) part of the year.

2. (a) secondary
   xylem; (b)
   annual rings;
   (c) early

3. The core of the wood in a tree is the (a)_____, which gives the tree mechanical strength. The outer xylem is called the (b)_____, and it continues to transport water.

3. (a) heartwood;
   (b) sapwood

4. The bark is produced by the meristem called the _____ _____.

4. cork cambium

19-10 Some stems become specialized and unusual.

1. (a)_____ are horizontal stems that grow at the ground surface or just below it. (b)_____ are horizontal stems that grow above ground. (c)_____ are swollen storage stems such as the Irish potato tuber.

1. (a) Rhizomes;
   (b) Stolons;
   (c) Tubers

2. An onion has a (a)_____, which is a structure made mostly of leaves that store food. A (b)_____ is an underground stem covered with a few thin leaves, such as that of a crocus or gladiolus.

2. (a) bulb; (c)
   corm

19-11 Leaves are built of parenchyma with a network of vascular tissue.

1. The three main features of a leaf are its (a)_____ or lamin; its (b)_____, which is the part that connects the leaf to the stem; and the (c)_____, which are the bundles of xylem and phloem.

1. (a) blade; (b) petiole; (c) veins

2. Most of the leaf interior is made of parenchymatous tissue called (a)_____. In the leaf there are two types of this tissue: the (b)_____ _____ which is an open tissue through which gases diffuse easily, and the (c)_____, which lies next to the upper epidermis and in which most of the chloroplasts are found.

2. (a) mesophyll; (b) spongy mesophyll; (c) palisade mesophyll

19-12 Stomates regulate the flow of gases through the leaf.

1. A (a)_____ is a pore in the epidermis of a leaf that is surrounded by two (b)_____ that can change shape and thus control the size of the pore.

1. (a) stomate; (b) guard cells

2. The size of stomates in the leaf depends on several different factors, including (a)_____ _____, (b)_____, and (c)_____.

2. (a) light intensity; (b) water supply; (c) carbon dioxide concentration

19-13 Phloem sap moves through a combination of osmotic forces and specific pumps.

1. The function of phloem is (a)_____, the distribution of organic material throughout the plant. This organic material enters the phloem at certain places called (b)_____, such as photosynthesizing leaves, and is removed at certain places called (c)_____ _____, where the organic material is consumed.

1. (a) translocation; (b) sources; (c) sinks

2. According to the (a)_____ theory, sucrose is actively loaded into the phloem at the source end and actively unloaded at the sink end. At both ends, (b)_____ is required.

2. (a) pressure-flow; (b) energy

3. Mittler was able to study the contents of the phloem by using an insect, (a)_____. The results of Mittler's experiments showed that (b)_____ _____ _____.

3. (a) aphid; (b)
the phloem sap
is under pres-
sure and that
the sap be-
comes less
concentrated
as it moves
away from the
source

*19-14 Water and ions flow from the root epidermis into the
xylem.*

1. Water moves into the root epidermal cells by (a)_____

_____ because the concentration of water in the

epdiermal cytosol is (b)_____(lower / higher)
than that of the surrounding soil. Potassium ions are

moved into the cell by means of an (c)_____

_____ because the concentration of these
ions may be a thousand times lower in the soil than in the
epidermal cytosol.

1. (a) diffusion;
(b) lower; (c)
ATP-activated
pump

2. Water ions can enter the xylem of the root only by passing

through the (a)_____ cells, whose intercellular

spaces are completely blocked by the (b)_____

_____, a layer of waterproof suberin.

2. (a) endodermal
(b) Casparian
strip

*19-15 Water is pulled into the shoot system by a combination
of forces.*

1. Root pressure _____(is / is not) explanation enough
for the transport of water in trees.

1. is not

2. Water vapor is lost from a plant in a process called

(a)_____. Water vapor passes through the

(b)_____ in the leaves.

2. (a) transpira-
tion;
(b) stomates

3. Water can be transported great distances up a tree because

_____

_____.

3. as water is
lost through
transpiration,
more is pulled
up the xylem,
since water
molecules co-
here to each
other

*19-16 Plants must balance several processes for optimal
activity.*

1. Water vapor moves out of plant leaf (a)_____
(faster / slower) than carbon dioxide coming into the
leaf. The concentration of carbon dioxide in the leaf

cannot be reduced below .01% because (b)_____

_____.

1. (a) faster;

2. The temperature of a leaf rises as (a)_____

264

(b) respiration keeps the carbon dioxide level up

2. (a) air temperature; (b) humidity; (c) sunlight

3. (a) convection; (b) transpiration

1. (a) Mesophytes; (b) Xerophytes

2. (a) C_4 photosynthesis; (b) hairs; (c) sunken stomates

1. (a) Halophytes; (b) too much salt surrounding the roots could lead to water loss from the plant; (c) high salt concentration inhibits most enzymes and

_____, (b)_____, and (c)_____
increase.

3. Heat is lost from a leaf through (a)_____

and (b)_____.

19-17 Many plants have special adaptations for water shortage.

1. (a)_____ are plants that live in an optimal

environment in terms of water supply. (b)_____
are plants that are adapted to very dry conditions.

2. Xeromorphic characteristics include (a)_____

_____, in which stomates are open during the cool
night and carbon dioxide is stored in organic acids.

Xeromorphic leaves may have (b)_____ or

(c)_____, both of which reduce
transpiration by trapping humid air so that it cannot be
blown away.

19-18 Similar adaptations are used with high salt conditions.

1. (a)_____ are plants that grow in saline
conditions. High salt concentration threatens a plant

because (b)_____

_____ and

(c)_____

_____.

2. Two adaptation of halophytes that allow them to live in

salty soils are (a)_____

_____ and (b)_____

_____

_____.

265

disrupt
membranes.

2. (a) ability to
absorb large
amounts of
sodium; (b)
collection of
excess salt in
leaves or ex-
cretion of ex-
cess salt from
salt glands

PRACTICE QUIZ

1. Which of the following is the <u>best</u> characteristic to use to distinguish a
   plant cell from an animal cell?
   a. the presence of a vacuole
   b. the presence of a cell wall
   c. the presence of a nucleus
   d. the presence of mitochondria

2. The plastid that is filled with carotenoid pigments and gives color to fruits
   is a:
   a. chloroplast.
   b. chromoplast.
   c. leucoplast.
   d. proplastid.

3. A complex hyrophobic polymer that toughens secondary cell walls is:
   a. lignin.
   b. the Casparian strip.
   c. cutin.
   d. cuticle.

4. If the phloem is removed from the trunk of a tree, the tree may die because:
   a. the roots cannot get enough water.
   b. the leaves cannot get enough water.
   c. the roots cannot get enough high-energy organic molecules.
   d. the leaves cannot get enough high-energy organic molecules.

5. A monocot plant will have:
   a. more leaves than a dicot plant.
   b. larger flowers than a dicot.
   c. bigger stems than a dicot.
   d. fewer seed leaves than a dicot.

6. Most storage roots store:
   a. water.
   b. proteins.
   c. lipids.
   d. carbohydrates.

7. Which of the rollowing organisms are the <u>most</u> important nitrogen fixers?
   a. fungi

    b. blue-green algae
    c. legumes
    d. cows

8. Wood is produced by:
    a. xylem.
    b. phloem.
    c. apical meristem.
    d. vascular cambium.

9. A stomate will be open:
    a. when guard cells close.
    b. when guard cells lose water.
    c. when guard cells are filled with water.
    d. when carbon dioxide levels increase in the guard cells.

10. The movement of sugars and the movement of water in a plant:
    a. occur in the same vascular tissue.
    b. can both be explained by the pressure-flow theory.
    c. are usually in opposite directions.
    d. occur in the apoplast of the plant.

11. Which of the following is an adaptation for water shortage and not for high salt conditions?
    a. glands that excrete materials by an active transport process
    b. stomatal closing during the day
    c. fibrous root system
    d. parenchyma tissue

REVIEW QUESTIONS

I. Use the following key to answer the next seven items about gas exchange.

    Key: a. more CO_2 going in than coming out; more O_2 coming out than going in

    b. more O_2 going in than coming out; more CO_2 coming out than going in

    c. as much CO_2 going in as coming out; as much O_2 coming out as going in

_____ 1. a green plant in the dark

_____ 2. a green plant in the light

_____ 3. an animal in the dark

_____ 4. an animal in the light

_____ 5. a plant with its stomates closed

_____ 6. a plant undergoing a high rate of photosynthesis

267

_____ 7. a plant with shrunken guard cells

II. Use the following key to answer the next nine items about water movement in a plant.

> Key: a.   Transpiration increases as a result.
>   b.   Transpiration decreases as a result.
>   c.   Caused by root pressure.
>   d.   Caused by transpiration.

_____ 1. Light intensity increases.

_____ 2. Relative humidity increases.

_____ 3. Guard cells shrink.

_____ 4. Clouds cover the sun.

_____ 5. Water rises in a plant before leaves come out in the spring.

_____ 6. Air temperature increases.

_____ 7. Soil dries out.

_____ 8. Water moves up a 200-foot tree.

_____ 9. Fluid rises in a tube placed on top of a cut stem.

III. Use the following key to answer the next twelve items.

> Key: a.   more important to terrestrial plants than to aquatic plants
>   b.   more important to aquatic plants than to terrestrial plants
>   c.   important to both terrestrial and aquatic plants

_____ 1. root hairs   _____ 7. cuticle

_____ 2. photosynthesis   _____ 8. vessels

_____ 3. chlorophyll   _____ 9. apical meristem

_____ 4. cell walls   _____ 10. nitrogen requirement

_____ 5. transpiration   _____ 11. stomates

_____ 6. sclerenchyma   _____ 12. specialized structures for water absorption

IV. Use the following key to answer the next eight items.

> Key: a.   related to primary growth
>   b.   related to secondary growth
>   c.   related to both primary growth and secondary growth

_____ 1. cork   _____ 5. phloem

_____ 2. wood   _____ 6. vascular bundle

_____ 3. apical meristem   _____ 7. growth in length of the plant

_____ 4. epidermis   _____ 8. growth in diameter in the plant

ANSWERS TO CHAPTER EXERCISES

Practice Quiz
1. b   4. c   6. d   8. d   10. c
2. b   5. d   7. b   9. c   11. b
3. a

Review Questions

I.   1. b   2. a   3. b   4. b   5. c   6. a   7. c

II. 1. a   2. b   3. b   4. b   5. c   6. a   7. b   8. d   9. c

III. 1. a   2. c   3. c   4. c   5. a   6. a
     7. a   8. a   9. c   10. c   11. a   12. a

IV. 1. b   2. b   3. a   4. a   5. c   6. a   7. a   8. b

Chapter 20

PLANT BIOLOGY II:
GROWTH AND GROWTH REGULATORS

WHAT'S IN THIS CHAPTER

Every organism begins its life as a single cell. Some primitive organisms remain as single-celled individuals throughout their life, but complex organisms are made up of millions, billions, or trillions of cells. In unicellular organisms, the single cell must perform all the processes of life by itself; in a complex organism there are specialized cells that have distinct functions, and it is the coordination of all these specialized cells that keeps the organism alive. In this chapter you will learn about the changes a young plant goes through on its way from a single cell to a complex, multicellular organism. Much of the growth of a plant is under the control of growth regulators, and you will be introduced to five important ones. Each of these regulators, as you will see, affects a number of processes, and there is much interaction among them. The effect these regulators have on cells in turn has an effect on the development of a plant. The chapter ends with a discussion about a very important light-receptor pigment, phytochrome, and the role it plays in the growth and reproduction of a plant.

By the end of this chapter you should be able to:

1. Name five different plant growth regulators.

2. Define the word "hormone."

3. Compare geotropism to phototropism and explain how auxin is involved with each.

4. Describe an experiment that helped demonstrate the effect of auxin on the growth of a plant.

5. Name two important effects that gibberellins have on the development of plants.

6. Explain the importance of cytokinins in the development of tissue culture studies.

7. Give an example of the interaction of two different plant growth regulators and their effects on the development of a plant.

270

8. Describe the phenomenon of apical dominance.

9. Explain the importance of abscission to plants, and describe the role that abscisic acid plays in the formation of the abscission layer.

10. Describe how ethylene differs from other plant growth regulators, and name two important uses of ethylene in agriculture.

11. Compare the growth of a vine to that of a tree.

12. Define photoperiodism and explain the role of phytochrome in this phenomenon.

WHAT YOU SHOULD ALREADY KNOW

Chapter 20 deals with plant growth and plant growth regulators, so you should review the general growth pattern of plants in Chapter 18. In Chapter 19, you should review the tissues involved in growth and the manner in which cells divide, elongate, and mature. In addition, you should be able to compare primary and secondary growth in plants and to list the inorganic molecules necessary for life that come to the plant through roots and stomates.

Pre-Test

1. Plants have (a)_____(determinate / inde-

   terminate) growth, meaning that (b)_____

   _____

   _____.

1. (a) indeter-
   minate; (b)
   growth occurs
   throughout
   the life of
   the plant with-
   out a definite
   number of
   structures
   produced

2. Growth in length in plants is (a)_____ growth, due to cell division in the stem's (b)_____

   _____. Growth in diameter in plants is

   (c)_____ growth, due to cell division in the

   (d)_____.

2. (a) primary;
   (b) apical meri-
   stem; (c)
   secondary; (d)
   vascular and
   cork cambium

3. In primary growth, after an (a)_____ cell divides, one of the newly formed cells remains meristema-

   tic while the other cell first (b)_____ and

   then (c)_____.

3. (a) initial;
   (b) elongates;
   (c) differen-
   tiates

4. The two inorganic molecules required in photosynthesis are

   (a)_____, which enters the leaf

271

through (b)_____, and (c)_____, which enters the plant through its (d)_____.

4. (a) carbon
   dioxide;
   (b) stomates;
   (c) water;
   (d) roots

GUIDED REVIEW OF THE CHAPTER

20-1 Plant growth is often directed by such influences as gravity and light.

1. Plant growth involves changes in cell (a)_____,

   (b)_____, and (c)_____.

1. (a) number;
   (b) size;
   (c) contents

2. Whereas a population of microorganisms increases through

   cell (a)_____, a plant root or stem increases

   in length primarily through cell (b)_____.

2. (a) division;
   (b) elongation

3. Plant growth is partially controlled by a small group of

   molecules called (a)_____

   _____ or (b)_____.

3. (a) plant
   growth regula-
   tors; (b) plant
   hormones

4. Plants have a movement directed by gravity called

   (a)_____ and a movement directed by light

   called (b)_____. If a root grows downward
   toward the source of gravitational attraction, it is said

   to be (c)_____.

4. (a) geotropism;
   (b) phototrop-
   ism; (c) posi-
   tively geo-
   tropic

20-2 Auxin controls cell elongation.

1. (a)_____ are the protective sheaths through
   which stems emerge from a grass seed. Boysen-Jensen
   showed that, when a mica slice is inserted into a slit on

   the dark side of an illuminated sheath, (b)_____

   _____.

1. (a) Coleop-
   tiles; (b)
   there is no
   bending toward

2. Normal bending of the coleoptile occurred if the tip was
   cut off and replaced with an intervening block of gelatin.

   This showed that _____

the light _____

_____.

2. the bending
was probably
due to a chem-
ical diffusing
through the
block and that
contact with
the tip was
unnecessary

3. In another experiment, when the coleoptile tip was cut off and replaced off-center, the shoot _____

_____

_____.

3. elongated on
the side with
the tip, in-
dicating that
that side was
still receiving
its chemical
influence

4. The oat coleoptile assay is_____

_____

_____

_____.

4. an assay based
on the idea
that the amount
of bending is
proportional to
the amount of
growth sub-
stance that has
diffused into
gelatin blocks
placed on
decapacitated
seedlings.

5. The growth substances that causes the bending of young stems toward a light source is (a)_____,

which is a derivative of the (b)_____ tryptophan.

20-3 Auxin controls several kinds of plant growth processes.

5. (a) auxin;
(b) amino acid

1. The general effect of auxin is to promote cell

(a)_____. Under the influence of IAA,

the (b)_____ inside the cell

increases while the wall (c)_____.

1. (a) elongation;
(b) turgor
pressure;
(c) loosens

2. The (a)_____ of plants produce auxin, which is then transported to the region of cell elongation. This

movement of auxin (b)_____(can / cannot) be accounted for by diffusion alone.

2. (a) meristems;
(b) cannot

3. In a young plant you would expect to find more auxin on

the (a)_____(light / dark) side of the stem and

more auxin on the (b)_____(top / bottom) of a root lying on the ground.

273

3. (a) dark;
   (b) bottom

4. Although auxin molecules may be too small to be affected by gravity, large particles called _____ may be involved in the distribution of auxin.

4. statoliths

5. (a)_____(Low / High) concentrations of auxin inhibit growth. A concentration of auxin in a stem great enough to cause bending will (b)_____(inhibit / stimulate) downward turning of roots.

5. (a) High;
   (b) inhibit

20-4 Gibberellins enhance growth and other processes.

1. Gibberellins were discovered in Japan in a (a)_____ growing on (b)_____ crops.

1. (a) fungus;
   (b) rice

2. Gibberellins stimulate growth in the (a)_____ of a plant but have little or no effect on a plant's

   (b)_____.

2. (a) shoot;
   (b) roots

3. Gibberellin is formed around the growing tips of young

   (a)_____. In germinating seeds it diffuses to the aleurone layer, where it stimulates the synthesis of

   (b)_____, an enzyme that (c)_____

   _____.

3. (a) leaves;
   (b) amylase;
   (c) partially
   converts starch
   to glucose

4. In addition to promoting stem growth, gibberellin is

   involved in (a)_____ and (b)_____

   _____.

4. (a) flowering;
   (b) seed
   germination

20-5 Cytokinins regulate cell division and differentiation.

1. Plants make their own vitamins in their _____.

1. leaves

2. Kinetin promotes _____ (cytokinesis / mitosis).

2. cytokinesis

3. Zeatin and kinetin are both compounds that promote cell

   division and are called (a)_____. These

   compounds work cooperatively with (b)_____ to promote cell division.

3. (a) cytokinins;
   (b) auxin

4. A small mass of new undifferentiated tissue is called a

   (a)_____. In a tissue culture, if the auxin level is kept constant and the cytokinin level

274

increased, the (b)_____ develops. If this concentration of growth factors is reversed, the

(b)_____ develops.

4. (a) callus; (b) shoot system; (c) root system

5. One practical aspect of plant tissue culture in the future is that _____

_____.

5. large numbers of superior plants can be grown quickly, or hybrid cells can be formed from different plants

6. One use of cytokinin that does not involve cell division is to _____

_____.

6. keep harvested plant products fresh

20-6 Several regulators interact to control plant shape and dormancy.

1. The conical shape of certain trees is the result of (a)_____, where the growth of a stem tends to be dominated by its terminal bud. This effect is due to the growth substance (b)_____.

Such domination can be overcome if (c)_____ is applied to the plant.

1. (a) apical dominance; (b) auxin; (c) cytokinin

2. The process of separating leaves, flowers, and fruit from the plant is called (a)_____. Just before separation occurs, an (b)_____ forms at the base of each part. This is important to a plant to prevent (c)_____ and

(d)_____.

2. (a) abscission; (b) abscission zone; (c) water loss; (d) entrance of pathogens

3. Abscission is controlled by the growth regulator (a)_____ _____. This regulator also causes stomates to (b)_____ (open / close) and induces (c)_____ in buds.

3. (a) abscisic acid; (b) close; (d) dormancy

4. The formation of abscisic acid is induced by _____ _____ days.

275

4. short or autumn

20-7 Ethylene enhances fruit ripening and other phenomena.

1. Ethylene differs from the other growth substances in its physical form: it is a _____.

1. gas

2. Ethylene has been used for many years by the Chinese to help (a)_____ by burning (b)_____.

2. (a) ripen fruit; (b) incense

3. Ethylene stimulates the formation of a (a)_____ in the stem of a very young seedling. This structure helps the young stem (b)_____.

3. (a) crook; (b) push through the soil

4. Ethylene production is autocatalytic, which means that _____ _____.

4. a small amount of ethylene will stimulate the production of much larger amounts of ethylene

5. Pineapple and melon growers use ethylene to _____ _____.

20-8 The vine habit is achieved through various growth mechanisms.

5. stimulate flowering

1. Vines, or (a)_____, are common in (b)_____ _____ where light beneath the canopy of trees is low.

1. (a) lianes; (b) tropical rain forests

2. Darwin distinguished among four types of climbing plants: (a)_____, (b)_____ _____, (c)_____, and (d)_____.

2. (a) hook climb- er; (b) root climber; (c) twiners; (d) plants with tendrils

3. An example of a hook-climbing plant is (a)_____, and an example of a twiner is (b)_____.

3. (a) black- berry or rose; (b) honey-

4. Roots of some climbing plants are (a)_____ _____ (geotropic / negatively phototropic). An

276

suckle, bind-
weed or
morning glory

4. (a) negatively
phototropic; (b)
grape or pea

20-9 Flowering and other phenomena are regulated by the photoperiod.

1. The period when it is light each day is called the (a)_____, and the process by which plants use cycles of light and dark as signals for flowering is called (b)_____.

1. (a) photo-
period; (b)
photoperiodism

2. In terms of photoperiodism, there are four different classes of plants (a)_____, (b)_____, (c)_____ _____, and (d)_____.

2. (a) short-day;
(b) long-day;
(c) interme-
diate-day; (d)
day-neutral

3. A short-day plant is one that will flower only if (a)_____ _____. An example of a short-day plant is (b)_____.

3. (a) it is sub-
jected to pho-
toperiods short-
er than a cer-
tain maximum
length; (b)
strawberries,
chrysanthemums,
dahlias, or
violets

4. A long-day plant will flower only if (a)_____ _____. An example of a long-day plant is (b)_____.

20-10 The photoperiod is measured by the phytochrome system.

4. (a) it is sub-
jected to pho-
toperiods long-
er than a cer-
tain minimum;
(b) lettuce,
spinach, wheat,
or potatoes

1. If a long-day plant is kept with a long dark period, it will (a)_____ (flower / not flower). If the plant is exposed to a brief burst of white light in the middle of the dark period, it will (b)_____ _____ flower / not flower).

1. (a) not flower;
(b) flower

2. The light-receptor pigment involved in photoperiodism is (a)_____. It exists in two forms: (b)_____, which absorbs red light, and (c)_____, which absorbs far-red light.

2. (a) phytochrome;
(b) P_r; (c) P_{fr}

3. Phytochrome detectors are located in the (a)_____ of the plant. The substance that promotes flowering

277

(b)_____(can / cannot) be transported from one part of the plant to another.

3. (a) leaves;
   (b) can

4. The condition in which a young plant has long internodes, a scraggly stem and thin yellowish leaves is called

   (a)_____. Such a plant has been grown in

   (b)_____ conditions.

4. (a) etiolation;
   (b) dark

PRACTICE QUIZ

1. _____ is not a plant growth hormone.
   a. Phytochrome
   b. Auxin
   c. Gibberellin
   d. Cytokinin

2. Auxin controls:
   a. photoperiodism.
   b. cell division.
   c. geotropism.
   d. fruit maturation.

3. You would expect to find cell elongation in:
   a. the illuminated side of stems.
   b. the top side of horizontal roots.
   c. the buds of lateral stems near the shoot apical meristem.
   d. the root apical meristem.

4. Gibberellin is important to seeds because it:
   a. promotes seed dormancy.
   b. breaks down starch.
   c. stimulates the synthesis of amylase.
   d. promotes formation of the seed coat.

5. Cytokinins are important to:
   a. gene splicing.
   b. flower production.
   c. seedless grape production.
   d. tissue culture.

6. A pine tree with its shoot apical meristem cut off will soon look like:
   a. a cone with its base at the bottom.
   b. a cone with its base at the top.
   c. an etiolated plant.
   d. a tree with long branches near its bottom and its top.

7. Which of the following is the most beneficial aspect of abscission layer formation for a plant?
   a. Leaves fall off.
   b. Carbon dioxide cannot enter the plant.

    c. Water cannot be lost from the plant.
    d. The oncoming winter is detected.

8. The origin of the phrase "One bad apple spoils the barrel" may have been related to the action of:
    a. auxin.
    b. ethylene.
    c. gibberellin.
    d. cytokinin.

9. Which of the following types of plants may show nutation?
    a. a hook-climbing plant
    b. a twining plant
    c. a dwarf plant
    d. a tobacco plant in short days

10. Photoperiodism is most likely to be important for:
    a. a plant living in the tropics.
    b. a twining plant.
    c. a lawn grass.
    d. a plant living where winters are harsh.

11. Which of the following is not related to phytochrome?
    a. photosynthesis
    b. long-day photoperiodism
    c. etiolation
    d. twining in plants

REVIEW QUESTIONS

I. Use the following graph and key to answer the next seven items.

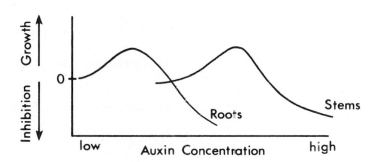

Key:
    a. supported by the graph
    b. refuted by the graph
    c. not related to the graph

_____ 1. Roots are more sensitive to auxin than stems.

_____ 2. Low concentrations of auxin stimulate stem growth.

_____ 3. High concentrations of auxin stimulate stem growth.

_____ 4. Root growth is stimulated by higher amounts of auxin than those that stimulate stem growth.

279

_____ 5. Gibberellin causes greater stem growth than root growth.

_____ 6. Roots do not respond to auxin.

_____ 7. Root growth is stimulated by stem growth.

II. Use the following diagrams to answer the next six items. Write True or False beside each statement.

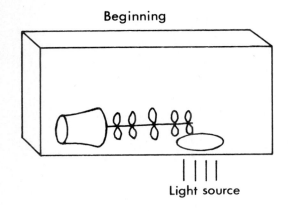

Beginning

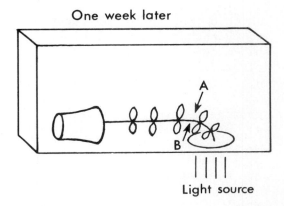

One week later

_____ 1. The plant's negative geotropism is stronger than its negative phototropism.

_____ 2. The plant's positive phototropism is stronger than its negative geotropism.

_____ 3. The plant's roots should be growing downward.

_____ 4. The concentration of auxin would be higher at point A than at point B.

_____ 5. Cells are elongating faster at point B than at point A.

_____ 6. The stem response could be called positive phototropism.

III. Use the following diagram and key to answer the next six items.

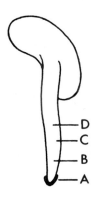

Key: a. region A
      b. region B
      c. region C
      d. region D

_____ 1. root cap

_____ 2. where most auxin is produced

_____ 3. where most cell differentiation occurs

_____ 4. where most cell elongation occurs

_____ 5. where most cell division occurs

_____ 6. where the effect of auxin would be greatest

IV. In which of the following circumstances would you expect flowering to occur? Write Yes or No beside each statement.

_____ 1. a long-day plant in the fall

_____ 2. a short-day plant in September in the United States

_____ 3. a short-day plant with a 1-minute exposure to white light in the middle of a 14-hour night

_____ 4. a short-day plant with a 1-minute exposure to red light in the middle of a 14-hour night

_____ 5. a short-day plant with a 1-minute exposure to far-red light in the middle of a 14-hour night

ANSWERS TO CHAPTER EXERCISES

Practice Quiz

1. a	4. c	6. d	8. b	10. d
2. c	5. d	7. c	9. b	11. d
3. b				

Review Questions

I. 1. a   3. a   5. c   7. c
    2. b   4. b   6. b

II. 1. False   3. True   5. False
    2. True   4. True   6. True

III. 1. a   3. d   5. b
     2. b   4. c   6. c

IV. 1. No   2. Yes   3. No   4. No   5. Yes

Chapter 21

INTEGRATION AND CONTROL SYSTEMS

WHAT'S IN THIS CHAPTER

The chapter begins with a description of each tissue: glandular and nonglandular
epithelium, connective, muscle, and nervous tissue. Differences in the matrices of
connective tissues, which account for differences in their structure and function,
are described. The three types of muscle tissue (smooth, cardiac, and skeletal)
are generally characterized. A description of nervous tissue leads into an
anatomical description and explanation of the role of the nervous system as one of
the two major integrating systems of the body. The physiological mechanisms that
are covered are the generation and maintenance of resting potential across the
plasma membrane of the neuron; the creation of an action potential, which
constitutes the propagated impulse; the generation of inhibitory and excitatory
postsynaptic potentials and the balance between them in determining the functional
state of a postsynaptic membrane; and the effect of drugs on synaptic functions,
particularly synapses between autonomic neurons.

The description of the other integrating system, the endocrine system, includes
coverage of the functional morphology of the pituitary and the mechanism of action
of hormones.

By the end of this chapter you should be able to:

1. List and describe the makeup of the four major groups of tissues and explain
    what these tissues do in the animal.

2. List and describe the two communication networks in a multicellular animal and
    explain the differences between the mechanisms of communication in the two.

3. Identify the anatomical and functional divisions of the vertebrate nervous
    system.

4. Identify and describe the parts of the basic unit and the integrative unit of
    the nervous system.

5. Explain ionic contributions to the establishment of a resting membrane
    potential, and outline the ionic changes that accompany the formation of an
    action potential and a return of the membrane to the resting state.

282

6. Distinguish between and understand the meaning of the terms polarized, depolarized, hyperpolarized, resting potential, and action potential, with respect to a nerve fiber and impulse propagation.

7. Describe the events of synaptic transmission and distinguish between the excitatory postsynaptic potential and the inhibitory postsynaptic potential.

8. Distinguish anatomically and functionally between the somatic and autonomic divisions of the nervous system; list effectors for each and chemical transmitter substances (ligands) secreted by neuron terminals in each component.

9. Relate the terms adrenergic, cholinergic, muscarinic, nicotinic, α-adrenergic, and β-adrenergic to somatic and autonomic divisions and their effectors.

10. Distinguish between the parts of the hypophysis, list some of the hormones secreted and their effects, and explain the mechanism of hypothalamic controls on target cells.

11. Explain the two known mechanisms whereby hormones exert their actions on target cells.

WHAT YOU SHOULD ALREADY KNOW

You will need to know the structure of biological membranes, factors that affect the permeability of membranes, and the function of cellular organelles (Chapters 3, 4, 11, and 12).

Pre-Test

1. The basic unit of function in an animal (as in all

organisms) is a (a)_____. Several of these units

with similar structures make a (b)_____, and several of the latter are often combined to make a

structure called an (c)_____ that is macroscopic (visible to the naked eye) and serves a distinct function. Finally, we often find several of the structures named in

(c) combined to make a (d)_____.

1. (a) cell;   2. The functions of all tissues are determined by the
   (b) tissue;
   (c) organ;   operation of their constituent _____.
   (d) system

2. cells   3. The boundary of a cell is the plasma membrane. Chemically

the membrane consists of (a)_____ and

(b)_____. The membrane is believed to con-

tain openings called (c)_____. The ability of

283

a substance to cross the membrane is called permeability. Because the plasma membrane permits entrance of some substances and not others, it is said to be (d)_____

_____.

3. (a) lipid; (b) protein; (c) pores; (d) differentially (or selectively) permeable

4. Features of molecules that allow them to permeate cell membranes easily include having a small (a)_____, not having a (b)_____, and being soluble in (c)_____. Features of cell membranes that allow molecules and ions to move through them more easily include having (d)_____ through which some molecules and ions can diffuse and having (e)_____ _____ for specific molecules and ions.

4. (a) size; (b) charge; (c) lipid; (d) pores; (e) transport mechanisms or proteins

5. The ability of an ion to traverse a membrane would depend on its (a)_____ and (b)_____. Some transport mechanisms in the membrane cause certain ions to move against their natural tendency. These are energy-requiring mechanisms referred to as (c)_____ _____.

5. (a) size; (b) charge; (c) active transport

6. The control center of the cell is the (a)_____, which contains the genetic material (b)_____. The cellular organelle that is responsible for the transformation of energy in the biologically useful form of ATP is the (c)_____. An organelle that functions in packaging cell secretions is the (d)_____.

6. (a) nucleus; (b) DNA; (c) mitochondrion; (d) Golgi complex

GUIDED REVIEW OF THE CHAPTER

21-1 Epithelia cover and protect.

1. Epithelial tissue as linings and coverings of various body

parts have the general functions of (a)_____,

(b)_____, and (c)_____.

1. (a) absorption; 2. Mucins chemically consist of proteins and _____

    (b) protection;

    (c) secretion   _____.

2. mucopolysac-

   charides   *21-2 Gland cells produce materials to be used elsewhere.*

    1. A gland, whose functional component consists of <u>epithelial</u> <u>cells</u>, may pour its secretions into a duct that empties into a specific location, thereby giving a relatively <u>localized effect</u> of the secretion. Such a gland is called

an (a)_____ gland. Blood-borne secretions,

produced by (b)_____ glands, have more wide-spread effects. These blood-borne secretory products are

called (c)_____.

1. (a) exocrine; 2. An <u>epithelial</u> membrane that lines a structure which opens

    (b) endocrine;

    (c) hormones   to the outside of the body is a _____ membrane.

2. mucous

             21-3 Connective tissues are fibrous structures that support, bind, and join other tissues.

    1. A dense regular arrangement of collagen or elastic protein fibers is found in places where forces are generated in one direction, such as the pull of muscle to move a

bone. Such an arrangement is found in (a)_____

and (b)_____.

1. (a) tendons; 2. The material outside the cells in connective tissue is

    (b) ligaments

called the (a)_____. This consists of a ground

substance made up of (b)_____ and (c)_____

_____.

2. (a) matrix; 3. True or False: An example of a mucopolysaccharide chain

    (b) protein;   is hylauronic acid and chondroitin sulfate.

    (c) mucopoly-

    saccharides

3. True   4. True or False: Connective tissue structures that connect bone to muscle are called ligaments.

4. False   5. The main protein filament in connective tissue matrices is

285

(a)_____. Large amounts of two amino acids are found in the protein. These are (b)_____ and (c)_____.

5. (a) collagen;
   (b) glycine;
   (c) proline

6. Triple helix molecules called _____ assemble into collagen fibers.

6. tropocollagen

7. True or False: Cells that break down hydroxyapatite crystals are called osteocytes.

7. False

21-4 There are three major types of muscle tissue.

1. Next to each of the following specific functions, give the muscle tissue that performs that function.

   (a) Contracts to eject blood from the heart. _____

   (b) Contracts to change the flow of blood in blood vessels. _____

   (c) Contracts to move bones. _____

1. (a) cardiac;
   (b) smooth;
   (c) skeletal

21-5 Animals must regulate themselves internally.

1. The term "milieu interieur" refers to the (a)_____ _____ space in tissues. A nineteenth-century physiologist who stressed the importance of proper regulation of this milieu interieur was (b)_____ _____.

1. (a) extracellular; (b) Claude Bernard

2. Cells in contact with the environment that detect environmental changes are called (a)_____ cells; those that respond to signals from the latter cells are called (b)_____ cells.

2. (a) sensor;
   (b) effector

3. A communication network that consists of neurons is the (a)_____ system; one that uses hormones as messengers is the (b)_____ system.

3. (a) nervous;
   (b) endocrine

21-6 A nervous system is made of neurons.

1. Identify the structures and locations that are labeled in the following diagram.

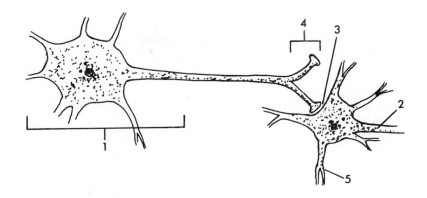

(a) presynaptic neuron _____

(b) neuronal synapse _____

(c) axon of postsynaptic neuron _____

(d) axon termination _____

(e) release of chemical transmitter _____

(f) dendritic receptors for chemical transmitters _____

1. (a) 1; (b) 3;
   (c) 2; (d) 4;
   (e) 3,4; (f) 5

2. False

3. False

4. neurotrans-
   mitter

5. (a) excitatory;
   (b) inhibitory

2. True or False: The person who theorized that the brain processes information received in the surface gray matter was Aristotle.

3. True or False: The synaptic cleft is located on the postsynaptic membrane.

4. Synaptic vesicles in axon terminations contain _____ _____ substances.

5. Actions of neurotransmitters at synapses may be (a)_____ _____ or (b)_____.

21-7 The general structure of the nervous system.

1. For simplicity of explantion, the nervous system is described in terms of central and peripheral portions. Classify the following parts as central (CNS) or peripheral (PNS), depending on their location.

   (a) ganglion _____

   (b) spinal nerve _____

(c) brain _____

(d) nerve tract _____

(e) cranial nerve _____

(f) nucleus _____

1. (a) PNS; (b)
(c) CNS;
   (d) CNS; (e)
   PNS; (f) CNS

2. The effectors for the autonomic nervous system are P N S ;

    (a)_____, (b)_____

    _____ (c)_____.

2. (a) smooth
   muscle; (b)
   cardiac
   muscle; (c)
   glands

3. A bundle of axons is called a _____.

3. nerve

4. Neurons that propagate messages from the periphery to the

    CNS are sensory, or (a)_____. Those that

    conduct from the CNS are motor, or (b)_____.

4. (a) afferent;
   (b) efferent

5. The somatic motor nervous system is (a)_____
    (excitatory / inhibitory / both). Somatic effectors are

    (b)_____ muscles.

5. (a) excitatory;
   (b) skeletal

21-8 A nervous system collects and disperses information.

1. Give the names of the structures that are labeled on the
    following diagram. Then use the labels in answering
    Question 2.

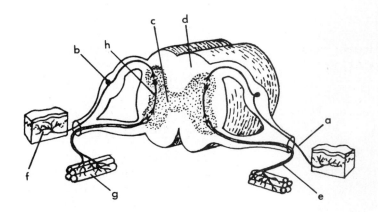

(a) _____

(b) _____

(c) _____

(d) _____

(e) _____

(f) _____

(g) _____

(h) _____

1. (a) sensory
   neuron; (b)
   ganglion; (c)
   gray matter;
   (d) white
   matter; (e)
   motor neuron;
   (f) receptor;
   (g) effector;
   (h) interneuron

2. Parts a, f, e, h, and g would make up a (a)_____

   _____. An example of a reflex action that

   would involve the latter is the (b)_____.

2. (a) simple re-
   flex arc; (b)
   knee jerk

21-9 A neuron maintains a potential across its plasma
     membrane.

1. Large axons found in _____ are used for studying
   neuron physiology.

1. squids

2. True or False: Axoplasm has a high concentration of Na^+
   and Cl^-.

2. False

21-10 A change in Na^+ permeability creates an action
      potential.

1. In a nonstimulated (resting) state of a neuron, the mem-

   brane is said to be (a)_____(polarized /
   depolarized). In this state, the cation that is more
   concentrated in the extracellular fluid than in the

   intracellular fluid is (b)_____ (Na^+ / K^+). The
   resting membrane potential is brought about by the net

   diffusion of (c)_____ (Na^+ / K^+) outward. This makes

   the outside of the membrane (d)_____(positive /
   negative) with respect to the inside. When a threshold
   strength voltage (stimulus) is applied to the membrane,

   the outside becomes (e)_____(positive /
   negative) with respect to the inside, and the membrane is
   said to be depolarized. The ionic change that occurs

   concurrently with depolarization is the movement of Na^+ to

289

the (f)_____(inside / outside) of the cell.

1. (a) polarized;
   (b) Na$^+$;
   (c) K$^+$;
   (d) positive;
   (e) negative;
   (f) inside

21-11 An action potential propagates itself along the axon.

1. True or False: Positive ions in the axomplasm are repelled by an increase in positive charges at the point of excitation and thus move away to hyperpolarize adjacent sections of the membrane.

1. False

2. A time following stimulation when an irritable membrane cannot respond to another stimulus is called the _____(absolute / relative) refractory period.

2. absolute

3. True or False: Increasing the strength of a stimulus increases the frequency of action potentials in the nerve fiber.

3. True

21-12 A nerve is a complex of nerve fibers and other cells.

1. Supportive neural cells in nerves that myelinate nerve fibers are called (a)_____. Cells in the CNS that do the same thing are the (b)_____ _____. A myelinated fiber propagates an impulse (c)_____(faster / slower) than a nonmyelinated fiber. This propagation, which is essentially a node-to-node depolarization, is called (d)_____ _____.

1. (a) Schwann cells; (b) oli-godendrocytes; (c) faster; (d) saltatory conduction

21-13 Impulses originate at the dendrites and soma.

1. An increase in <u>frequency</u> of stimuli to a single neuron is a (a)_____(spatial / temporal) summation effect. An increase in <u>number of nerve fibers</u> that are active in stimulating the neuron is a (b)_____ (spatial / temporal) summation effect.

1. (a) temporal;
   (b) spatial

2. Local depolarizations in postsynaptic membranes are called (a)_____ postsynaptic potentials; local hyperpolarizations are called (b)_____.

2. (a) excitatory;

(b) inhibitory   *21-15 Receptor cells are revealed by the action of drugs.*

1. Assign each of the following characteristics to the somatic nervous system (S) and/or to the sympathetic (Sy) or the parasympathetic (P) division of the autonomic nervous system.

   (a) cholinergic neurons _____

   (b) dominant during nonemergency state _____

   (c) adrenergic postganglionic neurons _____

   (d) increases heartrate and respiration rate _____

   (e) inhibits digestive activity _____

1. (a) S, P;
   (b) P; (c) Sy;
   (d) Sy; (e) Sy   *21-16 Animals are regulated by many different hormones.*

   1. The three classes of hormones are (a)_____

      _____, (b)_____, and

      (c)_____.

1. (a) amino acid
   derivatives;
   (b) peptides;   *21-17 The pituitary gland is a center of regulation.*
   (c) steroids

   1. An endocrine gland in the vertebrate that produces a number of hormones, some of which exert an effect on another endocrine gland, is the <u>pituitary</u>. The part of the pituitary that consists of axon endings of neurons

      originating in the hypothalamus is the (a)_____

      _____, which secretes (b)_____ and

      (c)_____. These two hormones are synthesized

      in the (d)_____.

1. (a) posterior   2. The anterior pituitary maintains a functional connection
   lobe; (b)
   oxytocin; (c)   to the hypothalamus via the (a)_____
   vasopressin;
   (d) hypothala-   _____. Substances produced
   mus
                        in the hypothalamus that regulate the secretion of

                        anterior pituitary hormones are called (b)_____

                        _____.

2. (a) hypothala-
   mic-hypophyseal
   portal system;

291

(b) releasing
factors

21-18 Extracellular ligands stimulate "second messengers" inside cells.

1. The mechanism of action of many hormones resides in their

    stimulating the production of (a)_____

    or (b)_____. These substances are

    referred to as the (c)_____(first / second)
    messenger. The hormones that do not act according to this
    mechanism, but rather act directly within the cell, are

    the (d)_____.

1. (a) cyclic AMP;
    (b) cyclic GMP;
    (c) second;
    (d) steroids

PRACTICE QUIZ

1. A tissue that functions in absorption of food from the intestine is _____
    tissue.
    a. muscle
    b. neural
    c. epithelial
    d. connective

2. Which of the following is <u>not</u> characteristic of the endocrine system?
    a. fast-acting control system
    b. secretion of chemicals called hormones
    c. long-lasting effects
    d. epithelial tissue

3. The portion of the nervous system that controls skeletal muscle contraction is
    the:
    a. parasympathetic motor.
    b. sympathetic motor.
    c. somatic sensory.
    d. somatic motor.

4. The basic functional unit of the nervous system is the:
    a. brain.
    b. neuron.
    c. reflex arc.
    d. spinal cord.

5. The ion that is <u>most</u> responsible for generating the resting potential in the
    cell is:
    a. K^+.
    b. Cl^-.

c. Na^+.

d. HCO_3^-.

6. If the difference in potential across an axon membrane is −70 mV, inside with respect to outside, and the potential changes to −80 mV, the change is a(an):
    a. action potential.
    b. excitatory postsynaptic potential.
    c. depolarization.
    d. hyperpolarization.

7. Which of the following is not characteristic of an inhibitory postsynaptic potential?
    a. local
    b. all-or-nothing
    c. graded
    d. hyperpolarization

8. Which of the following statements is not true of the sympathetic nervous system?
    a. It is located in thoraco-lumber nerves.
    b. It increases respiration rate.
    c. It stimulates the adrenal medulla.
    d. It has cholinergic postsynaptic neurons.

9. The neurohypophysis:
    a. is the anterior pituitary.
    b. is controlled by releasing factors from the hypothalamus.
    c. secretes hormones synthesized in the hypothalamus.
    d. is neural and therefore does not secrete hormones.

10. Which of the following is a "second messenger"?
    a. cyclic AMP
    b. oxytocin
    c. vasopressin
    d. a steroid hormone

11. Which of the following conditions would not exist at the peak of a spike action potential?
    a. The inside of the membrane is positive with respect to the outside.
    b. The concentration of K^+ ions is higher on the outside of the cell than inside.
    c. The concentration of Na^+ ions is higher inside the cell than it was prior to the action potential.
    d. There is a difference in potential across the membrane.

12. Four tissues are regarded as effectors of the nervous system. Which of the following is not such an effector?
    a. smooth muscle tissue
    b. glandular epithelial tissue
    c. bone tissue
    d. cardiac muscle tissue

13. Myelination in an axon permits:
    a. a higher threshold potential.
    b. a greater frequency of action potentials.

293

c. a higher-amplitude action potential.
d. faster impulse propagation.

14. A collection of the axon portions of neurons found in the peripheral nervous system is called a:
a. ganglion.
b. nucleus.
c. neuron.
d. nerve.

REVIEW QUESTIONS

I. Use the following diagram of a spike action potential to answer Questions 1-10. The readings reflect data for the inside of the membrane with respect to the outside. Here x = before stimulation, y = peak depolarization, and z = return to resting.

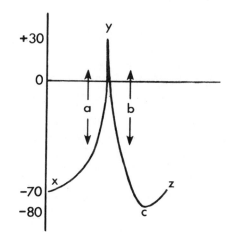

1. The resting potential is _____ mV.

2. The potential difference across the membrane at peak depolarization is _____ mV.

3. At what point (a, b, or c) is there any indication of hyperpolarization? _____.

4. The membrane is hyperpolarized by _____ mV.

5. What is the potential difference across the membrane in the hyperpolarized state? _____

6. Does -70mV to -80mV represent an increase or a decrease in the potential difference? an _____ of _____ mV

7. The total electrical change from the polarized to the depolarized state

   is _____ mV.

8. The value of the action potential, then, is _____ mV.

9. At what point is Na^+ moving into the cell? _____

10. At what point is K^+ moving out of the cell? _____

II. Listed below are a number of diseases that interfere with normal performance of parts of a reflex arc. On the basis of your knowledge of what the different parts of the reflex arc do, indicate what losses in function would result from each of these conditions.

1. Tabes dorsalis results in destruction of cells of the dorsal root ganglion.

   _____

2. Poliomyelitis destroys cell bodies of somatic motor neurons.

   _____

3. Multiple sclerosis results in demyelination of nerve fibers.

   _____

4. Accidental injury severs a nerve.

   _____

5. Myasthenia gravis is characterised by a deficiency in transmitter/receptor protein reactions in somatic motor neurons and skeletal muscle.

   _____

III. There are two systems that integrate and control an animal's activity. These differ in the mechanism and speed of communication and in the relative length of time of the effect. List the systems and enter the other information requested in the following table.

System	Method of Communication	Speed of Communication Time	Length of Time of Effect
1. _____	_____	_____	_____
2. _____	_____	_____	_____

ANSWERS TO CHAPTER EXERCISES

<u>Practice Quiz</u>

1. c	6. d	11. b
2. a	7. b	12. c
3. d	8. d	13. d
4. b	9. c	14. d
5. a	10. a	

<u>Review Questions</u>

I. 1. -70   3. c   5. 80   7. 100   9. a
    2. +30   4. 10   6. increase, 10   8. 100   10. b

II. 1. lack of sensation from the part affected
     2. paralysis of muscle due to lack of motor stimulation
     3. lack of propagation of impulses in CNS
     4. loss of sensation and motor functions in the part affected
     5. muscular weakness due to lack of stimulation by transmitter

III. 1. nervous   neurons   fast   shorter
     2. endocrine   hormones   slower   long-lasting

Chapter 22

CIRCULATION, RESPIRATION, AND EXCRETION

WHAT'S IN THIS CHAPTER

This chapter provides a description of the functional makeup of the circulatory, respiratory, and excretory systems of animals. Each of the three major sections of the chapter focuses on one of these systems. The chapter first shows that a circulatory system is only necessary in larger, more complex animals as opposed to small aquatic ones. Blood is then described as a tissue and the distinction is made between open and closed circulatory systems. Emphasis is placed on the functional anatomy of the vertebrate system and the physiological mechanisms involved in the exchange of materials between blood and tissues.

The section on respiration emphasizes the pickup, circulation, transport, and release of oxygen and carbon dioxide. An explanation of reciprocal relationships between the pickup of oxygen and the release of carbon dioxide (and vice versa) is included. The focus on respiration concludes with regulation of the rhythm of respiration and chemical factors involved in that regulation.

Removal of the waste products of nitrogen metabolism constitutes much of the section on excretion. The chapter includes the functional anatomy of the urinary system and the microanatomy of the nephron. The three methods of eliminating excess nitrogen (ammonotelism, ureotelism, and uricotelism) are covered, and comparisons are drawn among vertebrate groups. The kidney's role in ion balance, pH balance, and water balance is covered, along with mechanisms involved in the control of these functions.

By the end of this chapter you should be able to:

1. Describe the composition of blood.

2. Distinguish between open and closed circulatory systems, and describe in detail the components and differences in vertebrate circulatory systems and the sites of gaseous exchange.

3. Explain the factors involved in ultrafiltration through capillary walls.

4. List the main factors that determine blood pressure, and relate the lymphatic system to the blood volume component of blood pressure.

5. Describe the pick-up, circulatory transport, and release of O_2 and CO_2, noting the sites of pick-up and release and the chemical reactions involved.

6. Describe the respiratory organs in animals, relating those structures to air-breathers and aquatic animals; give the mechanism whereby breathing rhythm is controlled, and list factors that affect respiratory rate.

7. List the three main systems for removal of gaseous and nitrogenous wastes in animals.

8. Describe the gross and the microscopic structure of the kidney; relate the processes of filtration, reabsorption, and secretion to the nephron, and describe the events occurring in each process.

9. Explain the factors involved in determining the total effective filtration rate in the glomerulus/Bowman's capsule component of the nephron.

10. Explain the differences in the nitrogenous excretory products of fishes, amphibians, birds, reptiles, and mammals; relate these differences to the environment of the animal and the amount of water needed to excrete the product.

11. Describe the chemistry involved in ammonotelism, ureotelism, and uricotelism. Explain how some animals can switch from one mechanism to another.

12. Describe the mechanisms involved in the formation of urine in the mammalian kidney, including ion movements, water movements, and the countercurrent multiplier mechanism; explain how some animals can adjust ion movements according to environmental conditions.

13. Explain the mechanisms whereby the kidneys and lungs regulate the pH of plasma.

WHAT YOU SHOULD ALREADY KNOW

The background knowledge that you need in order to understand this chapter includes material from a number of chapters. You need to know the ionic distributions across membranes and the factors that affect the movement of water and ions. You need to be familiar with the passive processes of filtration, diffusion, and osmosis as well as with active transport mechanisms (Chapter 11). A knowledge of tissues and tissue fluid compartments is pertinent. A review of neural mechanisms, the autonomic nervous system, and endocrines will be helpful (Chapter 21) as will a review of the need for oxygen in metabolic reactions and the subsequent release of carbon dioxide (Chapter 7).

Pre-Test

1. Cardiac muscle cells are (a)_____(striated / nonstriated). The (b)_____(sympathetic / parasympathetic) division of the autonomic nervous system brings about an increased heartbeat.

1. (a) striated;   2. Identify the transport process involved in each of the

(b) sympathetic

following kinds of movement of material. Use A for active transport, D for diffusion, F for filtration, and O for osmosis.

(a) Movement of sodium against an electrical or concentration gradient _____

(b) Movement of a solute from a region of higher solute concentration to a region of lower solute concentration _____

(c) Movement of water from a region of lower solute concentration to a region of higher solute concentration _____

(d) Movement of a solute through a membrane because the solute is dissolved in a fluid that is being forced through a membrane by a mechanical pressure _____

2. (a) A; (b) D; (c) O; (d) F

3. Indicate which of the following terms below pertain to fluid inside (I) and which to fluid outside (O) the cell.

(a) interstitial _____

(b) extracellular _____

(c) intracellular _____

(d) intercellular _____

3. (a) O; (b) O; (c) I; (d) O

4. A hormone secreted from the posterior pituitary which functions in water balance is (a)_____. The hormone is synthesized in (b)_____.

4. (a) vasopressin or antidiuretic hormone; (b) a hypothalamic nucleus

5. Aldosterone is secreted from the (a)_____. Its role is to promote the retention of (b)_____.

5. (a) adrenal cortex; (b) sodium

6. An increase in solute concentration will (a)_____ (increase / decrease) the osmotic potential of a solution.

A gas will diffuse from a region of (b)_____ (higher / lower) pressure.

6. (a) decrease; (b) higher

7. In the degradation of glucose in a cell, oxygen is

299

(a)_____(utilized / given off) while carbon

dioxide is (b)_____(utilized / given off).
In the metabolism of amino acids, a by-product is

(c)_____.

7. (a) utilized;
   (b) given off;
   (c) ammonia

GUIDED REVIEW OF THE CHAPTER

22-1 Some small animals have no circulatory problems.

1. Short-distance exchanges of material between the environ-
    ment and the cell in small animals occurs by the process

    of (a)_____. Larger multicellular animals
    have cells too far removed from the environment, thus

    calling for a (b)_____ system to mediate
    the exchange.

1. (a) diffusion;
   (b) circulatory   *22-2 Blood is a tissue whose matrix is plasma.*

1. The three major blood cells, or cell fragments, are

    (a)_____, (b)_____, and

    (c)_____.

1. (a) erythro-   2. The fluid component of blood is called (a)_____.
   cytes; (b)   Within this component are inorganic substances such as
   leukocytes;
   (c) platelets   (b)_____ and organic substances such as

                        (c)_____.

2. (a) plasma;
   (b) salts;
   (c) proteins,   *22-3 Circulatory systems may be closed or open.*
   glucose, amino
   acids, or   1. In most animals the circulatory fluid is kept in a com-
   vitamins   partment distinct from the extracellular fluid compart-

                       ment. Such a system is said to be (a)_____
                       (closed / open). Circulatory systems typically consist of
                       two major components besides the fluid itself: a pump or

                       (b)_____ and tubelike structures called

                       (c)_____.

300

1. (a) closed;
   (b) heart;
   (c) blood
   vessels

22-4 General structure of the vertebrate circulatory system.

1. Which vessel--artery, vein, or capillary--fits each of the following descriptions?

    (a) returns blood to the heart _____

    (b) thickest muscular wall _____

    (c) carries oxygenated blood in the systemic circuit

    _____

    (d) carries oxygenated blood in the pulmonary circuit

    _____

1. (a) vein;
   (b) artery;
   (c) artery;
   (d) vein

2. Pressure is greatest in systemic arteries when the heart

    is in (a)_____(systole / diastole).   The

    large   systemic   artery   leaving   the   heart   is   the

    (b)_____; the major veins entering the heart

    are the (c)_____ and (d)_____

    _____.

2. (a) systole;
   (b) aorta; (c)
   venae cavae;
   (d) pulmonary

3. Which vertebrate group is characterized by each of the following descriptions?

    (a) double-circulation system with a complete septum separating the right and left sides of the heart

    _____

    (b) single-circulation system _____

    (c) first group to evolve a pulmonary system _____

    _____

3. (a) birds and
   mammals; (b)
   fishes; (c)
   amphibians

22-5 The heart has an internal pacemaker.

1. In the mammalian heart, heartrate is determined by the

    rate of firing of the (a)_____.

    This latter structure is modified (b)_____
    (cardiac/ neural) tissue. Its rate of firing is affected

    by the (c)_____(somatic / autonomic) portion
    of the nervous system.

301

1. (a) sinoatrial
   node;
   (b) cardiac;
   (c) autonomic

22-6 A circulatory system moves blood past a point of gas exchange.

1. The major routes of oxygen and carbon dioxide exchange in animals are (a)_____, (b)_____, and (c)_____. Air-breathing vertebrates use (d)_____ for gaseous exchange, whereas fish use (e)_____ to extract oxygen from the surrounding water.

1. (a) skin;
   (b) gills;
   (c) lungs;
   (d) lungs;
   (e) gills

22-7 The blood plasma exchanges with the interstitial fluid.

1. The two forces inside a capillary that affect the movement of fluid are (a)_____ and (b)_____. The only force present in interstitial fluid that normally would affect fluid movement is (c)_____.

1. (a) hydrostatic
   pressure;
   (b) osmotic
   pressure;
   (c) hydrostatic
   pressure

2. Hydrostatic pressure inside a capillary is (a)_____ (higher / lower) at the venous end than at the arterial end. There is a net tendency of fluid to move (b)_____(inward / outward) at the venous end.

2. (a) lower;
   (b) inward

3. Blood pressure is dependent on two major factors: (a)_____ and (b)_____. Increasing the diameter of a small artery (c)_____(increases / decreases) the peripheral resistance.

3. (a) cardiac
   output; (b)
   peripheral
   resistance;
   (c) decreases

22-8 The lymphatic system carries excess extracellular fluid.

1. An auxillary circulatory system that collects excess extracellular fluid is the (a)_____. This system contains structures called (b)_____ that filter the lymph.

1. (a) lymphatic
   system;
   (b) nodes

22-9 Oxygen must be transported into tissues.

1. The most common oxygen carrier in animals is (a)_____

_____. In many animals this substance is concentrated and carried in (b)_____(red / white)

blood cells. Packing it into cells (c)_____ (increases / decreases) the oxygen-carrying capacity of the blood.

1. (a) hemoglobin;
   (b) red;
   (c) increases

2. In terrestrial vertebrates, hemoglobin becomes almost fully saturated with oxygen in the (a)_____.
   In metabolizing tissues, oxygen is given up because of

   (b)_____(increased /decreased) oxygen pressure in the extracellular fluid, and this is accentuated by the

   presence of (c)_____ released from metabolizing cells.

2. (a) lungs;
   (b) decreased;

   (c) H^+ ions

22-10 Carbon dioxide must be transported out of tissues.

1. The major transport form of carbon dioxide is (a)_____.
   The substance is formed in red blood cells due to the

   presence of the enzyme (b)_____.

   Once formed, the substance travels in the (c)_____

   _____(red blood cell / plasma).

1. (a) HCO_3^-;
   (b) carbonic anhydrase;
   (c) plasma

22-11 The rhythm of breathing is controlled by an external circuit.

1. For each of the following events, indicate whether the phenomenon would be associated with inspiration (I) or expiration (E).

   (a) contraction of diaphragm _____

   (b) Hering-Breuer reflex _____

   (c) increase in size of chest cavity _____

   (d) stimulation of a brain center in the pons _____

   (e) elimination of CO_2 from lungs _____

   (f) increased O_2 content in lungs _____

1. (a) I; (b) E;
   (c) I; (d) E;
   (e) E; (f) I

22-12 Respiration is regulated by oxygen and hydrogen-ion levels.

1. Respiration rate is (a)_____(increased / decreased) by a decreased oxygen level in the blood. This

change in respiration rate is due to (b)_____ (stimulation / inhibition) of the carotid and aortic

bodies. Respiration rate is (c)_____(increased / decreased) by increased levels of H^+ ions in the brain.

Increased H^+ ion levels result from (d)_____ (increased / decreased) levels of CO_2.

1. (a) increased;
   (b) stimula-
   tion;
   (c) increased;
   (d) increased

22-13 Wastes are removed from blood as it passes through an excretory organ.

1. Excretory organs function in the removal of (a)_____

_____ wastes from the vertebrate. In addition to removing these wastes, the kidney functions in osmo-regulation, which involves maintaining a balance between

(b)_____ and (c)_____.

1. (a) nitro-
   genous;
   (b) water;
   (c) salts

2. Which of the following series of events, (a) or (b), describes the general mechanism whereby excretory systems operate?

   (a) ultrafiltration of waste products from blood into excretory units with retention of useful components such as glucose, water, and ions

   (b) ultrafiltration of waste, water, ions, glucose, and other useful components with reabsorption of useful components back into the bloodstream

2. series (b)

22-14 The nephron is a dead-end channel surrounded by specialized pumps.

1. The three main processes that occur in the mammalian kidney in the formation of urine are (a)_____, (b)_____, and (c)_____.

1. (a) filtration;
   (be) reabsorp-
   tion; (d)
   secretion

2. Glomerular filtration rate (GFR) is the amount of plasma filtered through the glomeruli per minute. Identify which of the following forces promote (P) and which retard (R) the filtration of fluid from the glomerulus to Bowman's capsule.

   (a) hydrostatic pressure of blood in the glomerulus _____

   (b) hydrostatic pressure of Bowman's capsule _____

   (c) osmotic pressure of blood in the glomerulus _____

   (d) osmotic pressure of Bowman's capsule fluid _____

2. (a) P; (b) R;   *22-16 Urea is made in a cycle of reactions.*
   (c) R; (d) P

1. Nitrogenous wastes may be primarily in the form of

   (a)_____ in aquatic vertebrates, (b)_____

   _____ in mammals, and (c)_____

   in animals such as birds, reptiles, and terrestrial in-
   vertebrates. The different forms of waste differ in the
   amount of water necessary for their removal. The least

   water is needed for the excretion of (d)_____

   _____. The waste product in mammals is synthesized

   in the (e)_____.

1. (a) ammonia;
   (b) urea;
   (c) uric acid;
   (d) uric acid;
   (e) liver

21-17 Many animals have to convert from one way of life to another.

1. Some animals can switch from ammonotelism to ureotelism.
   This process involves which of the following synthetic
   pathways?

   (a) a switch from the synthesis of carbamyl phosphate from
   ammonia to the combination of ammonia with glutamate

   (b) a switch from the formation of glutamine from glutamate plus ammonia to the formation of carbamyl
   phosphate from ammonia and carbon dioxide

1. pathway (b)

22-19 The loop of Henle is a countercurrent multiplier.

1. Indicate which of the following processes are active (A)
   and which passive (P).

Substance Moving	From	To	
(a) sodium ion	proximal convoluted tubule	bloodstream	_____
(b) water	proximal convoluted tubule	bloodstream	_____
(c) nutrients	glomerulus	Bowman's capsule	_____
(d) chloride ion	proximal convoluted tubule	bloodstream	_____
(e) urea	glomerulus	Bowman's capsule	_____
(f) chloride ion	ascending loop of Henle	interstitial fluid	_____

(g) sodium ion   ascending loop   interstitial   _____

                       of Henle   fluid

1. (a) A; (b) P;
(c) P; (d) P;
(e) P; (f) A;
(g) P

22-21 Na^+ concentration is closely related to extracellular volume.

1. Complete the following scheme related to sodium reabsorption in the kidney: The juxtaglomerulus apparatus releases (a)_____ in response to a decrease in blood pressure in the nephron. The latter substance is a(an) (b)_____(hormone / enzyme) that results in the conversion of angiotensinogen produced by the (c)_____ to active (d)_____. A further conversion results in the production of (e)_____.

1. (a) renin; (b) enzyme; (c) liver; (d) angiotensin I; (e) angiotensin II

2. The effect of angiotensin II on the adrenal cortex is to stimulate the release of (a)_____, which in turn (b)_____(increases / decreases) the reabsorption of sodium.

2. (a) aldosterone; (b) increases

22-22 Plasma acidity is regulated by the kidneys and lungs.

1. An increase in plasma pH above 7.4 is called (a)_____ and its decrease below 7.4 is called (b)_____. Three major systems that function in pH regulation are the (c)_____, (d)_____, and (e)_____ systems.

1. (a) alkalosis; (b) acidosis; (c) circulatory (blood); (d) excretory; (e) respiratory

22-24 Excess salt is sometimes removed by special glands.

1. Two groups of animals that have special adaptations for handling salt from salt water are (a)_____ and (b)_____.

1. (a) fish; (b) sea birds

PRACTICE QUIZ

1. In small animals in close contact with their environment, there is a direct exchange between the organism and its environment by way of:
    a. a circulatory system.
    b. the process of filtration.
    c. a respiratory system.
    d. the process of diffusion.

2. Which of the following components of blood is not cellular or a cell fragment?
    a. leucocyte
    b. erythrocyte
    c. platelet
    d. plasma

3. Which of the following animal groups have an open type of circulation?
    a. fish
    b. mammals
    c. insects
    d. amphibians

4. Arteries:
    a. carry blood toward the heart.
    b. in the pulmonary circuit contain oxygenated blood.
    c. in the systematic circuit carry unoxygenated blood.
    d. carry blood from the heart.

5. The largest vein in a mammal is the:
    a. vena cava.
    b. aorta.
    c. pulmonary artery.
    d. pulmonary vein.

6. The evolution of a double-circulation pattern was associated with:
    a. movement from salt water to fresh water.
    b. the development of the mammalian kidney.
    c. breathing air.
    d. development of closed circulation.

7. The rhythm of the heart is due to the:
    a. rate of discharge of the cardiac muscle cells.
    b. neural innervation to the heart.
    c. syncytial nature of the heart.
    d. intrinsic properties of modified cardiac fibers.

8. The actual exchange of gases between the environment and the bloodstream in the air breathers occurs in the:
    a. alveoli.
    b. trachea.
    c. bronchi.
    d. thoracic cavity.

9. A _____ increases blood presssure.
    a. decrease in heartrate
    b. decrease in the diameter of small blood vessels
    c. decrease in peripheral resistance
    d. decrease in cardiac output

307

10. Which of the following statements is <u>not</u> true of the lymphatic system?
   a. The vessels begin blindly in tissue spaces.
   b. The fluid contained in the vessels has the same composition as blood.
   c. There are nodes that filter lymph.
   d. Excess tissue fluid is drained into the lymphatic vesels.

11. Oxygen pressure is <u>greatest</u>:
   a. in a metabolizing cell.
   b. in the interstitial fluid surrounding a metabolizing cell.
   c. in the alveoli.
   d. in the bloodstream.

12. The Bohr effect refers to:
   a. the release of CO_2 from a metabolizing cell.
   b. the diffusion of O_2 into a metabolizing cell.
   c. the release of H^+ from H_2CO_3.
   d. the release of O_2 from hemoglobin as H^+ is picked up.

13. CO_2 is transported in the circulatory system mainly:
   a. in the form of HCO_3^-.
   b. attached to hemoglobin.
   c. in the form of H_2CO_3.
   d. in the red blood cell.

14. _____ bring about an increase in respiration rate.
   a. Increases in oxygen tension
   b. Decreased levels of CO_2
   c. Increased levels of H^+
   d. Increased levels of HCO_3^-

15. Stimulation of the carotid and aortic bodies:
   a. occurs when there is high oxygen tension in the blood.
   b. results in an increase in respiration rate.
   c. occurs when there is a deficiency in carbon dioxide in the blood cell.
   d. results in slow, shallow breathing.

16. Which of the following substances normally does <u>not</u> pass into Bowman's capsule?
   a. protein
   b. amino acid
   c. glucose
   d. water

17. At what site does the process of filtration in the mammalian kidney occur?
   a. proximal convoluted tubule
   b. loop of Henle
   c. glomerulus
   d. distal convoluted tubule

18. In a normally functioning kidney, which of the following would <u>not</u> significantly affect the total effective filtration pressure?
   a. hydrostatic pressure of Bowman's capsule
   b. osmotic pressure of Bowman's capsule

c. osmotic pressure of blood
d. hydrostatic pressure of blood

19. Ureotelism is a means of eliminating nitrogenous wastes in:
    a. birds.
    b. reptiles.
    c. fish.
    e. mammals.

20. _____ always move(s) passively in kidney functions.
    a. Water
    b. Na^+
    c. Amino acids
    d. K^+

REVIEW QUESTIONS

I. The blood, respiratory system, and excretory system play key roles in regulating the pH of body fluids. For each of the following phenomena, give the site of action and the mechanism.

1. $HbO_2 + H^+ \longrightarrow HHb + O_2$

   _____

   _____

2. $H^+ + HCO_3^- \longrightarrow H_2CO_3 \longrightarrow H_2O + CO_2$

   _____

   _____

3. H^+ stimulation of the respiratory center

   _____

   _____

4. release of H^+ via formation of ammonium ions

   _____

   _____

5. retention of H^+ ions in alkalosis with concurrent excretion of K^+ ions

   _____

   _____

309

II. When you hyperventilate you forcefully remove even normal amounts of carbon dioxide from the bloodstream. A decrease in carbon dioxide levels below normal has consequences in both circulation and respiration. You get "light-headed" and may faint, and your respiration rate decreases. What would be the expected effects of low carbon dioxide levels on each of the following factors? Give a one-statement explanation.

1. blood pressure _____

_____

2. stimulation of inspiratory center _____

_____

3. H^+ level in the blood _____

_____

4. pH of blood _____

_____

III. The total effective filtration pressure promoting the movement of water, salts, ions, and the like from the glomerulus to Bowman's capsule depends on the osmotic pressure of plasma, the osmotic pressure of fluid in Bowman's capsule (if present), and the hydrostatic pressure in the bloodstream and fluid within Bowman's capsule. Given the values in the following example, answer the next six questions.

Hydrostatic pressure in glomerulus   = 65 torr
Hydrostatic pressure in Bowman's capsule   = 25 torr
Osmotic pressure in glomerulus   = 10 torr
Osmotic pressure in Bowman's capsule   = 0 torr

1. Is the total hydrostatic factor working in favor of or against filtration?

By how much? _____

2. Is the osmotic pressure in the glomerulus in favor of or against

filtration? _____

3. What is the total effective filtration pressure in this example?

_____

4. What would happen to the filtration process if blood pressure dropped to 35

torr? _____

5. If the tube draining urine from the kidney were blocked by a kidney stone, causing the urine to "back up" and thereby increasing the hydrostatic pressure in Bowman's capsule to 55 torr, what would happen to the

filtration process? _____

6. Suppose that in nephrosis, a disease of the kidney, protein were able to move from the glomerulus into Bowman's capsule. What would this do to the osmotic pressure of Bowman's capsule fluid? What would it do to the total EFP?

_____

_____

ANSWERS TO CHAPTER EXERCISES

Practice Quiz

1. d	6. c	11. c	16. a
2. d	7. d	12. d	17. c
3. c	8. a	13. a	18. b
4. d	9. b	14. c	19. d
5. a	10. b	15. b	20. a

Review Questions

I. 1. Bloodstream. H^+ released from metabolizing cells promotes the release of O_2 and is picked up by hemoglobin.

2. Bloodstream at the site of the lungs. H^+ released when hemoglobin is picked up reacts with HCO_3 in the red blood cell, due to the action of carbonic anhydrase, forming carbonic acid which dissociates to release the CO_2, which in turn diffuses into the lungs.

3. H^+ stimulation of the respiratory center in the medulla of the brain increases respiratory rate to promote the reaction $H^+ + HCO_3^- \longrightarrow H_2CO_3 \longrightarrow H_2O + CO_2$, whereby CO_2 is lost.

4. Kidney. Some nephron cells can break down glutamine to glutamate to release ammonium ions formed from H^+ and ammonia.

5. Kidney. Parts of the nephron can exchange K^+ ions for H^+ ions by active transport.

II. 1. Decreases, due to a decreased heartrate as well as increased diameter of small blood vesels. This is the reason for fainting following hyperventilation.

2. Decreases, resulting in a decreased respiration rate. Underwater swimmers use this "physiological trick" to swim longer distances.

3. Decreases, because of the lack of CO_2 to promote the reaction $CO_2 + H_2O \longrightarrow H_2CO_3 \longrightarrow H^+ + HCO_3^-$.

4. Increases, because there would be a decrease in H^+ ions.

311

III.   1. in favor of by 40 torr
        2. against
        3. EFP = 30 torr
        4. Filtration would stop.
        5. Filtration would stop.
        6. It would increase the osmotic pressure, which would increase the EFP.

Chapter 23

NUTRITION, DIGESTION, AND DISTRIBUTION

WHAT'S IN THIS CHAPTER

This chapter covers the nutritional needs of animals, particularly humans, and explains how nutrients are obtained from ingested food after processing through the digestive tract. It begins with an introduction to the digestive tube of animals, variation in feeding methods, and the mechanical breakdown of food. The remainder of the chapter emphasizes the human digestive system. The functional anatomy of the system is covered, along with the reactions involved in the digestive breakdown of all three classes of foods--carbohydrates, protein, and fats. In addition to the digestive reactions themselves, hormonal control mechanisms for the release of enzymes and other actions of the digestive tract are explained.

The explanation of the process of distributing the products of digestion begins with a description of the absorptive surface of the intestine--that is, the area where the products actually move from the lumen of the intestine to the bloodstream. Also included are the circulatory transport of lipids, hormonal regulation of blood glucose levels, and of blood calcium levels, circulatory transport and storage of iron, the contribution of amino acids to nitrogen balance, and the complex nature of the nutritional interactions in the organism.

By the end of this chapter you should be able to:

1. Describe the anatomy of the tubular and nontubular parts of the digestive system, and explain the role of each component in the function of the digestive system.

2. List different mechanisms of feeding in animals, and distinguish between the mechanical and the chemical breakdown of food.

3. Trace the passage of carbohydrates, proteins, and fats through the entire digestive system, and explain where digestive actions occur and what the product of each digestive action is.

4. Become familiar with enzymes involved in the digestion of each of the three classes of food and with the control mechanisms that regulate enzymatic secretions.

5. Cite the functions of the liver in digestion and food storage.

313

6. Explain how lipids are transported throughout the body.

7. List and describe the source and action of four hormones that regulate glucose levels in the bloodstream.

8. List and describe the source and action of the two hormones that regulate calcium levels in the bloodstream.

9. Explain how iron is transported in the bloodstream and stored in the body.

10. Explain the need for amino acids, and tell what is meant by essential amino acids and by positive and negative nitrogen balance.

11. Give an account of the order in which stored foods in the body are utilized when food is not available through ingestion.

12. Become aware of the complex nature of interactions between nutrients.

WHAT YOU SHOULD ALREADY KNOW

You will need to know the basics of the hydrolytic reactions of digestion (Chapter 6). Material on endocrine and neural control (Chapter 21) is essential to an understanding of the hormonal interactions related to digestion in the present chapter. You need to know the chemical components of the three classes of foods: carbohydrates, fats, and proteins (Chapter 4). You will need to know the relationship between the circulatory system and the lymphatic system (Chapter 22).

Pre-Test

1. A hydrolytic reaction is one that breaks up large molecules into smaller units with the addition of

   (a)_____. In synthesis reactions the same

   substance is (b)_____(lost / gained) in the reaction.

1. (a) water; (b) lost

2. The division of the nervous system that affects digestive

   functions is the (a)_____(autonomic / somatic). The particular branch of the latter that increases

   digestive function is the (b)_____ division.

2. (a) autonomic; (b) parasympathetic

3. Hormones may be proteins and, as such, are made up of

   (a)_____. Each hormone affects certain target cells whose membranes contain specific

   (b)_____ for that hormone.

3. (a) amino acids; (b) receptors

4. The major carbohydrate foodstuffs are (a)_____

   from plants and (b)_____ from animals. The

314

basic units of both of these are (c)_____.

Fat molecules consist of two components: (d)_____

and (e)_____.

4. (a) starch;
   (b) glycogen;
   (c) glucose;
   (d) glycerol;
   (e) fatty acids

GUIDED REVIEW OF THE CHAPTER

23-1 The digestive tract is a long tube to which digestive enzymes are added.

1. More advanced animals have a tubular digestive system beginning with the (a)_____ and ending with the (b)_____. The three major functions of the digestive tract are (c)_____, (d)_____ _____, and (e)_____.

1. (a) mouth;
   (b) anus;
   (c) ingestion;
   (d) digestion;
   (e) absorption

23-2 Animals use many different mechanisms for feeding.

1. Two types of feeding that do not require tearing and chewing food are (a)_____ and (b)_____.

1. (a) sucking juices; (b) filter feeding

2. An example of a filter feeder is _____.

2. *Daphnia*

3. Whales use a structure called the baleen for _____ _____.

3. filter feeding

23-3 Food must generally be broken down mechanically.

1. What organ(s) is(are) involved in the mechanical breakdown of food by (a) birds? _____ (b) mammals? _____ The chemical breakdown of food utilizes digestive (c)_____.

315

1. (a) gizzard;
   (b) teeth;
   (c) enzymes

2. crop

3. (a) incisors;
   (b) canines;
   (c) premolars
   and molars

4. ruminants

1. (a) mouth; (b)
   esophagus; (c)
   stomach; (d)
   small intes-
   tine; (e) colon
   (large intes-
   tine);
   (f) rectum

2. peristalsis

3. chyme

4. False

2. A storage organ for food in the bird is the _____.

3. The teeth of mammals that are used for cutting are the
   (a)_____. Those used for tearing are
   (b)_____, and those used for grinding or
   crushing are (c)_____.

4. Animals that have a pouch in the stomach where food can be
   stored and later regurgitated are called _____.

23-4 *An overview of the digestive system.*

1. List in proper order the parts of the digestive tube.

   (a)_____   (d)_____

   (b)_____   (e)_____

   (c)_____   (f)_____

2. Muscular actions that propel food down the esophagus and
   through the digestive tract are called _____
   _____.

3. The thick souplike material that leaves the stomach following digestive action is called _____.

4. True or False: Pancreatic enzymes exert their action in
   the colon.

23-5 *Carbohydrate digestion begins in the mouth.*

1. Starch and glycogen digestion begins in the (a)_____
   with the enzyme (b)_____. It is completed
   in the intestine, where intestinal enzymes break down
   (c)_____(starch / disaccharides). What
   three monosaccharides are the major end products of carbohydrate digestion? (d)_____, (e)_____,

316

and (f)_____.

1. (a) mouth; (b)
amylase; (c)
disaccharides;
(d) glucose;
(e) galactose;
(f) fructose

2. Which of the following are sources of enzymes for carbohydrate digestion? (a) salivary glands, (b) stomach glands, (c) pancreas, (d) intestinal glands

2. (a), (c) and
(d)

3. Some _____ can digest cellulose.

3. microorganisms

23-6 Proteins are attacked by a series of enzymes.

1. Protein digestion begins in the (a)_____

_____(oral cavity / stomach / small intestine) and

is completed in the (b)_____, where

the breakdown product is (c)_____.

1. (a) stomach;
(b) small
intestine; (c)
amino acids

2. What is the source of each of the following digestive substances?

(a) pipsinogen _____

(b) hydrochloric acid _____

(c) trypsinogen _____

(d) enterokinase _____

2. (a) chief cells
/stomach; (b)
parietal cells/
stomach; (c)
pancreas; (d)
intestinal
cells

3. Complete the following expression, which suggests the relationship among pepsin, pepsinogin, hydrochloric acid

(HCl): (a)_____ activates pepsin-

ogen by converting it to (b)_____.

3. (a) HCl;
(b) pepsin

4. Inactive forms of enzymes, such as pepsinogen and

trypsinogen, are called _____.

4. proenzymes

23-7 Secretion is regulated by a series of hormones.

1. Secretion of digestive enzymes and other materials is

regulated by both (a)_____ and (b)_____
mechanisms.

1. (a) neural;
(b) hormonal

2. Give the specific source of each of the following hormones.

(a) gastrin _____

317

(b) secretin _____

(c) enterogastrone _____

3. Secretion from chief cells and parietal cells is mucosa;

stimulated by _____.

*23-8 Hormones from the small intestine stimulate pancreatic
secretion.*

1. Two hormones that stimulate alkaline secretions to raise

the pH of the small intestine are (a)_____

and (b)_____.

2. Two hormones that stimulate secretion of digestive enzymes

which act in the small intestine are (a)_____

and (b)_____.

3. The trigger for bicarbonate secretion from the pancreas

and intestine is the _____ condition of
the contents coming into the intestine from the stomach.

4. Two intestinal cells that are stimulated by the substance

enterocrinin are (a)_____ and

(b)_____.

5. The first hormone to be discovered was (a)_____.

This hormone was discovered by (b)_____ and

(c)_____.

6. True or False: The release of PZ-CCK is stimulated by the
presence of carbohydrate in the small intestine.

23-9 Bile aids the digestion and absorption of lipids.

1. Bile is synthesized in the (a)_____ and acts

in the (b)_____ to promote absorp-

tion of (c)_____. The stimulus for release
of bile from the gall bladder is provided by the hormone

(d)_____.

(b) small intestine
(c) fats (or lipids); (d) cholecystokinin

23-10 The intestine has an enormous absorptive surface.

1. Three surface specializations of the intestine that increase surface area for digestion and absorption are

   (a)_____, (b)_____, and

   (c)_____.

1. (a) plicae (or folds);
   (b) villi;
   (c) microvilli

2. Projections on the surface of cells lining the intestine

   are called _____.

2. microvilli

23-11 The products of digestion are distributed to all tissues.

1. A circulatory pathway that carries absorbed food from the

   small intestine to the liver is called the (a)_____

   _____. The storage form of

   glucose in the liver is (b)_____(glycogen /
   starch). Excess glucose that is not stored as carbohy-

   drate is converted to (c)_____.

1. (a) hepatic portal system;
   (b) glycogen;
   (c) fat (or lipid)

2. True or False: Excess amino acids may be oxidized for energy, but most are converted to fatty acids and glycogen.

2. True

3. A vitamin that promotes absorption of calcium from the in-

   testine is (a)_____. A deficiency of this vitamin

   can lead to the condition known as (b)_____.

3. (a) D_3;
   (b) rickets

23-12 Lipids are transported in special ways.

1. The two forms in which lipids are transported are

   (a)_____ and (b)_____.

1. (a) chylomicrons; (b) lipoproteins

2. Chylomicrons are absorbed into the _____ portion of a villus.

2. lacteal

3. True or False: Chylomicrons consist of a lipid bilayer attached to carrier proteins.

3. False

4. True or False: Very low-density lipoproteins carry triglycerides to various tissues.

319

4. True

5. Lipoproteins that carry phospholipids to other tissues are

_____ lipoproteins.

5. low-density

23-13 Metabolic patterns change during a fasting period.

1. In what order are foods metabolized during fasting or

starvation? (a)_____, (b)_____,

(c)_____

1. (a) carbohy-
drates; (b)
fats; (c)
proteins

23-14 The plasma glucose level is kept within a narrow range.

1. List the two islet of Langerhans hormones that regulate
glucose availability, their source, and their action.

(a)_____

_____

_____

_____

(b)_____

_____

_____

_____

1. (a) insulin,
beta cells of
pancreas, pro-
mote glucose
entrance into
muscle, adi-
pose, and
liver cells;
(b) glucagon,
alpha cells of
pancreas, pro-
mote release of
glucose from
liver and adi-
pose cells

2. A complex consisting of nicotinic acid and (a)_____

_____ ion called (b)_____

_____ works along with insulin to maintain proper
plasma glucose levels.

2. (a) chromium;
(b) glucose
tolerance
factor

23-15 The concept of a reaction cascade.

1. A series of reactions that can take a small input signal
and produce a much larger final reaction is called a

_____.

1. reaction cascade

23-16 Other hormones are superimposed on this system.

1. Two hormones that regulate glucose levels and whose release is under hypothalamic control are (a)_____ and (b)_____.

1. (a) epinephrine; (c) somatotropin

23-17 Plasma calcium levels are regulated by two hormones.

1. What is the effect of parathyroid hormone on each of the following organs with respect to calcium levels?

    (a) kidney _____

    (b) intestine _____

    (c) bone _____

1. (a) increased reabsorption; (b) increased absorption; (c) increased release

23-18 Iron is transferred and stored by two proteins.

1. Iron that is absorbed from the intestine combines with a protein called (a)_____. The storage form of iron is (b)_____.

1. (a) transferrin; (b) ferritin

2. About 70% of the body's iron is found in the _____ molecule.

2. hemoglobin

3. The two pigments that are produced by the breakdown of hemoglobin are (a)_____ and (b)_____. These both become a part of (c)_____.

3. (a) biliverdin; (b) bilirubin; (c) bile

23-20 Several amino acids must be supplied in food.

1. Amino acids that an animal cannot make are called (a)_____. Amino acids are used to synthesize (b)_____. A positive nitrogen balance means that the body is (c)_____(synthesizing / breaking down) protein.

1. (a) essential; (b) proteins; (c) synthesizing

321

1. Which of the following is <u>not</u> a source of digestive enzymes?
    a. certain intestinal lining cells
    b. pancreatic acinar cells
    c. chief cells of the stomach lining
    d. parietal cells of the stomach lining

2. Which of the following is <u>not</u> a major function of the digestive system?
    a. chemical breakdown of food
    b. excretion of nitrogenous wastes
    c. absorption of breakdown products
    d. ingestion of bulk food

3. Filter feeding occurs in:
    a. whales.
    b. birds.
    c. mammals.
    d. reptiles.

4. The gizzard:
    a. is present in mammals.
    b. is responsible for chemical breakdown of food.
    c. is a digestive organ in fish.
    d. is involved in mechanical breakdown of food.

5. The first enzyme to act on carbohydrate foods in mammals is:
    a. pancreatic amylase.
    b. intestinal maltase.
    c. salivary amylase.
    d. intestinal sucrase.

6. Which of the following is <u>not</u> an absorbed product of carbohydrate digestion?
    a. fructose
    b. maltose
    c. galactose
    d. glucose

7. Cellulose can be digested by certain:
    a. fishes.
    b. mammals.
    c. birds.
    d. microorganisms.

8. The major products of protein digestion that are absorbed into the bloodstream are:
    a. amino acids.
    b. peptides.
    c. dipeptides.
    d. proteases.

9. Which of the following statements is <u>not</u> true of pepsinogen?
    a. It is secreted from chief cells.
    b. It is an active form of enzyme.
    c. Hydrochloric acid influences its activity.
    d. It is secreted in the stomach.

10. An inactive form of a proteolytic enzyme is called a:
    a. nuclease.
    b. peptidase.
    c. protease.
    d. proenzyme.

11. Which of the following is a source of alkaline secretions?
    a. zymogen cells of the stomach
    b. pancreatic duct cells
    c. parietal cells of the stomach
    d. paneth cells of the intestine

12. A substance that is not an enzyme, but promotes fat digestion and absorption, is:
    a. lipase.
    b. cholecystokinin.
    c. bile.
    d. nuclease.

13. Chylomicrons are a transport form of:
    a. fats.
    b. amino acids.
    c. glucose.
    d. iron.

14. Which of the following hormones does not regulate glucose levels in some way?
    a. insulin
    b. somatotropin
    c. cholecystokinin
    d. epinephrine

15. _____ promotes the entrance of glucose into fat cells.
    a. Cholecystokinin
    b. Secretin
    c. Epinephrine
    d. Insulin

16. Which of the following statements about calcium levels in blood is not true?
    a. Reabsorption via the kidney increases blood calcium.
    b. Blood levels are affected by calcitonin.
    c. The release of calcium from bone increases blood calcium.
    d. Blood levels are affected by vasopressin.

17. The storage of iron in the liver is:
    a. transferrin.
    b. ferritin.
    c. elemental iron.
    d. bilirubin.

18. The breakdown of amino acids does not contribute to the formation of:
    a. proteins.
    b. glucose.
    c. urea.
    d. fatty acids.

19. An essential amino acid is one that:
    a. is abundant in all protein foods.

323

b. the body cells cannot metabolize.
c. does not have to be supplied in the diet.
d. the body cells cannot synthesize.

REVIEW QUESTIONS

I.   Carbohydrate is taken into the body in the form of starch or glycogen, or smaller units, and ends up as glucose in a cell where it is metabolized for energy. Use the following scheme to trace the fate of starch from its ingestion to its entry into a cell.

Enzymatic action occurring in oral cavity

1.   Starch is broken down to _____ units.

2.   What is the enzyme? _____

3.   What is the source of the enzyme? _____

Enzymatic action occurring in the small intestine

4.   What enzyme in the intestine converts starch to disaccharide units?

_____

5.   What is the source of this enzyme? _____

6.   What enzyme breaks down the disaccharide maltose? _____

7.   What is the product of the latter? _____

8.   What is the source of the enzyme for the breakdown of maltose? _____

_____

Absorption of glucose

9.   Into what specialized structure of the intestinal lining is glucose

absorbed? _____

10. It is absorbed into the (j)_____(capillary / lymphatic) portion of that specialized structure.

Transport of glucose

11. To what organ is glucose first taken? _____

12. Through what system of vessels? _____

Cellular uptake of glucose

13. What hormone promotes the entrance of glucose into certain cells where it

is metabolized? _____

14. What is the source of this hormone? _____

15. Into what cells is the entrance of glucose promoted by this hormone?

_____, _____, and _____

II. There are a number of examples of enzymes that are actually secreted as inactive proenzymes. This mechanism is protective in nature. Give two examples of proenzymes. What consequences would result if these enzymes were not secreted as inactive forms?

_____

_____

_____

_____

III. It is possible for an individual to become overweight by ingesting excess amounts of any food. Show how this can happen by completing the following scheme showing conversions.

1. ingested protein ⟶ (a)_____ some types

                  other types ╱ ↓

      (b) _____ ⟶ acetyl-CoA ⟶ fat in cells

2. ingested fat ⟶ (a)_____ and (b)_____ ⟶ fat in cells

3. ingested carbohydrates ⟶ (a)_____ ⟶ (b)_____

                              ⟶ fat in cells

ANSWERS TO CHAPTER EXERCISES

Practice Quiz

1. d	6. b	11. b	16. d
2. b	7. d	12. c	17. b
3. a	8. a	13. a	18. a
4. d	9. b	14. c	19. d
5. c	10. d	15. d	

Review Questions

I. 1. disaccharide
     2. salivary amylase
     3. salivary glands
     4. pancreatic amylase

     5. pancreatic acinar tissue
     6. maltase
     7. glucose
     8. intestinal cells

9. villus
10. capillary
11. liver
12. hepatic portal system
13. insulin
14. pancreatic beta cells of the islets of Langerhans
15. adipose, muscle, liver

II. Pepsinogen, chymotrypsinogen, trypsinogen, or procarboxypepidase. The active forms of these enzymes are proteolytic; if they were present within cells in the active form, they would digest one another within the cell, and perhaps the cell itself.

III. 1. (a) amino acids, (b) glucose
2. (a) glycerol, (b) fatty acids
3. (a) glucose, (b) acetyl-CoA

Chapter 24

INFECTION, INFLAMMATION, AND IMMUNITY

WHAT'S IN THIS CHAPTER

This chapter introduces infectious disease and some of the mechanisms used by animals--especially mammals--to fight disease. It begins with a historical account of the discovery of "germs" as the causal agents of disease and then discusses the routes through which disease-causing organisms can spread and infect animals. There is then a discussion of the ways in which pathogenic organisms infect their hosts and the mechanisms used by hosts to fight infection.

Most of the chapter focuses on the process of acute inflammation and the immune system that acts in concert with inflammation. Inflammation turns out to be a process in which the microcirculation in an injured area becomes more permeable so that large numbers of white blood cells--especially neutrophils--can move in to fight infection and clean up injured tissue. At the same time, macrophages and lymphocytes initiate the synthesis of antibodies against prospective invaders. There is a detailed explanation of our current view of antibody production, and some attention is given to the question of how an animal can make such an enormous variety of different antibodies. The chapter closes with a brief look at some of the processes, such as allergy, in which the immune system "backfires" to injure an animal and perhaps even kill it.

Much of the chapter focuses on details of the inflammatory process that you should not try to learn all at once. A pictorial summary of the whole process is given on page 589. It involves three cascades--kinin, complement, and blood clotting--and several kinds of leukocytes with specific roles. Get an overall picture before trying to learn any details.

By the end of this chapter you should be able to:

1. Define the term "infectious agent," list routes of infection in humans, and explain what is meant by host, reservoir of infection, and vector.

2. Describe the three major lines of defense an organism has against infection.

3. Explain what is meant by virulence and what factors determine virulence.

4. Describe and explain the major events that occur in the three phases of inflammation.

327

5. Outline the three reaction cascades that characterize the vascular phase of inflammation.

6. Discuss the processing of lymphocytes to form T cells and B cells, and explain the different functions of each type of cell.

7. List the classes of immunoglobulins, discuss the role of B cells in their synthesis, diagram their basic structure, and explain the mechanism of the antigen-antibody reaction.

8. Tell what is meant by <u>clonal selection theory</u>, <u>idiotype</u>, <u>committed lymphocyte</u>, and <u>plasma cell</u>, and explain their relationship to one another.

9. Discuss the role of the antigen-antibody complex in the activation of complement.

10. Explain generally the genetic coding for immunoglobulins.

11. Explain the role of T-lymphocyte effector cells.

12. Explain the mechanism of at least one allergic reaction.

WHAT YOU SHOULD ALREADY KNOW

You should know the general structure of the human body and be familiar with the cells of the blood, cells commonly found in connective tissues, and the concept of paratactic surfaces (Chapter 21). You should know what is meant by biological specificity of proteins and understand the genetic basis for that specificity (Chapters 4 and 9). You should also know the structure of the microcirculation, the effects of vasodilation and vasoconstriction, and what is meant by a reaction cascade (Chapter 22).

Pre-Test

1. The organ systems that are exposed to the environment through external openings are the (a)_____, (b)_____, (c)_____, and (d)_____ systems.

1. (a) respiratory; (b) digestive; (c) urinary; (d) reproductive

2. Which of the four major groups of tissues covers the body and lines the structures that open to the outside?

_____

2. epithelial

3. The major components of blood are (a)_____, (b)_____, (c)_____, and (d)_____.

3. (a) plasma;
   (b) leuko-
   cytes; (c)
   erythrocytes;
   (d) platelets

4. The cells found in connective tissue that synthesize collagen and other proteins of the matrix are called

   _____.

4. fibroblasts

5. The specificity of proteins resides in their sequence of

   (a)_____. This sequence is determined by

   the nucleotide sequence in cytoplasmic (b)_____,
   whose nucleotide sequence is, in turn, determined by

   (c)_____.

5. (a) amino
   acids; (b)
   RNA; (c) DNA

6. The part of the vascular system where the major exchange of material between the blood and tissue spaces takes

   place is the (a)_____. Vasodilation at the arterial end and vasoconstriction at the venous end

   (b)_____(increase / decrease) the amount of fluid within a capillary.

6. (a) capil-
   laries;
   (b) increase

7. A reaction cascade begins with a (a)_____(small / large) input and ends with a (b)_____(small / large) final reaction.

7. (a) small;
   (b) large

8. A membrane that lines a surface which opens to the outside

   of the body is called a _____ membrane.

8. mucous

GUIDED REVIEW OF THE CHAPTER

24-1 Parasitic microorganisms cause infectious diseases.

1. Match each of these important names in microbiology with the proper contribution to the field.

   Charles Cagniard-Latour and Theodor Schwann
   Louis Pasteur
   Joseph Lister
   Robert Koch

   (a) _____ showed that wine fermentation is due to microorganisms.

   (b) _____ introduced sterilization techniques in surgery.

   (c) _____ invented a process

329

of heating milk or other foods to a temperature that kills microorganisms.

(d) _____ developed four conditions that must be satisfied before a causal relationship between an organism and a disease can be established.

1. (a) Cagniard-Latour, Schwann; (b) Lister; (c) Pasteur; (d) Koch

2. A parasite that lives on the outside of its host is called an _____.

2. ectoparasite

3. The process whereby wine or other food is heated just enough to kill the worst microorganisms without ruining the food is called _____.

3. pasteurization

24-2 *Infectious agents must be transmitted to new hosts as part of their life cycles.*

1. The condition wherein one organism inhabits tissues of another but does no harm is called (a)_____. An organism that lives within another and damages the host is a (b)_____.

1. (a) commensalism; (b) pathogen or parasite

2. An organism that accommodates a pathogen but does not contract the disease produced by the pathogen is called _____.

2. reservoir

3. Some animals, called _____, transmit pathogens from one host to another.

3. vectors

4. Rabies is caused by a (a)_____ and transmitted through (b)_____. The reservoir for the agent is (c)_____.

4. (a) virus; (b) saliva; (c) various mammals, including dogs

5. Can the rabies virus survive in poikilothermic animals? _____

5. no

6. The four routes through which humans can be infected with pathogens are (a)_____, (b)_____, (c)_____,

330

and (d)_____.

6. (a) respira-
   tory tract;
   (b) mouth/
   intestinal
   tract; (c)
   urogenital
   tract; (d)
   broken skin

7. True or False: In humans, the organisms *Streptococcus sal-ivarius* and *S. mutans* are pathogens.

7. False

8. The arthropod vector for the malaria protozoan is a _____.

8. mosquito

24-3 Animals have several defense mechanisms against infection.

1. The three lines of defense that animals have against in-fectious organisms are (a)_____

   _____, (b)_____

   _____, and

   (c)_____.

1. (a) mechanical
   and chemical
   barriers such
   as unbroken
   skin and lyso-
   zyme; (b)
   phagocytic
   white blood
   cells;
   (c) immunity

2. Vomiting and coughing are part of the _____(first / second / third) line of defense.

2. (a) first

3. A substance produced by the skin that inhibits bacterial and fungi growth is _____.

3. sebum

4. An enzyme present in tears which attacks bacteria that get into the eyes is called _____.

4. lysozyme

24-4 Pathogens produce disease through invasion and toxin production.

1. The virulence of the organism *Clostridium perfringens* de-pends on its (a)_____ and its ability to

331

produce (b)_____.

1. (a) invasive-
ness;
(b) toxins

2. *Clostridium botulinum* is extremely virulent. Its invasive-

ness is (a)_____(strong / weak) and it produces a

(b)_____(strong / weak) toxin.

2. (a) weak;
(b) strong

3. Two or three substances (such as those produced by
Clostridium   perfringens) that enhance invasiveness are

_____

_____

3. collagenase,
hemolysin;
lecithinase,
and various
cytolytic
enzymes

4. The toxin produced by *Clostridium tetani* is a _____

_____.

24-5 Inflammation is a general reaction to injury.

4. neurotoxin

1. The four cardinal signs of acute inflammation are _____

_____

_____

1. swelling,
pain, redness,
and heat

2. True or False: The four cardinal signs of inflammation
were not described until the early nineteenth century.

2. False

3. List the most abundant white blood cells that have a role
in inflammation, and give their general function.

(a)_____ _____

(b)_____ _____

(c)_____ _____

3. (a) lympho-
cytes, immu-
nity; (b)
neutrophils,
phagocytes;
(c) monocytes,
phagocytes

4. Monocytes of the bloodstream migrate to tissue spaces and

become phagocytic _____.

4. macrophages

5. The most abundant granulocytes are _____.

5. neutrophils

6. The reticuloendothelial system consists of (a)_____

_____ that line the sinuses of organs such as

(b)_____.

6. (a) macro-
phages; (b)
lymph nodes,
spleen, liver,
or bone marrow

7. mast

7. Basophils of the bloodstream are apparently the same as
_____ cells in tissues.

24-6 An outline of inflammation.

1. The primary response in the inflammatory process is

(a)_____ of microvessels and (b)_____
(increase / decrease) in the capillary permeability. Fol-

lowing this is an invasion by (c)_____

and (d)_____, which are phagocytic cells.

Other cells, the lymphocytes, produce (e)_____
that can inactivate potential pathogens and their toxins.

1. (a) vasodila-
tion; (b) in-
crease; (c)
neutrophils;
(d) macro-
phages; (e)
antibodies

2. True or False: The term "prophylaxis" refers to prevention.

2. True

3. The term that is opposite to prophylaxis and pertains to

allergic reactions is _____ .

3. anaphylaxis

4. Histamine causes (a)_____(vasodilation /
vasoconstriction) of vessels of the microcirculation and

(b)_____(increased / decreased) capillary
permeability.

4. (a) vasodila-
tion;
(b) increased

24-7 Three reaction cascades are activated in inflammation.

1. The most common result of an injury is (a)_____,
so it makes sense that one cascade should result in blood

(b)_____. A second cascade produces

(c)_____, which cause pain and also have an
effect on the microcirculation similar to the effect of

(d)_____, which is produced by mast cells.

A third cascade activates the (e)_____ proteins, which are effective in lysing bacteria and promoting chemotaxis of leukocytes.

1. (a) bleeding;
(b)clots or
clotting;

2. Substances in the complement system that activate the
release of histamine from mast cells and neutrophil

333

(c) kinins;
(d) histamine;
(e) complement

migration are called _____.

2. anaphylatoxins

3. Activation of a substance called _____ initiates the kinin cascade.

3. Hageman factor

4. Large cells called megakaryocytes produce which formed element of blood? _____

4. platelets

5. The substance that initiates the reaction cascade leading to blood clot formation is called _____.

5. Hageman factor

24-8 Neutrophils, the major phagocytes, invade the inflamed area.

1. Fever accompanying inflammation is produced by substances called (a)_____ that are released from neutrophils. These substances affect the temperature-control centers in the (b)_____.

1. (a) pyrogens;
(b) hypo-
thalamus

2. True or False: Fever is a useless, maladaptive reaction that can only damage the host.

2. False

3. True or False: In an inflamed area, the environment becomes more acid and the acidity kills neutrophils.

3. True

4. A reduction in circulation to a tissue resulting in a lack of oxygen is called _____.

4. ischemia

24-9 Lymphocytes enter and attract the macrophages.

1. Two roles of lymphocytes in inflammation are to (a)_____ and to (b)_____.

1. (a) attract
macrophages;
(b) produce
antibodies

2. _____ make up 20-40 percent of the total white blood cell count.

2. Lymphocytes

3. True or False: Lymphocytes produce a signal ligand that attracts monocytes to an injured area and another signal ligand that keeps them there.

3. True

4. An important lymphokine produced in response to viral infection is _____.

334

4. interferon

24-10 The damaged area is finally cleaned up and repaired.

1. An early event in wound healing is the formation of new connective tissue, which is called (a)_____ tissue. The connective tissue fibers are produced by cells called (b)_____. When they become crowded, tissue cells eventually stop growing because of (c)_____.

1. (a) granulation; (b) fibroblasts; (c) contact inhibition

2. Three components of the purulent exudate (pus) in an inflamed area are (a)_____, (b)_____ _____, and (c)_____ _____.

2. (a) leukocytes; (b) tissue debris; (c) partially digested bacteria.

3. Two substances produced by eosinophils in the inflammatory response are (a)_____ and (b)_____ _____.

3. (a) histaminase; (b) fibrinolysin

24-11 A specific defense system is superimposed over inflammation.

1. Fill in the following table to show the two parts of the immune system, what type of lymphocyte is responsible for each part, and in what structure in birds these cells are processed.

Part of System	Lymphocyte	Where Processed in Birds
(a)_____	_____	_____
(b)_____	_____	_____

1. (a) humoral, B, bursa; (b) cellular, T, thymus

2. Humoral immunity operates through the synthesis of specific (a)_____. This type of immunity is primarily effective against (b)_____ and (c)_____.

2. (a) antibodies; (b) bacteria; (c) extracellular viruses

3. Lymphocytes that function in immune surveillance are _____.

3. T cells

335

24-12 Lymphocytes synthesize specific immunoglobulins.

1. Antibodies belong to a class of proteins called (a)_____

_____. A substance that elicits the

production of antibodies is called an (b)_____.

1. (a) immuno-
globulins;
(b) antigen

2. A hapten (a)_____(is / is not) immunogenic and

(b)_____(can / cannot) bind to cognate antibodies.

2. (a) is not;
(b) can

3. An antigen-antibody reaction that involves clumping of

bacteria is called a _____ reaction.

3. precipitin

4. True or False: An antiserum is a serum containing specific antigens for a certain antibody.

4. False

5. The titer of antibodies is higher in a _____ (primary / secondary) response.

5. secondary

26-13 All immunoglobulins have the same basic structure.

1. The (a)_____(light / heavy) chain of immunoglobulins determines the class to which it belongs. The idiotype of the immunoglobulin consists of the

(b)_____(constant / variable) region of

(c)_____(the H / the L / both H and L) chain(s).

1. (a) heavy;
(b) variable;
(c) both H
and L

2. The most common type of immunoglobulin is _____.

2. IgG

3. Make a simple sketch of an IgG molecule, labeling the L and H chains.

3.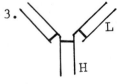

4. Circle the sites on this molecule where antigens bind.

4.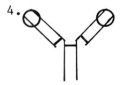

24-14 Each idiotype is made by one kind of differentiated
   lymphocyte.

1. A clone of committed lymphocytes in a postnatal mammal is

specialized for making (a)_____(a single / numerous) idiotype(s). Upon initial exposure of the cell

to an antigen, (b)_____(IgG/ IgM) immunoglobulins are produced.

1. (a) a single;
   (b) IgM

2. The theory that explains the synthesis of specific anti-

   bodies of a group of lymphocytes is called the _____

   _____ theory.

2. clonal
   selection

3. A B lymphocyte differentiates to form a _____

   cell, which produces antibodies.

3. plasma

24-15 Antibodies activate the complement cascade.

1. Blood proteins that are activated as a result of antigen-antibody reactions and that result in lysis of bacteria

   are referred to as _____.

1. complement

2. Initiation of the complement cascade in a bacterial in-

   vasion is by way of immunoglobulins (a)_____ and

   (b)_____ binding to the bacteria.

2. (a) M; (b) G

3. Among the products of the complement cascade are small

   peptides called _____ that stimulate
   general inflammatory reactions.

3. anaphylatoxins

24-16 Immunoglobulins are coded by several gene segments.

1. Humans and mice have clusters of genes for three families

   of immunoglobulins. They are for (a)_____ chains,

   (b)_____ chains, and (c)_____
   chains. Each cluster of genes contains one gene for each

   type of the (d)_____(C / V) region.

1. (a) kappa;
   (b) lambda;
   (c) all heavy;
   (d) C

24-17 The T lymphocytes become various kinds of effector cells.

1. Two effector T cells are (a)_____ and

   (b)_____.

1. (a) helper
   cells;
   (b) killer
   lymphocytes

2. Three organisms that are targets for T cells are (a)_____

   _____, (b)_____, (c)_____

337

_____. Tumor cells are recognized and

destroyed by (d) _____(T / B) cells.

2. (a) fungi;
   (b) worms;   *24-18 Some immune reactions can damage the host.*
   (c) intracellu-
   lar viruses   1. The class of immunoglobulins that are responsible for
   (d) T

                          allergic reactions are (a)_____.   The Fc portion of

                          these antibodies binds to the membrane of (b)_____
                          cells; binding to the cognate antigen results in release

                          of (c)_____.

1. (a) IgE;   2. High levels of immunoglobulin _____ are
   (b) mast;   produced in parasitic infections.
   (c) histamine

2. E   3. Two types of antigen-antibody reactions that are harmful

                          to the body are (a)_____

                          _____ and (b)_____.

3. (a) hypersen-
   sitivity
   reaction;
   (b) anaphylaxis

PRACTICE QUIZ

1. An organism that lives at the expense of another is called a:
    a. host.
    b. reservoir.
    c. parasite.
    d. symbiont.

2. The person responsible for introducing sterilization techniques in medicine
    is:
    a. Lister.
    b. Pasteur.
    c. Koch.
    d. Schwann.

3. An organism that transmits a parasite from one host to another is called a:
    a. host.
    b. vector.
    c   reservoir.
    d. pathogen.

4. A common route for the spread of contagious disease is the:
    a. unbroken skin.
    b. bloodstream .

c. respiratory system.

d. nervous system.

5. The third line of defense in a bird or mammal is:

a. the skin.

b. phagocytosis.

c. neutrophil invasion.

d. immunity.

6. Which of the following statements is not true of the virulence of a pathogen?

a. It may depend on the pathogen's ability to invade the host tissue.

b. If may depend on the pathogen's ability to produce toxic substances.

c. A pathogen may be highly virulent but relatively noninvasive.

d. *Clostridium tetani* is highly invasive and relatively nontoxic.

7. Which of the following cells make up the reticuloendothelial system?

a. macrophages

b. lymphocytes

c. erythrocytes

d. eosinophils

8. Cells in the bloodstream that are similar to the mast cells found in connective tissue are:

a. eosiniphils.

b. monocytes.

c. basophils.

d. fibroblasts.

9. Most of the visible effects of redness and edema in inflammation are due to:

a. neutrophil invasion of injured areas.

b. vasodilation and increased permeability.

c. antibody production by plasma cells.

d. local action of macrophages.

10. A substance that is involved in both the kinin cascade reaction and the blood clotting mechanism is:

a. Hageman factor.

b. fibrinogen.

c. complement.

d. platelet factor.

11. Which of the following is not considered a reaction cascade?

a. kinin activation

b. blood clotting

c. antibody formation

d. complement activation

12. _____ process antigens to aid lymphocytes in their role in antibody production.

a. Most cells

b. Basophils

c. Monocytes

d. Macrophages

13. Eosinophils:

a. do not have a role in inflammation.

b. produce fibrinolysins that dissolve blood clots.

339

c. are similar to mast cells.
d. are important phagocytes for bacteria.

14. Cells that are directly involved in the production of circulating immunoglobulins are:
a. B-cell lymphocytes.
b. T-cell lymphocytes.
c. macrophages.
d. neutrophils.

15. Immunoglobulins that are primarily bound to mast cell membranes are:
a. IgE.
b. IgM.
c. IgG.
d. IgD.

16. Which of the following correctly describes the structure of immunoglobulins?
a. one light chain and one heavy chain
b. two light chains and two heavy chains
c. one light chain and two heavy chains
d. two light chains and one heavy chain

17. _____ are cytotoxic to foreign cells.
a. T cells
b. B cells
c. Fixed macrophages
d. Neutrophils

REVIEW QUESTIONS

I. Allergic reactions are adverse reactions of the immune system. Anaphylactic shock is a severe allergic reaction. The following are some of the events involved in this reaction. Arrange them in their proper order of occurrence.

a. binding of IgE to mast cell membranes
b. movement of fluid from blood vessels to tissue spaces
c. release of histamine from mast cells
d. drop in blood pressure
e. synthesis of IgE
f. antigen-IgE combination
g. vasodilation and increased capillary permeability

Correct order: _____

II. The surface of the skin and mucous membranes is an important first line of defense against invasion by microorganisms. The skin and mucous membranes have evolved a number of features that allow them to serve this important function. Give the particular feature that is responsible for each of the following protective actions.

1. Prevention of growth of microorganisms that require a moist, nutrient-filled tissue

_____

340

2. Inhibition of growth of fungi and bacteria on the surface of the skin

_____

3. Trapping of microorganisms invading respiratory passages

_____

4. Movement of trapped microorganisms out of the respiratory tract

_____

5. Digestion of bacteria in the eyes and mouth

_____

III. Some vaccinations require more than one injection, and long-lasting immunity is only acquired after several injections. Briefly explain this phenomenon in terms of antibody titers.

_____

_____

_____

_____

IV. Explain briefly why a person who is having a skin graft or an organ transplant is given a drug that will suppress the cellular immune system and why that person temporarily becomes more susceptible to the development of cancer.

_____

_____

_____

_____

_____

V. The details of the following story are imaginary, but as a whole it is probably quite realistic. Suppose that <u>all</u> the various V regions that can be made on human antibodies are coded by specific genes and that among them are V_{L37} and V_{L498}, and $V_{H2,30}^9$ and V_{4219}, which inform light and heavy V regions, respectively. Suppose also that the four idiotypes that can be made by using these genes have the fol-

341

lowing uses. $V_{L37}V_{H219}$ form an idiotype cognate to an obscure virus that has not been seen since about 35,000 B.C. $V_{L37}V_{H2,309}$ form an idiotype that is cognate to measles virus. $V_{L498}V_{H219}$ form an idiotype that is cognate to a form of influenza that appears at least once a century somewhere in the world. $V_{L498}V_{H2,309}$ form an idiotype that is cognate to tetanus toxin.

1. Do you think the average person today has few or many lymphocytes in his or her system making the $V_{L37}V_{H219}$ combination? _____

2. The L37-H219 combination is apparently useless today, so why aren't the genes that inform these regions lost from the human genome?

    _____

    _____

3. An obscure tribe of South American Indians has, in fact, lost the gene for V_{L37} by accident. They have recently become hosts to a group of American missionaries. Predict at least one thing that is likely to happen to these Indians.

    _____

    _____

4. Tetanus toxoid is an inactivated tetanus toxin that is immunogenic but not toxic. Outline what happens when a person is given an injection of this toxoid for the first time.

    _____

    _____

    _____

    _____

ANSWERS TO CHAPTER EXERCISES

Practice Quiz

1.	c	7.	a	13.	b
2.	a	8.	c	14.	a
3.	b	9.	b	15.	a
4.	c	10.	a	16.	b
5.	d	11.	c	17.	a
6.	d	12.	d		

I. e, a, f, c, g, b, d, h

II. 1. dry, dead, horny cells
    2. fatty acid secretion of sebaceous glands
    3. mucus
    4. ciliated epithelium
    5. lysozyme secretion

III. The first injection elicits a primary response with a rapid rise, then a drop, in antibody titer. The second injection elicits a secondary response with a higher titer that is more long-lasting

IV. T cells are the cells that kill foreign cells, as in tissue grafts or organ transplants, through cell-mediated immunity. Suppressing these allows a graft or transplant to be better accepted. The T cells also seek out and destroy cancer cells that are recognized as foreign. Suppressing T cells will enhance their development.

V. 1. very few

    2. The gene for V_{L39} is required every generation to fight measles, and the V_{H219} gene is needed frequently to fight influenza, so natural selection (if nothing else) keeps them in the human genome.

    3. They can't make antibodies against measles virus, so there is a good chance that they will succumb to a measles epidemic. And notice that they can't be immunized against this disease.

    4. The toxoid will be processed (somehow) by macrophages and B lymphocytes that are making immunoglobulins with the L498-H2,309 idiotype. These lymphocytes will be stimulated to start proliferating, and some of them will become plasma cells that will make large amounts of antibody, primarily IgM, bearing the antitetanus idiotype.

343

Chapter 25

NERVOUS SYSTEM I: SENSORY RECEPTORS

WHAT'S IN THIS CHAPTER

Chapter 25 considers the classification and function of sensory receptors. Early sections in the chapter explain the general mechanisms whereby receptors receive sensory stimuli, respond via formation of the generator potential or receptor potential, and amplify and encode stimuli. Increased stimulus strength is represented in a neuron as an increased frequency of impulses.

The five classes of general sense receptors representing five sensory modalities are introduced, and each is then treated individually with specific examples and explanations of mechanisms. General sense receptors which are covered are chemoreceptors that respond to particular chemicals, such as taste and smell receptors, and mechanoreceptors stimulated by mechanical distortion.

Special sense organs are covered also. These include the inner ear receptors for equilibrium and hearing, which respond to mechanical distortion of hair cells, and the retina, which consists of photoreceptors that respond to light via a change in photopigments. Information on the special sensory receptors in olfactory epithelium and taste buds is provided in the section on chemoreception. Two exercises are included to help you apply some of this information.

By the end of the chapter you should be able to:

1. Explain what is meant by receptor encoding, amplification, transduction, and generator potential.

2. List the two types of receptors on the basis of whether or not they adapt to constant stimulation.

3. Explain the mechanism of receptor adaptation and what is meant by differential threshold.

4. Classify receptors according to whether they respond to internal or external stimuli.

5. Classify receptors according to the five sense modalities.

6. List the two major types of chemoreceptor exteroceptors found in animals and

the kinds of molecules that stimulate them.

7. List the four basic qualities of taste and give the functional significance of each.

8. Cite experiments that have shed light on the interaction between stimulus molecules and receptor proteins.

9. Explain the concept primary odors and chemoreceptor proteins.

10. Explain what is meant by a mechanoreceptor and list two mechanoreceptors found in skin and one found in muscle.

11. Define statocyst, lateral line organ, and labyrinth apparatus; explain how hair cells function in these receptors.

12. Diagram the structure of the mammalian ear.

13. Trace the path of events in the mammalian ear from the reception of sound waves in the external ear to the stimulation of the receptor cells in the inner ear, giving the function of all parts.

14. List some temperature receptors in mammals and explain the functional significance of thermoreceptors in the pits of pit vipers.

15. Explain what is meant by a photopigment and how it functions in photo-reception.

16. Define rhabdomeric and ciliary photoreceptors and list the two types of ciliary photoreceptors in the human eye.

17. Diagram the structure of the vertebrate eye and explain the parts that are involved in accommodation.

WHAT YOU SHOULD ALREADY KNOW

As background material for this chapter, you should know the terms relating to membrane potentials and changes in membrane potentials, including action potential. You should know also the components of a reflex arc and what is meant by temporal summation (Chapter 21).

Pre-Test

1. The difference in electrical potential across a non-stimulated plasma membrane is called the (a)_____ _____. A decrease in amplitude of that potential difference is called a (b)_____ (depolarization / hyperpolarization).

1. (a) resting potential; (b) depolari-

2. (a)_____ and (b)_____ ions are involved in the generation of the potential difference across the membrane.

345

zation.

2. (a) Na$^+$;

(b) K$^+$

3. action
potential

4. (a) receptor;
(b) sensory
neuron; (c) in-
terneuron; (d)
motor neuron;
(e) effector

5. (a) Temporal
(b) receptor

3. The total electrical change associated with the passage of an impulse in an axon is called the _____ _____.

4. In order, beginning with the receptors, the components of a reflex arc are, (a)_____, (b)_____ _____, (c)_____, (d)_____ _____, and (e)_____.

5. (a)_____(Temporal / Spatial) summation refers to the adding together of stimuli that occur at about the same time. If this occurred in a sensory neuron, where would the stimuli be initiated? (b)_____

GUIDED REVIEW OF THE CHAPTER

25-1 Receptors transduce, encode, and amplify.

1. The "language" of the nervous system takes the form of (a)_____ energy. The fact that a sensory receptor can translate an external form of energy into the latter makes it a (b)_____.

1. (a) electro-
chemical;
(b) transducer

2. As the intensity of a stimulus increases, the amplitude of the generator potential (a)_____(increases / decreases). As the amplitude of the generator potential increases, the (b)_____ of nerve impulses in the sensory neuron increases.

2. (a) increases;
(b) frequency

25-2 Receptors respond primarily to changes in the environment.

1. An animal may cease to be aware of a stimulus that is constantly applied. Such a phenomenon is due to receptor (a)_____. A (b)_____ receptor sends impulses at a decreasing rate with prolonged application of a stimulus, whereas one that continues to

generate action potentials with prolonged stimulation is

called (c)_____.

1. (a) adaptation;
   (b) phasic;
   (c) tonic

2. The change in intensity of stimulus that can be detected

   as a new stimulus by a receptor is known as the (a)_____

   _____. The law that defines this

   is called (b)_____ law.

2. (a) differen-
   tial threshold;
   (b) Weber's

25-3 There are at least five classes of receptors.

1. The five classes of receptors in animals, based on mo-

   dality, are (a)_____, (b)_____

   _____, (c)_____

   _____, (d)_____, and

   (e)_____.

1. (a) chemorecep-
   tors; (b) pho-
   toreceptors;
   (c) thermore-
   ceptors; (d)
   mechanorecep-
   tors; (e) elec-
   troreceptors

2. List three classes of receptors based on location, and
   give an example of each.

   (a)_____   _____

   (b)_____   _____

   (c)_____   _____

2. (a) interocep-
   tor, osmorecep-
   tors; (b) ex-
   teroceptor,
   rods and cones;
   (c) propriocep-
   tor, stretch
   receptors in
   muscle

3. Proprioceptors all belong to which class of receptor

   according to modality? _____

25-4 Chemoreceptors are basic and widely distributed.

1. Match each of the following external chemoreceptors with
   the appropriate statement.

3. mechanoreceptor

                              smell
                              taste

   (a) Detects general classes of molecules that bind to

       specific receptor proteins _____

   (b) Detects specific shapes of all kinds of molecules

       _____

   (c) Olfactory receptor _____

347

(d) Gustatory receptor _____

1. (a) taste;
   (b) smell;
   (c) smell;
   (d) taste

2. In air-breathing animals, the sensation of (a)_____ (tasting / smelling) involves a component of (b)_____ _____(tasting / smelling). Animals that have taste receptors all over the surface of their body are (c)_____.

2. (a) tasting;
   (b) smelling;
   (c) fish

3. Chemical signal ligands from animals of the same species that induce a certain behavior pattern in the animal receiving the ligand are called _____.

3. pheromones

4. List the four general receptors in animals and give the functional significance of the sensation.

   (a)_____   _____

   (b)_____   _____

   (c)_____   _____

   (d)_____   _____

4. (a) salty, ion concentration;
   (b) sweet, energy source;
   (c) bitter, avoidance of poisonous compounds; (d) sour, avoidance of high-acidity substances

5. Taste buds in mammals are located in specific structures on the tongue called (a)_____. Each of these structures contains (b)_____(few / many) taste buds. In order for a substance to be tasted, the substance must be (c)_____.

5. (a) papillae;
   (b) many;
   (c) in solution

25-5 *Mechanoreceptors respond to certain tensions and pressures.*

1. A touch receptor located in the deeper layers of the skin is the (a)_____. Proprioceptors that respond to stretch placed on muscle fibers are (b)_____.

1. (a) Pacinian corpuscle; (b) muscle spindles

2. True or False: Ordinary skeletal muscle fibers are called intrafusal fibers, whereas those of muscle spindles are called extrafusal fibers.

2. False

3. A receptor involved in the knee-jerk response is the (a)_____. When the patellar tendon is tapped, the intrafusal receptors of the receptor

(b)_____(stretch / relax).

3. (a) muscle
   spindle;
   (b) stretch

4. contract

4. Gamma fiber stimulation of intrafusal fibers makes them

_____(contract / relax).

25-6 Many mechanoreceptors employ hair cells.

1. Match each hair-cell receptor with the particular animal group in which it is found.

> lateral line organ
> labyrinth apparatus
> statocyst

(a) crustaceans _____

(b) mammals _____

(c) fish and amphibians _____

1. (a) statocyst;
   (b) labyrinth
   apparatus; (c)
   lateral line
   organ

2. In a statocyst receptor, the position of the _____ tells the animal how to orient itself.

2. statolith

3. Hair cells of the labyrinth apparatus detect two kinds of

forces: (a)_____ and

(b)_____. Structures in this apparatus that are comparable to statoliths are

called (c)_____ and they consist of (d)_____

_____.

3. (a) the pull of
   gravity; (b)
   acceleration
   of movement;
   (c) otoliths;
   (d) calcium
   carbonate

25-7 Hair cells in the ear detect sound vibrations.

1. Name the structures that are indicated in the following diagram. All are involved in transmitting vibrations in air to vibrations in fluid in the inner ear.

349

(a)_____   (b)_____

(c)_____   (d)_____

(e)_____   (f)_____

1. (a) tympanic
   membrane; (b)
   middle ear; (c)
   malleus or ham-
   mer; (d) incus
   or anvil; (e)
   stapes or stir-
   rup; (f) oval
   window

2. Most of the pressure applied to the oval window in the

   form of vibrations is tranmitted to the (a)_____

   _____, one of the two membranes of the receptor for

   hearing called the (b)_____ of _____.
   The part of the membrane which vibrates depends on what

   characteristic of sound? (c)_____

2. (a) basilar
   membrane; (b)
   organ of Corti;
   (c) pitch or
   frequency

25-8 Some thermoreceptors detect infrared radiation.

1. Thermoreceptors in snakes, particularly pit vipers, which
   help them locate prey by way of small differences in

   temperature, are the _____.

1. infrared
   detectors

25-9 The sensation of pain is complex and still mysterious.

1. Internal analgesics produced by the brain are called

   _____.

1. endorphins

2. True or False: Bradykinin, released when tissue is
   damaged, is one agent that produces the sensation of pain.

2. True

*25-10 Light is absorbed by photopigments in specialized mem-
        branes.*

1. Organic molecules that undergo a change when they absorb

   light are called (a)_____. In the

   retina, this change ultimately results in a (b)_____

   _____.

1. (a) photopig-
   ments; (b)
   nerve impulse

2. Rhabdomeric type photoreceptors are found in what groups

   of animals? _____

2. molluscs and
   arthropods

3. The two ciliary photoreceptors found in the human eye are

   (a)_____ and (b)_____. Which of these

   are receptors for color vision? _____

3. (a) rods;
   (b) cones;
   (c) cones

4. chromatophore

5. True

6. False

4. The component of a photopigment that actually absorbs the

   light is the _____.

5. True or False: Absorption of light by rhodopsin changes retinal to all-trans-retinal.

6. True or False: The form of retinal that recombines with opsin is the all-trans form.

25-11 The vertebrate eye focuses light on a layer of receptor cells.

1. Label the structures indicated in the following diagram of the vertebrate eyeball.

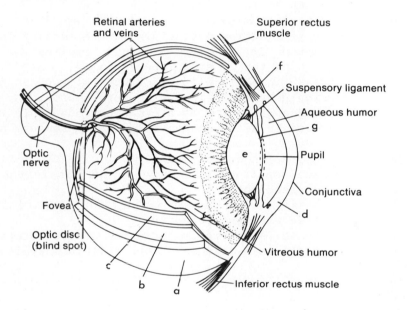

(a)_____   (b)_____

(c)_____   (d)_____

(e)_____   (f)_____

(g)_____

1. (a) sclera;
   (b) choroid;
   (c) retina;
   (d) cornea;
   (e) lens; (f) ciliary body;
   (g) iris

2. (a) cornea;
   (b) lens

2. The two structures that bend light rays to focus an image

   on the retina are the (a)_____ and the

   (b)_____.

351

PRACTICE QUIZ

1. The action of a sensory receptor in converting one form of energy into electrochemical changes of neurons is called:
   a. amplification.
   b. encoding.
   c. transduction.
   d. interpretation.

2. Which of the following statements is not true of the generator potential?
   a. It occurs in sensory receptors.
   b. It is a change in membrane potential.
   c. Its amplitude increases with stimulus strength.
   d. It will increase in phasic receptors with prolonged stimulation.

3. Which of the following relationships of stimuli, receptors, and sensory neurons is not stated accurately?
   a. An increase in stimulus strength applied to a receptor lowers the frequency of action potentials in the sensory neuron.
   b. An increase in stimulus strength applied to a receptor increases the amplitude of the generator potential.
   c. A decrease in the amplitude of generator potential decreases the frequency of action potentials in the sensory neuron.
   d. Prolonged application of a stimulus to a tonic receptor does not result in a decrease in action potentials in the sensory neuron.

4. Receptor adaptation would result in:
   a. decreased amplitude of action potentials in the sensory neuron associated with the receptor.
   b. a decrease in frequency of action potentials in the sensory neuron associated with the receptor.
   c. an increase in generator potential of the receptor.
   d. an increase in awareness of the stimulus applied to the receptor.

5. Which of the following receptors is sensitive to mechanical changes?
   a. rod
   b. end-bulb of Kraus
   c. Ruffini ending
   d. muscle spindle

6. In _____ a chemical reaction occurs between application of a stimulus to the receptor and the electrochemical events in the neurons.
   a. muscle spindles
   b. thermoreceptors
   c. rods and cones
   d. Pacinian corpuscles

7. Which of the following is not a taste sensation?
   a. pepperminty
   b. sweet
   c. sour
   d. salty

8. The Weber fraction for the sense of weight is 1/50, so you could just tell the difference between weights of:
   a. 500 and 505 grams.
   b. 290 and 300 grams.

352

c. 1,000 and 1,020 grams.

d. 250 and 270 grams.

9. Meissner's corpuscles are _____ receptors.

a. heat

b. cold

c. pain

d. touch

10. Muscle spindles:

a. are stimulated when a muscle shortens.

b. are innervated by gamma motor neurons.

c. contain both intrafusal and extrafusal fibers, which contract when a muscle is stretched.

d. relax when a tendon is tapped in the knee-jerk reflex.

11. Which of the following receptors is(are) <u>not</u> concerned with balance?

a. semicircular canals

b. vestibular apparatus

c. organ of Corti

d. lateral line organ

12. Mineral granules such as calcium phosphate are a functional part of all the following receptors except the:

a. organ of Corti.

b. labyrinth apparatus.

c. statocysts.

d. vestibular apparatus.

13. The _____ would <u>not</u> be seen in a cross section through the cochlea.

a. organ of Corti

b. oval window

c. tympanic canal

d. vestibular canal

14. Receptors on the head of pit vipers that help them locate prey are:

a. mechanoreceptors.

b. pain receptors.

c. touch receptors.

d. thermoreceptors.

15. In the retina of the human eye:

a. there are both rhabdomeric and ciliary receptors.

b. rods are responsible for color vision and cones for vision in dim light.

c. there is one layer of cells.

d. the cells whose fibers make up the optic nerve are ganglion cells.

16. The vascular coat of the eyeball is the:

a. retina.

b. sclera.

c. choroid.

d. cornea.

REVIEW QUESTIONS

I. An increase in intensity of a sensation is ultimately determined at the level of interpretation, the brain. This, however, depends on activity that begins with a sensory receptor. Using a touch receptor, explain the series of changes that connect an increase in stimulus intensity to an increase in sensation, with the generator potential and action potentials in the sensory neuron in between.

_____

_____

_____

_____

II. A number of intermediate events take place between the formation of sound waves in the air and the generation of nerve impulses in the auditory nerve fibers connected to the inner ear. List in order the structures that undergo vibrations before the ultimate stimulation of receptor cells.

_____

_____

III. Relate the following terms to one another: hair cell, organ of Corti, basilar membrane, mechanoreceptor, and exteroceptor.

_____

_____

_____

_____

_____

IV. Some receptors adapt to the continuous application of a stimulus. An example of this is the sensation of cold you get when you jump into a body of cold water, only to find that the water feels warmer in minutes. Obviously, you do not heat up the water by being in it. Using the following guide words, give a reasonable explanation, using concepts you have learned in this chapter: stimulus, generator potential, action potential, and intensity of sensation.

_____

_____

_____

_____

V. Match each specific receptor with one of the following five classifications of receptors.

     a. chemoreceptor   d. mechanoreceptor
     b. photoreceptor   e. electroreceptor
     c. thermoreceptor

_____   1. all proprioceptors

_____   2. receptor for pheromones

_____   3. rods and cones

_____   4. gustatory receptors

_____   5. camphoric receptor

_____   6. Pacinian corpuscle

_____   7. lateral line organ

_____   8. rhabdomeric receptor

_____   9. muscle spindle

_____ 10. Meissner's corpuscles

_____ 11. Kraus end bulb

_____ 12. Ruffini ending

ANSWERS TO CHAPTER EXERCISES

Practice Quiz

1. c	5. d	9. d	13. b
2. d	6. c	10. b	14. d
3. a	7. a	11. c	15. d
4. b	8. c	12. a	16. c

Review Questions

I. An increase in intensity of the touch stimulus brings about an increase in the amplitude of the generator potential. An increase in the amplitude of the generator potential brings about an increase in the frequency of action potentials in the sensory neuron. An increase in the frequency of action potentials brings about an increase in sensation.

II. Tympanum, middle ear bones, oval window membrane, fluid in inner ear, basilar membrane.

III. The organ of Corti is the receptor for hearing. The receptor cells are hair cells located on the basilar membrane along with support cells. The receptor cells are mechanoreceptors in that they respond to mechanical distortion, and they are exteroreceptors because they respond to stimuli from the external environment.

IV. With the constant application of a <u>stimulus</u>, the <u>generator potential</u> of the receptor decreases; this brings about a decrease in frequency of <u>action potentials</u>, which reduces the <u>intensity of sensation</u>.

V. 1. d   4. a   7. d   10. d
    2. a   5. a   8. b   11. c
    3. b   6. d   9. d   12. c

Chapter 26

NERVOUS SYSTEM II: THE BRAIN AND ITS ACTIVITIES

WHAT'S IN THIS CHAPTER

This chapter provides a comprehensive introduction to the functional anatomy of the brain and its role in integrating the body's activities.   Information on the development of the vertebrate brain from the three primary regions--prosencephalon, mesencephalon, and rhombencephalon--provides a basis for study of adult structures. The parts of the brain are covered in order from the lower brainstem or medulla, to the cerebellum, diencephalon, and finally the cerebrum.   The role of the cerebrum in the reception of sensory informtion, the generation of motor information, and the integration of these activities precedes coverage of several functional neural systems.   The latter include the system for handling somesthetic sensations, such as touch and temperature; analysis of visual information between the retina and visual cortex; localization of certain functions in one or the other cerebral hemisphere and information gained from "split-brain" experiments; and the limbic system and its role in emotional behavior.   Emphasis is also placed on the role of chemicals in both the normal and abnormal functions of the brain, such as learning and behavioral disorders.

By the end of this chapter you should be able to:

1. List the five major divisions of the brain, specify which brain parts belong to each division, and give the general function of each part.

2. Define and give the composition of gray matter and white matter, and discuss the function and composition of ascending and descending tracts.

3. Discuss the significance of the crossing over of motor and sensory fiber tracts.

4. List and give the function of components of the lower brain stem, including the reticular activating system.

5. Describe the evolution of the cerebral hemispheres in terms of paleocortex, archicortex, corpus striatum, neoccrtex, and rhinencephalon.

6. Describe the surface of the cerebral hemispheres with respect to the lobes, and define <u>sulcus</u>, <u>gyrus</u>, and <u>fissure</u>.   List the sensory and/or motor functions of the lobes.

7. Define <u>somesthetic senses</u> and describe the relaying of somesthetic information from the receptors through ascending pathways to the cerebral cortex.

8. Discuss points in the visual system where visual information is analyzed and the mechanisms involved in this analysis.

9. Explain what is meant by "split-brain" experiments and what useful information has been derived from such experimentation.

10. Explain what is meant by the limbic system, what its major components are, and what behavioral activities are associated with it.

11. Name some neurotransmitters of the CNS, areas where they serve as transmitters, and conditions that result from deficiencies or defects in their metabolism.

12. Name some neuropeptides that may serve as CNS transmitters.

13. Explain what is meant by the <u>internal opiate</u>, and give examples and actions.

14. Explain the differences between long-term and short-term neural changes, and suggest mechanisms that may be involved.

WHAT YOU SHOULD ALREADY KNOW

Basic terminology associated with the structure and function of neural tissue is essential to an understanding of this chapter. You should be thoroughly familiar with the contents of Chapter 25. You should know the anatomical and functional aspects of motor and sensory activities of the nervous system, as well as the role of neurotransmitters. You should also know the general structure of the vertebrate eye.

Pre-Test

1. A neuron consists of a soma (cell body) portion located in the (a)_____ (ganglia / nuclei) in the CNS and in the (b)_____ (ganglia / nuclei) in the PNS. The fiber portion of the neuron is located in (c)_____ in the PNS and in (d)_____ in the CNS.

1. (a) nuclei; (b) ganglia; (c) nerves; (d) nerve tracts or fiber tracts

2. The area where the axon ending of one neuron forms a functional connection with the soma of another is called a (a)_____. A message crosses this junction in the form of a (b)_____.

2. (a) synapse; (b) chemical ligand; (neuro-

3. Neurotransmitters in the PNS are (a)_____ and (b)_____.

transmitter)

3. (a) acetylcho-
line; (b) no-
repinephrine

4. Information is propagated from one place to another via nerve fibers in the nervous system in the form of

(a)_____. Messages on their

way to the brain are referred to as (b)_____,

whereas those on their way from the brain are referred to

as (c)_____.

4. (a) action po-
tentials; (b)
sensory or
afferent; (c)
motor or
efferent

5. Give the specific location of each of the following components of a reflex arc.

(a) receptor _____

(b) peripheral fiber of sensory neuron _____

(c) cell body of sensory neuron _____

(d) central fiber portion of sensory neuron _____

(e) cell body of interneuron _____

_____

(f) axon of interneuron _____

(g) cell body of motor neuron _____

(h) axon of motor neuron _____

5. (a) peripheral
tissues; (b)
nerve; (c)
ganglion; (d)
CNS; (e) Nu-
cleus and basal
ganglia; (f)
fiber tract;
(g) nucleus;
(h) nerve

6. List the three layers of the retina of the eye, and give the significance of each.

(a)_____   _____

(b)_____   _____

(c)_____   _____

6. (a) rods and
cones, recep-
tors; (b) in-
termediate
cells, connect
to ganglion
cells; (c)
ganglion cells,
cell bodies of
neurons of
optic nerve

7. Control over cardiac and smooth muscle and glands is by

way of the (a)_____ portion of the nervous system. The component of the latter that is dominant during an emergency or "fight, fright and flight" response

is the (b)_____ portion.

359

7. (a) autonomic;
   (b) sympathetic

GUIDED REVIEW OF THE CHAPTER

26-1 The vertebrate brain develops from a tube.

1. Using the major divisions of the brain given below, match each of the following specific brain parts with the division to which it belongs.

   1. telencephalon
   2. diencephalon
   3. mesencephalon
   4. metencephalon
   5. myelencephalon

   (a) medulla _____   (e) hypothalamus _____

   (b) cerebral hemisphere _____   (f) pituitary _____

   (c) pons _____   (g) pineal _____

   (d) thalamus _____   (h) cerebellum _____

1. (a) 5, (b) 1;
   (c) 4; (d) 2;
   (e) 2; (f) 2;
   (g) 2; (h) 4

2. Spaces within the brain that contain cerebrospinal fluid are the (a)_____. If fluid accumulates here, the condition is called (b)_____.

2. (a) ventricles;
   (b) hydro-
   cephalus

3. The three connective tissue meninges of the CNS in order, beginning with the innermost layer, are (a)_____, (b)_____, and (c)_____.

3. (a) pia; (b) arachnoid;
   (c) dura

4. True or False: The rhombencephalon is the forebrain.

4. False

5. The stem "cephalo-" refers to the _____.

5. head

26-2 Information is transmitted primarily up and down the neuraxis.

1. The substance of the CNS consists of gray matter and white matter. Identify each of the following parts or characteristics as gray (G) or white (W) matter.

   (a) fiber tracts _____   (d) unmyelinated axons _____

   (b) cell bodies _____   (e) commissure _____

   (c) myelinated axons _____

1. (a) W; (b) G;
   (c) W; (d) G;
   (e) W

2. Information ascends toward and descends from the brain in nerve fibers contained in anatomical units called _____ _____.

2. nerve tracts

3. A nerve tract in the CNS that connects the cerebral cortex with the spinal cord is called a _____ tract.

3. corticospinal

4. A type of tract that connects the right and left cerebral hemispheres is called a (a)_____. A specific example of such a tract is the (b)_____ _____.

4. (a) commissure;
   (b) corpus
   callosum

5. True or False: The CNS functions as two isolated halves.

5. False

26-3 The lower brainstem contains major control and relay centers.

1. Match each particular function or characteristic with the proper lower brainstem part.

    1. medulla oblongata
    2. reticular formation
    3. cerebellum
    4. pons
    5. superior colliculi
    6. inferior colliculi

(a) Contains a part, the RAS, that is responsible for maintaining an alert state _____

(b) Coordinates skeletal muscle activity _____

(c) Seven cranial nerves emerge from this region _____

(d) A component may serve as a "filter" for incoming sensory stimuli _____

(e) Contains the center for respiration and cardiac control _____

(f) A commissural tract that contains centers for respiration, facial muscle contractions, and feeding

_____

(g) Center for vision reflexes _____

(h) Auditory centers located here _____

26-4 *The diencephalon is primarily the thalamus and hypo-thalamus.*

1. The part of the diencephalon that contains important relay

   centers for incoming sensory signals is the (a)_____

   _____. The part that contains important centers which
   control feeding, eating, reproductive activities, and

   emotions is the (b)_____. The pineal body

   protrudes from the (c)_____.

26-5 *The cerebrum exerts control over many lower brain centers.*

1. The ability of an animal to integrate large amounts of
   information (including visual information, proprioception
   and movement) developed with the evolution of a large

   (a)_____. The (b)_____
   were the first group of animals with a neocortex.

2. The hippocampus of the mammalian brain came from the

   (a)_____(paleocortex / archicortex

   / corpus striatum). It is a part of the (b)_____

   _____(neocortex / basal ganglia / rhinencephalon).

3. The two nuclei in the corpus striatum are (a)_____

   and (b)_____.

4. Match the area of the cerebral cortex with the appropriate
   lobe.

   1. frontal lobe
   2. parietal lobe
   3. temporal lobe
   4. occiptal lobe

   (a) somesthetic area _____   (c) vision area _____

   (b) motor area _____   (d) auditory area _____

26-6 *Somesthetic information is carried through two major pathways.*

1. The location of the somesthetic area of the cortex is the

(a)_____(precentral / postcentral) gyrus. The greater the sensitivity of a part of the body, the

(b)_____(greater / less) the area of the cortex associated with that part.

1. (a) post-
central;
(b) greater

2. Ascending spinal pathways that convey information about touch, pain, and temperature are the (a)_____

_____ and (b)_____

_____ pathways. The fibers in these tracts

are (c)_____(crossed / uncrossed).

2. (a) lateral
spinothalamic;
(b) ventral
spinothalamic;
(c) crossed

26-7 Information from the visual receptors is partially analyzed in the retina.

1. Visual information is first analyzed in the (a)_____

_____(retina / optic nerve / brain). Luminosity units in the intermediate layer of the retina are

assumed to get their information from (b)_____(rods / cones), whereas chromaticity units receive information

from (c)_____(rods / cones).

1. (a) retina; (b)
rods; (c) cones

26-8 Vision depends on a hierarchy of cells in the visual cortex.

1. To what part of the thalamus do fibers of optic nerves go?

(a)_____. An area where fibers from the two optic nerves cross over is

called the (b)_____. The crossing over enables information from the left half of

each retina to be recorded in the (c)_____(left / right) of the visual cortex.

1. (a) lateral
geniculate
body; (b) optic
chiasma;
(c) left

2. The three areas where visual processing occurs are the

(a)_____, (b)_____

_____, and (c)_____.

2. (a) retina;
(b) lateral
geniculate
body; (c)
visual cortex

3. According to investigations by Hubel and Wiesel, there are cells in the visual cortex that are stimulated by certain features of a structure moving before the eye. List these cell types and the features that stimulate them.

(a)_____   _____

363

(b)_____ _____

(c)_____ _____

3. (a) simple,
   each line; (b)
   complex, line
   movement; (c)
   hypercomplex,
   corners

26-9 Some functions are lateralized in the human cerebrum.

1. Split-brain experiments have shown that, in humans, mani-
   pulospatial activities are controlled by the (a)_____
   (right / left) cerebral hemisphere, whereas speech is controlled by the (b)_____(right / left).

1. (a) right;
   (b) left

2. Broca's area is located in the (a)_____(right /
   left) cerebral hemisphere. Damage to this area produces
   (b)_____.

2. (a) left; (b)
   motor speech
   disorders

3. Wernicke's area is located in the (a)_____(right /
   left) motor cerebral hemisphere. Damage to this area
   produces problems with (b)_____.

3. (a) left;
   (b) speech
   comprehension

26-10 The limbic system is associated with emotional behavior.

1. Three components of the limbic system are (a)_____
   _____, (b)_____, and (c)_____
   _____. The limbic system is associated with the
   emotions of (d)_____, (e)_____,
   and (f)_____.

1. (a)-(c) fornix,
   hippocampus,
   thalamus, hypo-
   thalamus, amyg-
   dala, or cingu-
   late gyrus;
   (d) rage; (e)
   fear; (f)
   sexuality

2. Psychosurgery performed to treat patients suffering from
   depression or anxiety involves cutting through the
   _____ region of the cerebrum.

2. prefrontal

*26-11 Many transmitters are used for different pathways and
   functions.*

1. The two major classes of central nervous system neurotransmitters are (a)_____ and (b)_____
   _____. These two have in common a positively
   charged (c)_____. The two possible effects
   of the neurotransmitter are (d)_____ and
   (e)_____.

1. (a) monamines;
(b) amino
acids; (c)
nitrogen; (d)
excitatory;
(e) inhibitory

2. Match each statement with the proper transmitter.

  1. GABA
  2. catechdamine
  3. serotonin
  4. dopamine

  (a) Implicated in dreaming and maintaining an arousal

  state _____

  (b) Parkinson's disease results from a deficiency of this

  _____

  (c) Implicated in temperature regulation _____

  (d) Secreted by cerebellar Purkinje neurons _____

  (e) Implicated in sleep onset _____

  (f) Schizophrenia may result from a problem with

  metabolism of this _____

2. (a) 2; (b) 4;
(c) 3; (d) 1;
(e) 3; (f) 4

26-12 Many peptides have roles in the nervous system.

  1. List three neuropeptides, other than internal opiates,
  that are possible neurotransmitters. (a)_____
  _____, (b)_____, and
  (c)_____.

1. (a) angioten-
sin II; (b)
vasopressin;
(c) cholecysto-
kinin

26-13 Some neuropeptides are internal opiates.

  1. Three neuropeptides that appear to serve as natural internal painkillers are (a)_____. (b)_____
  _____, and (c)_____.

1. (a) enkepha-
lins; (b) beta-
endorphin; (c)
neurotensin

  2. True or False: Pro-ACTH includes both ACTH and MSH.

2. True

  3. True or False: Excesses of ACTH and glucocorticoids
  produce schizophrenic-like symptons.

3. True

365

26-14 Longer-term neural changes may be effected by cyclic nucleotides.

1. Ion-channel protein receptors are responsible for (a)_____(long / short)-term effects of a neurotransmitter on membrane potentials. Cyclic nucleotides may be involved in (b)_____(long / short)-term effects.

1. (a) short;
   (b) long

PRACTICE QUIZ

1. The hindbrain is called the:
   a. prosencephalon.
   b. mesencephalon.
   c. rhombencephalon.
   d. rhinencephalon.

2. The thalamus and hypothalamus belong to which division of the brain?
   a. metencephalon
   b. diencephalon
   c. telencephhalon
   d. myelencephalon

3. The lateral ventricles:
   a. contain cerebrospinal fluid.
   b. are located in the diencephalon.
   c. are within the cerebellar hemispheres.
   d. are also called the third and fourth ventricles.

4. Sensory and motor impulses get to and from the brain by way of what part of the spinal cord?
   a. gray matter
   b. white matter
   c. ganglia
   d. nuclei

5. Important brain centers for cardiac control, vasomotion, and respiratory control are located in the:
   a. thalamus.
   b. basal ganglia.
   c. cerebellum.
   d. medulla oblongata.

6. The superior colliculi are concerned with _____ reflexes.
   a. auditory
   b. visual
   c. olfactory
   d. proprioceptive

7. The part of the brain through which most sensory impulses are relayed is the:
   a. cerebellum.
   b. pons.
   c. thalamus.
   d. caudate nucleus.

8. The first group of animals in which a neocortex appeared were the:
   a. reptiles.
   b. amphibians.
   c. birds.
   d. mammals.

9. An "island" of gray matter that is embedded within the white matter of the cerebrum and is concerned with motor functions contains the:
   a. thalamus.
   b. cerebral cortex.
   c. basal ganglia.
   d. limbic system.

10. The occipital lobe of the cerebrum is where the sensation of _____ is registered and interpreted.
    a. gustation
    b. olfaction
    c. hearing
    d. vision

11. Somesthetic sensations:
    a. are sensations such as olfaction and vision.
    b. from the right side of the body are represented on the right cerebral hemisphere.
    c. are represented on the postcentral gyrus.
    d. make synaptic connections in the hypothalamus.

12. Primary visual analysis occurs first in the:
    a. lateral geniculate body.
    b. retina.
    c. visual cortex.
    d. superior colliculus.

13. The cell body portion of neurons whose axons make up the optic nerve are located in the:
    a. ganglion layer of the retina.
    b. superior colliculus.
    c. lateral geniculate body.
    d. intermediate cells of the retina.

14. The area of the cerebral cortex concerned with articulating spoken words is:
    a. Wernicke's area.
    b. located on the right cerebral hemisphere.
    c. Broca's area.
    d. the primary motor area on the frontal lobe.

15. The limbic system:
    a. is concerned with control over motor functions.
    b. is made up of areas including the caudate and lenticular nuclei.
    c. contains nuclei for the vagus nerve.
    d. includes the fornix, hippocampus, and hypothalamus.

367

16. An inhibitory CNS neurotransmitter that is released from Purkinje neuron axon endings is:
    a. GABA.
    b. serotonin.
    c. dopamine.
    d. norepinephrine.

17. A CNS neurotransmitter that is also important in the peripheral autonomic nervous system is:
    a. serotonin.
    b. norepinephrine.
    c. GABA.
    d. dopamine.

18. A CNS transmitter whose imbalance is associated with schizophrenia and Parkinson's disease is:
    a. serotonin.
    b. norepinephrine.
    c. GABA.
    d. dopamine.

19. A neuropeptide that may be a CNS neurotransmitter is:
    a. GABA.
    b. dopamine.
    c. serotonin.
    d. cholecystokinin.

20. Which of the following substances secreted by CNS neurons binds to the same receptor sites as opiates?
    a. beta-endorphin
    b. cholecystokinin
    c. serotonin
    d. vasopressin

REVIEW QUESTIONS

I. All parts of the brain are important in normal sensory, motor, and integration functions. Damage to any part will be manifested in some abnormality in behavior of motor and/or sensory functions. Based on the information provided in this chapter, match the following disturbances with the particular brain part or parts whose damage might result in the disability.

a. Broca's area   h. corpus striatum
b. medulla oblongata   i. Wernicke's area
c. Purkinje neurons   j. corpus callosum
d. precentral gyrus   k. postcentral gyrus
e. occipital lobe   l. hypothalamus
f. thalamus   m. superior colliculus
g. lateral geniculate body of thalamus   n. cerebellar nuclei

_____ 1. Disturbances in emotional, sexual, and feeding behavior

_____ 2. Loss of somesthetic sensations

_____ 3. Loss of control of skeletal muscle activity

_____ 4. Disturbances in vision or visual reflexes

_____ 5. Inability to articulate words

_____ 6. Inability to initiate voluntary movements

_____ 7. The right cerebral "doesn't know" what the left cerebral hemisphere is doing

_____ 8. Major parasympathetic irregularities in the viscera

_____ 9. Inability to comprehend words

II.   A number of anatomical components of the nervous system are involved in transmitting information from a receptor for pain and temperature to the point where it is finally perceived as a sensation.   Arrange the following components in

the proper order, beginning with the receptor. _____

            a.   receptor for pain
            b.   spinothalamic pathway
            c.   somesthetic cortex
            d.   thalamus
            e.   dorsal root of spinal nerve

III. Nerve tracts in the CNS are named according to the major parts they connect. Based on your knowledge of the functional anatomy of the vertebrate brain, list the parts that the following tracts would connect, indicating the direction of information and the division of the brain where the parts are located.

   1. corticopontine _____

       _____

   2. thalamocortical _____

       _____

   3. spinothalamic _____

       _____

   4. corticospinal _____

       _____

   5. spinocerebellar _____

       _____

6. pontocerebellar _____

_____

IV. A nucleus in the cerebellum is the dentate. "Rubro-" refers to the red
nucleus of the midbrain. What would be the nature of the nerve tract with the name
dentatorubrospinal?

_____

_____

_____

ANSWERS TO CHAPTER EXERCISES

Practice Quiz

1. c	5. d	9. c	13. a	17. b
2. b	6. b	10. d	14. c	18. d
3. a	7. c	11. c	15. d	19. d
4. b	8. a	12. b	16. a	20. a

Review Questions

I. 1. 1	4. e, m, g	7. j
2. f, k	5. a	8. b
3. h, c, n	6. d	9. i

II. a, e, b, d, c

III. 1. From the cerebral cortex of the telencephalon to the pons of the
metencephalon
2. From the thalmus of the diencephalon to the cerebral cortex
3. From the spinal cord to the thalamus
4. From the cerebral cortex to the spinal cord
5. From the spinal cord to the cerebellum of the metencephalon
6. From the pons to the cerebellum

IV. This tract would relay information from the dentate nucleus of the cerebellum
to the red nucleus of the midbrain to the descending spinal tract.

Chapter 27

MUSCLE AND THE CONTROL OF MOVEMENT

WHAT'S IN THIS CHAPTER

In this brief chapter, specific attention is given to the descending motor pathways--the pyramidal and extrapyramidal--and the types of skeletal activity associated with them. The feedback pathways involving the cerebellum, cerebral basal ganglia, cerebral cortex, and brainstem nuclei are explained.

The introduction to neuromuscular transmission includes an explanation of the junction itself, generation of the end plate potential or EPP, and initiation of an action potential in the muscle fiber. Preliminary to the explanation of the actual contractile process in skeletal muscle fibers is the subcellular structure of the fiber--that is, myofibril, sarcomere, actin, and myosin myofilaments. The sliding filament action, which is dependent on the release of calcium from the sarcoplasmic reticulum, is explained.

By the end of this chapter you should be able to:

1. List the parts of mammalian and nonmammalian brains concerned with initiation and control over skeletal muscle action.

2. Describe and explain the anatomical and functional differences between the pyramidal and extrapyramidal motor pathways.

3. Correlate the relative size of areas of the cerebral cortex with the degree of control over a skeletal muscle and the size of a motor unit.

4. Diagram a typical feedback loop involving initiation and control over contraction of a skeletal muscle.

5. Explain the role of the cerebellum in skeletal motor activity.

6. Describe the makeup of a muscle from the muscle itself down to the protein myofilaments.

7. Diagram a sarcomere and label its component parts.

8. Explain what is meant by neuromuscular tranmission and excitation-contraction coupling.

9. List, in order, the events in the sliding-filament action in muscle

371

contraction, beginning with depolarization of the motor end plate.

10. Define <u>end plate potential</u>, <u>sarcoplasmic reticulum</u>, and <u>T tubule</u>, and explain how they are involved in muscle contraction.

WHAT YOU SHOULD ALREADY KNOW

Background material you should know for this chapter includes the functional anatomy of both the central and the peripheral nervous system. You should know the components of a reflex arc and how the peripheral components are associated with the central nervous system. You should also know mechanisms of synaptic transmission. You should understand the anatomical and functional differences represented by the terms somatic, autonomic, sympathetic, and parasympathetic. In addition, you should be familiar with the three types of muscle tissue. Review the electrical properties of membranes and the concepts of resting potential, depolarization, and action potential. Background material is found in Chapters 21, 25, and 26.

<u>Pre-Test</u>

1. The major parts of the brain that are important in motor

   activity are the (a)_____, (b)_____

   _____, and (c)_____.

1. (a) cerebral cortex; (b) basal ganglia; (c) cerebellum

2. Match each of the following tissues with the component of the nervous system that innervates them.

   1. somatic
   2. autonomic

   (a) skeletal _____

   (b) cardiac _____

   (c) smooth _____

2. (a) 1; (b) 2; (c) 2

3. The axon of a somatic motor neuron is a part of the

   (a)_____(central / peripheral) nervous system.

   The cell body of the neuron is located in a (b)_____

   (nucleus / ganglion) in the (c)_____(central / peripheral) nervous system.

3. (a) peripheral; (b) nucleus; (c) central

4. Another name for a skeletal muscle cell is (a)_____.

   These cells are (b)_____(longitudinal / fusiform) in shape, are (c)_____

   (uninucleate / multinucleate), and have nuclei (d)_____

_____ (centrally / peripherally) located.

4. (a) fiber; (b) longitudinal; (c) multinucleate; (d) peripherally

5. Transmission of impulses across most synapses is _____ _____ (electrical / chemical).

5. chemical

6. The basic components of a reflex arc are (a)_____,

(b)_____, (c)_____,

(d)_____, and (e)_____.

6. (a) receptor; (b) sensory neuron; (c) interneuron(s); (d) motor neuron; (e) effector

7. A decrease in the mV value of the membrane resting potential is a (a)_____ (depolarization / hyperpolarization). The total electrical change associated with the passage of an impulse along a membrane is called the (b)_____.

7. (a) depolarization; (b) action potential

GUIDED REVIEW OF THE CHAPTER

27-1 Motor activity is governed by complex feedback mechanisms.

1. Give the function of each of the following brain parts.

   (a) Cerebral basal ganglia in nonmammalian vertebrates

   _____

   (b) Cerebral cortex in mammals _____

   _____

   (c) Cerebral basal ganglia in mammals _____

   _____

1. (a) primary motor control; (b) primary motor control; (c) muscle tone, stereotyped muscular activites

2. Identify the correct motor tract.

   1. extrapyramidal
   2. pyramidal

   (a) Responsible for skilled movements. _____

   (b) Involves synapse in brainstem nuclei. _____

   (c) Nerve fibers cross to other side. _____

373

(d) Includes a feedback system that involves a complete

reflex arc. _____

(e) Collateral axons from neurons in this tract are sent to the cerebellum to inform the cerebellum of the

intended movement. _____

2. (a) 2; (b) 1; (c) 2; (d) 1; (e) 2

3. True or False: Larger areas of the motor cerebral cortex are devoted to the trunk and upper limbs than to the hands.

3. False

4. The reticular formation is a component of the (a)_____

_____(pyramidal / extrapyramidal) motor system and

is (b)_____(inhibitory / excitatory).

4. (a) extra-pyramidal; (b) excitatory

5. The three major components of the extrapyramidal system

are the (a)_____, (b)_____

_____, and (c)_____.

5. (a) thalamus; (b) red nucleus; (c) cerebellum

6. The part of the brain that compares the intended movement with what is actually happening in the muscle is the

_____.

6. cerebellum

7. An "intention tremor" is related to damage in the

_____.

7. cerebellum

27-2 *A neuron activates a muscle fiber by eliciting a membrane potential in it.*

1. Arrange the following in ascending order according to size: (a) myofibril, (b) sarcomere, (c) fiber, (d) myofilament, (e) muscle. _____

1. d, b, a, c, e

2. A motor neuron and all the muscle fibers it controls is

called a (a)_____. If the latter contains relatively few muscle fibers in a particu-

lar muscle, there will be (b)_____(more / fewer) cerebral cells assigned to the muscle and the movement

will be (c)_____(delicately / grossly) controlled.

2. (a) motor unit; (b) more; (c) delicately

3. The plasma membrane of the muscle fiber at the neuromus-

cular junction is called the (a)_____.

374

This structure has receptor proteins for the neurotrans-

mitter (b)_____(norepinephrine /
acetylcholine).   The effect of the neurotransmitter on the

motor end plate is (c)_____
(hyperpolarization / depolarization) and this change in

potential is called the (d)_____

_____.

3. (a) motor end-
plate; (b)
acetylcholine;
(c) depolariza-
tion; (d) end
plate potential

4. True or False: Activation of the proteins at a motor end
plate that bind acetylcholine results in an increase in
sodium permeability.

4. True

5. True or False: The end-plate potential itself produces
muscle fiber contraction.

5. False

6. True or False: Excitation-contraction coupling refers to
the role of the sarcoplasmic reticulum in the muscle
fiber.

6. True

*27-3 A muscle is a highly organized system of contractile
proteins.*

1. Label the components of the sarcomeres shown in
longitudinal section in the following diagram.

(a)_____

(b)_____

(c)_____

(d)_____

(e)_____

(f)_____

1. (a) Z line; (b)
A band; (c) I
band; (d) actin
protein; (e)

2. The I bands contain (a)_____(actin / myosin)

protein.   The heavy filaments are (b)_____
(actin / myosin).

375

myosin protein;
(f) H zone;

2. (a) actin;
   (b) myosin

3. α-actinin

4. True

5. False

6. False

3. The protein found in the Z lines is _____.

4. True or False: The I bands contain actin only, whereas the A bands contain actin and myosin.

5. True or False: When a sarcomere shortens, the actin and myosin filaments decrease in length.

6. True or False: The ends of the myosin filaments pull in the same direction.

27-4 Muscle contraction is regulated by calcium ions.

1. The energy supply for the sliding action in muscle contraction is in the form of (a)_____. The enzyme that hydrolyzes the latter is located in the (b)_____.

1. (a) ATP: (b)
   myosin heads

2. Match each statement with the correct protein.

   1. troponin   2. tropomyosin

   (a) Prevents actin and myosin from interacting _____

   (b) Has sites that bind calcium ions _____

   (c) Blocks sites paratactic to myosin heads _____

2. (a) 2; (b) 1;
   (c) 2

3. The four proteins that have a functional role in muscle contraction are (a)_____, (b)_____, (c)_____, and (d)_____.

3. (a) actin; (b)
   myosin; (c)
   troponin; (d)
   tropomyosin

4. The two ligands that initiate conformational changes and the building of muscle proteins into complexes are (a)_____ and (b)_____.

4. (a) calcium;
   (b) ATP

27-5 The membrane potential triggers the release of calcium ions.

1. Depolarization of the muscle cell plasma membrane is carried to the interior of the cell via the (a)_____. Depolarization of the latter structure causes the release of calcium ions from the (b)_____

_____.

| 1. (a) T tubules; (b) sarcoplasmic reticulum | 2. True or False: Myofibrils are about 100 μm in diameter. |

2. False

3. The "T" in T tubules stands for _____.

3. transverse

4. True or False: The T tubule membrane is continuous with the plasma membrane of the muscle fiber.

4. True

5. The space within the T tubule _____(is / is not) continuous with the extracellular space.

5. is

6. A place in the muscle fiber where calcium ions are stored

is the _____.

6. sarcoplasmic reticulum

PRACTICE QUIZ

1. Somatic motor neurons innervate:
   a. glands.
   b. smooth muscle.
   c. skeletal muscle.
   d. cardiac muscle.

2. Somatic motor activity in humans is <u>initiated</u> in the:
   a. cerebral cortex.
   b. thalamus.
   c. basal ganglia.
   d. cerebellum.

3. The pyramidal tract:
   a. is a sensory tract.
   b. is responsible for gross body movements.
   c. has fibers that synapse in basal ganglia.
   d. has fibers that cross to the other side of the body.

4. Large areas of both the motor and sensory cortex of the human brain are associated with the:
   a. trunk.
   b. thighs.
   c. fingers and fingertips.
   d. arms.

5. The extrapyramidal pathway:
   a. originates in the precentral cortex.
   b. has fibers that synapse in basal ganglia.
   c. originates in the postcentral cortex.
   d. has fibers that cross over in the medulla oblongata.

377

6. The part of the brain that has input both from the motor cortex and from the muscle whose contraction is initiated at the motor cortex is the:
   a. basal ganglia.
   b. thalamus.
   c. cerebellum.
   d. sensory cortex.

7. The _____ is a part of the pyramidal motor tract.
   a. cerebral cortex
   b. basal ganglia
   c. thalamus
   d. cerebellum

8. Which of the following gives the proper ascending order of structures in the morphology of skeletal muscle?
   a. fibers, myofilaments, myofibrils, sarcomeres
   b. sarcomeres, myofilaments, fibers, myofibrils
   c. myofilaments, sarcomeres, myofibrils, fibers
   d. myofibrils, myofilaments, sarcomeres, fibers

9. A number of muscle fibers make up a:
   a. myofibril.
   b. motor unit.
   c. sarcomere.
   d. myofilament.

10. You would expect to find motor units with the _fewest_ muscle fibers in the:
   a. muscles controlling the fingers.
   b. muscles of the upper arm.
   c. muscles of the thigh.
   d. abdominal muscles.

11. Inhibition of cholinesterase:
   a. causes a rapid breakdown of acetylcholine.
   b. reduces the synaptic synthesis of acetylcholine.
   c. increases the synaptic concentration of acetylcholine.
   d. causes fewer receptor proteins at the motor end plate to be activated.

12. A depolarization at the motor end plate:
   a. is due to the presence of cholinesterase.
   b. is an increase in resting potential.
   c. is blocked by the presence of minute amounts of acetylcholine.
   d. results in an end plate potential.

13. The end plate potential is:
   a. all-or-nothing.
   b. propagated.
   c. a hyperpolarization.
   d. a local change.

14. The protein that prevents interaction of actin and myosin is:
   a. troponin.
   b. tropomyosin.
   c. α-actinin.
   d. cholinesterase.

15. When a muscle fiber contracts:
    a. the sarcomere length decreases.
    b. the A band decreases in length.
    c. the I band increases in length.
    d. myofilaments shorten.

16. Which of the following has(have) sites that bind calcium?
    a. tropomyosin
    b. α-actinin
    c. troponin
    d. myosin heads

17. The source of calcium ions in the contractile process is the:
    a. T tubule.
    b. sarcoplasmic reticulum.
    c. Z line.
    d. mitochondria.

REVIEW QUESTIONS

I. The sequence of events leading to muscle contraction is an orderly process. The following are a number of events, including activities in neurons and muscle cells. List these events in proper order from the beginning to the end of muscle contraction and through relaxation.

Proper order: _____

    a. Release of acetylcholine from axon ending
    b. Generation of end plate potential
    c. Release of calcium ions from sarcoplasmic reticulum
    d. Release of the inhibition by tropomyosin of actin and myosin interaction
    e. Diffusion of acetylcholine across the synapse
    f. Sequestering of calcium ions into sarcoplasmic reticulum
    g. Action potential in motor neuron
    h. Relaxation
    i. Action potential on muscle fiber plasma membrane
    j. Interaction of actin and myosin for sliding action and contraction
    k. Binding of acetylcholine to receptor proteins at motor end plate
    l. Binding of calcium to troponin molecules
    m. Repolarization of T tubule
    n. Spread of depolarization through T tubule

II. The following events are involved in control over skeletal muscular activity. Put these in the proper order to show the sequence of events leading to a controlled, intended movement.

Proper order: _____

    a. Impulses traveling via the pyramidal tract to muscle B with collateral signals sent to cerebellum
    b. Sensory impulses traveling to cerebellum from muscle B
    c. Contraction of muscle B
    d. Signals from the cerebellum through the thalamus to the motor cortex
    e. Initiation of a signal in the motor cortex

f. Stimulation of proprioreceptors in muscle B
g. Comparison in cerebellum of intended movement to actual movement
h. New modified signal from motor cortex through pyramidal tract to muscle B

III. Because synaptic transmission is by way of a chemical transmitter, a number of substances can affect synapses. Using the information given below, answer the questions that follow.

The chemical transmitter at the neuromuscular junction is acetylcholine. Acetylcholine binds to receptor proteins at the motor end plate. The drug atrophine competes with acetylcholine for the same receptor proteins. The enzyme cholinesterase breaks down acetylcholine. Organophosphate insecticides bind to cholinesterase and inhibit it.

1. What effect would organophosphates have on acetylcholine concentration at the neuromuscular junction?

   _____

2. What would be the effect of organophosphates on muscle fibers?

   _____

3. What would be the effect of atropine on neuromuscular transmission?

   _____

4. What would be an effective treatment for organophosphate poisoning?

   _____

ANSWERS TO CHAPTER EXERCISES

Practice Quiz

1. c	4. c	7. a	10. a	13. d	16. c
2. a	5. b	8. c	11. c	14. b	17. b
3. d	6. c	9. b	12. d	15. a	

Review Questions

I. g, a, e, k, b, i, n, c, l, d, j, m, f, h

II. e, a, c, f, b, g, d, h

III. 1. increase
     2. continuous stimulation by acetylcholine
     3. block transmission
     4. atropine

Chapter 28

FUNDAMENTALS OF ANIMAL BEHAVIOR

WHAT'S IN THIS CHAPTER

This chapter introduces the field of ethology, the study of animal behavior. In this chapter behavior is explained in terms of fixed action patterns and learning. Fixed action patterns (FAP) form a basic concept of ethology. Releasing stimuli are required to initiate a fixed action pattern, and releasers of FAPs can be altered through maturation, experience, and learning. Releasing stimuli are selected by releasing mechanisms that are a part of the innate physiological makeup of an animal. Complex behavior patterns, such as the courtship behavior of the stickleback fish, are explained as a series of FAPs. Fundamental concepts in the chapter include imprinting, habituation, hierarchical arrangements of behavior patterns from broad appetitive behavior to consummatory behavior, sign stimuli, motivation and drive, complex learned behavior where tradition becomes a part of an animal's behavior, and the internal clock mechanism and visual cues from stars and the sun that guide birds in migration. One or more examples are given to illustrate each of these concepts. There is also a word of caution, for studying animal behavior requires observations that cannot necessarily tell us anything about neural mechanisms inside an animal. Included in the chapter are four exercises to help you apply the information you have learned.

By the end of this chapter you should be able to:

1. Define an FAP and the related concept of taxis.

2. Explain the relationship between the FAP, releasing stimulus, innate releasing mechanism (IRM), imprinting, and conditioning.

3. Explain behavioral chains, such as the feeding of *Hydra* and the behavior of the digger wasp *Ammophila*, in terms of fixed action patterns.

4. Give examples of how fixed action patterns can be refined by maturation.

5. Define imprinting and cite some examples.

6. Explain what is meant by a sign stimulus and what is involved in the selection of this stimulus.

7. Discuss the use of the concepts of motivation and drive, and give examples.

8. Define and relate the terms <u>hierarchical behavior patterns</u>, <u>appetitive behavior</u>, and <u>consummatory behavior</u>, and give an example that illustrates the definitions.

9. Explain differences between long and short feedback loops with regard to behavior.

10. Relate the terms <u>learning</u>, <u>imprinting</u>, and <u>habituation</u> to behavior patterns.

11. Describe two general patterns of conditioning; explain the differences and give examples that illustrate the differences.

12. Relate the terms <u>reinforcer</u> and <u>extinction</u> to conditioning.

13. Explain the significance of traditional behaviors, which are passed on through imitation rather than via the genes.

14. Explain how birds orient themselves in migration.

WHAT YOU SHOULD ALREADY KNOW

Background that you should have for this chapter includes an understanding of the structure and function of the genetic apparatus and its role in protein synthesis (Sections 3-6, 3-7, and 9-12). You should know the general structure of the nervous system, the pattern of nerve cells making up a reflex arc (which is necessary for a stimulus-response phenomenon), and the classification of sensory receptors (Sections 21-6, 21-7, 21-8, and 25-3). You should know also the function of hypothalamic centers (Section 26-4) and the meaning of the terms <u>adrenergic</u>, <u>cholinergic</u> (Section 21-15), <u>osmotic potential</u> (Section 11-3), and <u>antidiuretic hormone</u> (Section 21-17).

Pre-Test

1. The transfer of a message that resides in DNA to a sequence of nucleotides in RNA is called (a)_____ _____. Use of the latter message to direct the synthesis of a specific order of amino acids is called (b)_____.

1. (a) transcription; (b) translation

2. The basic information on which an organism operates resides in the _____ of its cells.

2. genome

3. The components of a reflex arc, beginning with the receptor, are the (a)_____, (b)_____, (c)_____ _____, (d)_____, and (e)_____.

3. (a) sensory re-
ceptor; (b)
sensory neuron;
(c) interneu-
ron; (d) motor
neuron; (e)
effector

4. List the five categories of sensory receptors and the stimulus modality for each.

(a)_____   _____

(b)_____   _____

(c)_____   _____

(d)_____   _____

(e)_____   _____

4. (a) chemorecep-
tor, chemical;
(b) photorecep-
tor, light; (c)
thermoreceptor,
temperature;
(d) mechanore-
ceptor, mechan-
ical distor-
tion; (e) elec-
troreceptor,
electric cur-
rent

5. A neuron that releases acetylcholine as a neurotrans-

mitter is said to be (a)_____, whereas

an adrenergic neuron releases (b)_____.

5. (a) choliner-
gic; (b)
noradrenalin

6. Feeding and thirst centers are located in the (a)_____

_____ portion of the diencephalon. A stimulus for

an animal to drink water is a(an) (b)_____
(increase / decrease) in the osmotic pressure of the
blood.   When the osmotic pressure of the blood is

elevated, ADH secretion (c)_____(increases /

decreases). The source of ADH is the (d)_____

_____.

6. (a) hypothala-
mus; (b)
increase;
(c) increases;
(d) anterior
pituitary

GUIDED REVIEW OF THE CHAPTER

28-2 A general paradigm for understanding behavior.

1. The term for the scientific study of behavior is

(a)_____. A fixed action pattern is (b)_____

_____(learned / innate), but requires a (c)_____

_____ to be initiated. The mechanism
whereby the animal selects and responds to releasers is

called an (d)_____

_____.

1. (a) ethology;
   (b) innate; (c)
   releasing
   stimulus; (d)
   innate releas-
   ing mechanism

2. taxis

2. A directing or orienting movement related to a fixed

action pattern is called a _____.

*28-3 A fixed action pattern is a highly stereotyped behavior
pattern.*

1. Small animals such as *Hydra*, *Ammophila* and *Sphex* exhibit

fixed action patterns that (a)_____(are / are not)

altered by experience. This is demonstrated in (b)_____

_____ and (c)_____ in the pattern of
securing prey and returning it to a burrow that has been
prepared for egg laying.

1. (a) are not;
   (b) *Ammophila;*
   (c) *Sphex*

2. The stimulus for the *Sphex* wasp FAP of dragging prey to

the threshold of the burrow is _____

_____.

2. sight of prey
   that is not
   yet in position
   on the thresh-
   old

28-4 Some fixed action patterns must be refined by experience.

1. The behavior pattern of pecking in small chicks is an

example of (a)_____

_____(imprinting / one that is fully developed
with practice). The pattern demonstrated by the gray lag
gosling in following the first large, moving object is an

example of (b)_____.

1. (a) one deve-
   loped with
   practice; (b)
   imprinting

2. List four examples of imprinting, citing the animal, the
    behavior pattern, and what specific event fills in the
    genetically determined pattern to complete the fixed
    action pattern.

	Animal	Pattern	Information Necessary
(a)	_____	_____	_____
(b)	_____	_____	_____
(c)	_____	_____	_____

2. (a) gray lag goose, following, large moving object; (b) salmon, homing, stream odor; (c) white crowned sparrow, singing, early exposure to proper song version

3. False

1. (a) sign stimulus; (b) innate releasing

2. (a) mimicry; (b) adaptive

1. (a) zig-zag dance; (b) sticking head in nest; (c) butting base of female's tail with snout

3. True or False: In the process of imprinting, the information needed to complete a genetically determined behavior pattern can come at any time during development.

28-5 Releasing stimuli are highly selected pieces of the environment.

1. A particular releaser that signals a specific behavior

   pattern is called a (a)_____.

   Selection of the latter is due to an (b)_____

   _____ mechanism.

2. The evolution of large eyespots on the wings of insects is

   a form of (a)_____ and is (b)_____
   (adaptive / nonadaptive).

28-6 More complex behavior patterns are often chains of simpler fixed action patterns.

1. What particular action of the male stickleback triggers the responses of the female that are listed below?

   (a) Display of belly swollen with eggs

   _____

   (b) Slipping into nest with head and tail protruding

   _____

   (c) Spawning

   _____

28-7 The role of motivation and drive in behavior.

1. A particular internal condition of an animal that drives it to behave in a certain way--for example to drink when

   thirsty--is called (a)_____. Two particular actions that would be classified as drives are (b)_____ and (c)_____.

1. (a) motivation;
   (b) drinking;
   (c) feeding

2. Give an example of a neuroendocrine mechanism that accompanies a thirst-motivated drive to satisfy the body's water needs.

   _____

   _____

2. stimulation of hypothalamic centers, release of ADH, or reabsorption of water

3. The drive that motivates an animal to drink water is due to (a)_____(increased / decreased) osmotic potential of fluids present in the hypothalamus.

3. decreased (or increased osmotic pressure)

28-8 Behavioral patterns are often organized hierarchically.

1. Searching for a mate is (a)_____(consummatory / appetitive) behavior, whereas mating is (b)_____(consummatory / appetitive).

1. (a) appetitive;
   (b) consummatory

2. An animal's initial behavior that leads to the final act of mating is _____(broadly / narrowly) directed toward that act.

2. broadly

3. Once a male stickleback has established his territory, what would provide the stimulus for aggressive display behavior? _____

3. appearance of another male

28-9 Learning is a mechanism for rapid adaptation to new situations.

1. Compared to genetically encoded stereotyped behavior patterns, learning operates with a (a)_____(long / short) feedback loop. Learning that is based on refining a genetically encoded pattern is called (b)_____, whereas learning that involves ignoring a continuing stimulus is called (c)_____. An experiment by Otto Koehler demonstrated that birds are capable of (d)_____(imprinting / habituation / concept development).

1. (a) short; (b) imprinting; (c) habituation; (d) concept development

2. The ability to learn seems to be the _____(rule / exception) among animals.

2. exception

28-10 There are two general patterns of conditioning.

1. Two types of conditioning are (a)_____ and

   (b)_____.

1. (a) respondent;
   (b) operant

2. In respondent conditioning, the conditioned stimulus must

   come _____(before / after) the releaser.

2. before

3. The animal will work harder at displaying the desired

   behavior if it is _____(occasionally / consistently) rewarded.

3. occasionally

4. Disappearance of a conditioned behavior when it is no

   longer reinforced is called _____.

4. extinction

5. The fact that a dog conditioned to salivate at the sound
   of a bell with a 500-cycle/second tone will also salivate
   at the sound of a higher-pitched tone is an example of

   _____.

5. stimulus
   generalization

6. Give an example (other than the honeyguide) of a behavior
   pattern that has been learned and retained in a species
   through imitation rather than genetic inheritance.

   _____

   _____

6. English chick-
   adee opening
   milk bottles
   and drinking
   cream

7. What has happened to the behavior pattern of the honeyguide leading people of Africa to beehives as a result of
   the people being able to acquire honey at local grocery
   stores?

   _____

7. extinction be-
   cause it is
   no longer
   reinforced

28-12 Animals can use various cues to orient themselves.

1. Bird migration and navigation are explained in terms of

   (a)_____ combined with the

   visual cues of (b)_____

   and (c)_____.

1. (a) internal
   clocks; (b)
   position of the
   sun; (c) star
   patterns

2. True or False: Birds use landmarks as important means of
   orienting themselves during migration.

387

2. False

3. True or False: Birds always follow the same route in their migrations.

3. True

4. True or False: Young birds learn the migratory route from older birds.

4. False

5. A stimulus that initiates bird migration is _____ _____.

5. length of day

6. Three anatomical or physiological changes that take place in birds in the spring of the year are (a)_____ _____, (b)_____, and (c)_____.

6. (a) increase in gonad size; (b) extra fat; (c) increased activity

PRACTICE QUIZ

1. A fixed action pattern:
   a. is not stereotyped.
   b. does not require a releaser.
   c. may also require a taxis.
   d. is basic to only a few behavioral patterns.

2. Taxis is defined as:
   a. a decrease in response to a consistent stimulus.
   b. an orienting movement in response to a stimulus.
   c. repetition of a response that is reinforced.
   d. the internal drive that motivates a certain behavior pattern.

3. The experiment that demonstrated the FAP of the gray lag goose's retrieval of an egg was performed by:
   a. Bolle.
   b. Lorenz.
   c. Matthews.
   d. Kramer.

4. An animal's ability to pick out a particular stimulus that releases a fixed action pattern is due to:
   a. ability to learn.
   b. imprinting.
   c. habituation.
   d. an innate releasing mechanism.

5. Which of the following involves more than simply a series of fixed action patterns?
   a. reproductive behavior of the digger wasp

b. feeding behavior in *Hydra*
c. use of tools by chimps to get food
d. retrieval of a "lost" egg by the gray lag gocse

6. The fact that salmon return to the stream where they are hatched is an example of:
   a. concept formation
   b. motivation
   c. habituation
   d. imprinting

7. The stimulus for homing in salmon is:
   a. visual.
   b. olfactory.
   c. auditory.
   d. tactile.

8. The functional signficance of a bird song is not related to:
   a. feeding of young.
   b. species recognition.
   c. finding a mate.
   d. defining territory.

9. Zig-zag behavior in the male stickleback is part of:
   a. establishing a territory.
   b. agonistic behavior.
   c. courtship behavior.
   d. defense of nesting site.

10. Release of sperm by a male stickleback is called:
    a. spawning.
    b. milting.
    c. fertilzation.
    d. homing.

11. A consummatory act is:
    a. broadly directed.
    b. an orientation in response to a stimulus.
    c. exemplified by copulation.
    d. an example of imprinting.

12. The fact that a hydra will respond to jets of water, but not to a steady stream, is an example of:
    a. classical conditioning.
    b. operant conditioning.
    c. habituation.
    d. imprinting.

13. The experiment performed by Pavlov with salivation in dogs provides an example of:
    a. respondent conditioning.
    b. trial-and-error.
    c. operant conditioning.
    d. extinction.

14. The animal will work harder at the desired behavior if the rewards are:
    a. taken away for extended periods.

b. given every time the desired behavior is performed.
c. given occasionally when the desired behavior is performed.
d. given any time within 24 hours of performance of the desired behavior.

15. Which of the following is not a behavioral pattern that has been acquired
through cultural tradition?
a. guiding behavior by *Indicator*
b. nest building by sticklebacks
c. English chickadees drinking cream from bottles of milk
d. potato washing by certain nonhuman mammals

16. Birds orient themselves in migration by:
a. the position of stars.
b. landmarks.
c. wind currents.
d. day length.

REVIEW QUESTIONS

I. Some types of learning are listed below. For each activity that follows,
identify the type of learning that it demonstrates.

a. imprinting
b. habituation
c. respondent conditioning
d. operant conditioning
e. insight

_____ 1. Chimpanzees use a stick to get termites from a nest.

_____ 2. A butterfly flies away in response to a sudden puff of air, but it does
not in response to a steady wind.

_____ 3. The first moving object a newly hatched chick sees is a motorized toy,
which the chick claims as its mother.

_____ 4. The homing behavior of salmon results in their returning to the stream
where they were hatched.

_____ 5. A bird's song is sung in its proper version only if it is heard by the
bird at a critical time.

_____ 6. A dog salivates at the sound of a bell.

_____ 7. A dog is given a bone when he responds to his master's call. He will
continue to come for a pat on the head rather than a bone.

II. Give the relationship among (not the definition of) the members of each of the
following groups of terms.

1. Ethology, fixed action pattern, releasing stimulus, innate releasing
mechanism

---

2. Releasing stimulus, innate releasing mechanism, imprinting

_____

_____

_____

3. Sign stimulus, evolution, adaptive behavior, releaser

_____

_____

_____

4. Salivation in Pavlov's dogs, fixed action pattern, releaser, conditioned stimulus, respondent conditioning

_____

_____

_____

ANSWERS TO CHAPTER EXERCISES

Practice Quiz

1. c	3. b	5. c	7. b	9. c	11. c	13. a	15. b
2. b	4. d	6. d	8. a	10. b	12. c	14. c	16. a

Review Questions

I. 1. e   2. b   3. a   4. a   5. a   6. c   7. d

II. 1. A basic concept in ethology is the fixed action pattern, a behavior pattern that is triggered by a releasing stimulus identified via an innate releasing mechanism.
  2. Imprinting is a process in which the details of a releasing stimulus are specified in an innate releasing mechanism.
  3. Sign stimuli are releasers that become intensified through evolution if the behavior pattern they evoke is adaptive.
  4. The conditioned stimulus in Pavlov's experiment, the sound of a bell, evokes the fixed action pattern, salivation, through respondent conditioning when it is associated with the releaser, meat powder in the dog's mouth.

Chapter 29

SOCIAL BEHAVIOR

WHAT'S IN THIS CHAPTER

This chapter covers specific interactions that take place between animals of the
same species that form social groups. Advantages of social groups, (such as
security from predators) and disadvantages (such as susceptibility to epidemics)
are described. Characteristics and methods of communication (such as visual,
auditory and olfactory mechanisms) are described for animals that exhibit social
behavior. Division of labor and altruistic characteristics of certain animal
groups are explained in terms of the way they promote the survival of the species
and as a basis for interaction among members of a species. The chapter provides an
explanation of the term territoriality and outlines the advantages that establishment of a territory offers a species. More detailed descriptions are given for
three species of social animals: honeybees, herring gulls, and Japanese macaque
monkeys. Honeybee societies exemplify a division of labor among three
castes--worker, drone and queen--and exhibit various forms of communication.
Herring gulls display behavior which, like that of honeybees, depends on a series
of fixed action patterns. Macaques display complex behavior that is modified
through experience and cultural innovations.

By the end of this chapter you should be able to:

1. List some animals that form social groups.

2. Cite advantages and disadvantages of social behavior, and give examples
    wherein it has been detrimental to a species.

3. Make a general statement about the range in size of social groups.

4. Explain the types of bonds that may organize animals into social groups.

5. List various ways in which animals communicate.

6. Define and distinguish among the terms territoriality, home range, and
    personal space, and explain the significance or functional importance of each.

7. Define altruism and explain the general reason why animals may be altruistic.

8. Define dominance hierarchy and cite examples of social groups that display it.

392

9. Explain the caste system of honeybees and the division of labor among members of the hive.

10. Describe the methods of communication in honeybees and the events with which these communication patterns are associated.

11. List and describe some social behavior patterns observed in herring gulls, and comment on whether these would be classified primarily as fixed action patterns or as cultural innovations.

12. Explain what is meant by the "uncertainty principle" in studies of the behavior of animals in captivity.

13. Describe the dominance hierarchy in macaque social groups, and explain how male dominance is established. Identify behavior patterns in which male dominance is important and others in which it is not.

14. Describe the courtship and mating behavior of macaques.

15. Cite examples of cultural innovations in macaque social groups.

WHAT YOU SHOULD ALREADY KNOW

Background material generally applicable to this chapter is found in Chapter 28. Specifically applicable are the role of fixed action patterns and the modification of behavior through learning and experience. You should know what is meant by releasing stimuli. You should know also the definition and role of chemoreceptors.

Pre-Test

1. A pheromone is a (a)_____(mechanical / chemical) stimulus. An example of an animal that produces a pheromone is the (b)_____.

1. (a) chemical;
   (b) ant

2. A fixed action pattern is (a)_____(stereotyped / nonstereotyped) and requires a (b)_____ to be initiated. The recognition of such a stimulus is due to an (c)_____.

2. (a) stereo-
   typed; (b)
   releaser; (c)
   innate releas-
   ing mechanism

3. A complex behavior pattern may be dependent on, or a manifestation of, at least two factors. These are

   (a)_____ and

   (b)_____.

3. (a) chain of
   simpler FAPs;
   (b) modifi-
   cation by
   learning

4. Cultural transmission of behavior patterns _____(is / is not) restricted to humans.

393

4. is not

5. is

GUIDED REVIEW OF THE CHAPTER

29-1 Social behavior entails a balance of advantages and disadvantages.

1. List two advantages of social behavior between members of the same species.

   (a)_____

   _____

   (b)_____

1. (a) increased chance of finding food and other resource; (b) protection from predators

2. List two possible disadvantages for an <u>individual</u> in a flock or herd.

   (a)_____

   (b)_____

2. (a) disease due to epidemic; (b) subordination of individuals

3. True

3. True or False: Social behavior patterns in animal groups have advantages and disadvantages, but overall, there are more advantages for the species.

29-2 Social groups may reach enormous sizes.

1. What species became extinct because of its social tendency

   to form large flocks? _____

1. passenger pigeon

2. True

2. True or False: Some societies may have as many as 20 million members.

29-3 Societies may be organized through various types of bonds.

1. List four types of interactions between members of a society.

   (a)_____   (b)_____

   (c)_____   (d)_____

1. (a) communica-

2. List three means by which animal societies may be

tion; (b) ter-
ritoriality;
(c) altruism;
(d) dominance
hierarchy

organized.

(a)_____   (c)_____

(b)_____

2. (a) parental
bonds; (b)
sexual bonds;
(c) division
of labor

*29-4 Social behavior requires communication between members of
the group.*

1. The most common means of communication among animals is

(a)_____. A common nonvocal means

of communication utilizes chemicals called (b)_____

_____.

1. (a) vocaliza-
tion; (b)
pheromones

2. Gesturing in humans is regarded as a genetically encoded

_____.

2. fixed action
pattern

3. Fireflies signal to potential mates by _____

_____.

3. lantern
flashing

4. True or False: Lantern flashing patterns are the same for
all species of fireflies.

4. False

*29-5 Territoriality is a mechanism for dividing space and
resources.*

1. When an animal claims an area as its own, the area is

called the animal's (a)_____. In what two
groups of animals is this behavior most highly developed?

(b)_____ and (c)_____.

1. (a) territory;
(b) birds;
(c) mammals

2. A smaller area of space that an animal maintains around

itself is called its _____.

2. personal
space

3. A major advantage of an established territory is _____

_____.

3. division of
resources

4. A bird's mating area is called a (a)_____, whereas

a collection of the latter is called a (b)_____.

4. (a) court;
(b) lek

5. An example of an animal group that forms coteries is

_____.

5. prairie dogs

6. True or False: In human cultures, personal space is

always about one foot, regardless of the culture.

6. False

29-6 Social animals often display altruistic behavior.

1. What is Darwin's answer to the question of how altruism benefits an individual? _____

_____

1. perpetuation of genes similar to one's own

29-7 Dominance hierarchies often mark social behavior.

1. A common example of dominance hierarchies in a species is

   (a)_____. Physical combat that occurs in establishing the hierarchy is one

   example of (b)_____ behavior.

1. (a) pecking order in chickens; (b) agonistic

2. Agonistic behavior in some male animals is correlated with

   levels of _____ hormones.

2. androgen

3. True or False: A beta hen may not peck an alpha hen but may peck all others beneath it.

3. True

29-8 Honeybees exhibit an extreme division of labor between castes.

1. Four groups of social insects are (a)_____,

   (b)_____, (c)_____, and

   (d)_____.

1. (a) wasps; (b) bees; (c) termites; (d) ants

2. Match each of the following characteristics with the proper caste of bees: queens (Q), workers (W), or drones (D).

   (a) Mate with queen _____

   (b) Diploid females _____

   (c) Develop in the presence of royal jelly _____

   (d) Produce royal jelly _____

   (e) Nurse larvae and construct brood cells _____

   (f) "Field bees" and "house bees" _____

   (g) Produced parthogenetically _____

(h) Produce trans-9-ketodecenoic acid _____

(i) Haploid males _____

(j) Lay eggs _____

(k) Have unbarbed stinger _____

2. (a) D: (b) QW;
   (c) Q; (d) W;
   (e) W; (f) W;
   (g) D; (h) Q;
   (i) D; (j) Q;
   (k) Q

3. The structure in the queen where sperm are stored is the

   _____.

3. spermatheca

4. True or False: A queen bee mates with only one drone.

4. False

5. True or False: Worker bees can, within limits, control
   the temperature of the beehive.

5. True

29-9 *Honeybees communicate through dancing, sounds, and
scents.*

1. The medium of communication in honeybees when a food

   source has been discovered is (a)_____.
   Depending on whether the food source is near or far away

   from the hive, the dance is (b)_____ or

   (c)_____.

1. (a) dancing;
   (b) round;
   (c) wagging;

2. Bees obtain information about the direction in which a

   food source is located from (a)_____
   (sound / vision / pheromones). The pattern of dancing
   conveys information about direction by analogy with a

   (b)_____(clock / compass / map).

2. (a) sound;
   (b) compass

3. When a food source is close to the beehive, a _____
   (round / wagging) dance is used.

3. round

29-10 *Herring gull societies operate through fixed action
patterns.*

1. Five behavior patterns in herring gulls are (a)_____

   _____, (b)_____,

   (c)_____, (d)_____

   _____, and (e)_____. An
   apparently irrelevant behavior that animals show as a

397

means of releasing built-up energy is called (f)_____

_____.   An example of the latter is

(g)_____.

29-11 Macaques have complex societies in which culture plays a large part.

1. (a) pair for-
mation; (b)
courtship feed-
(c) nest build-
ing; (d) copu-
lation; (e)
fighting
males); (f)dis-
placement acti-
vity; (g) grass
pulling

1. A major difference between the social behavior of bees and gulls and that of macaques is that the behavior of

_____ does not depend almost entirely on FAPs.

1. macaques

2. The monkey at the top of the dominance hierarchy in

macaque societies is called the (a)_____

_____. Attaining this position depends on (b)_____

_____.   There (c)_____(is /
is not) a correlation between hierarchical rank and androgen level.   The position of the male in the dominance

hierarchy is relatively unimportant in (d)_____.

2. (a) alpha male;
(b) social
status; (c) is
not; (d) mating

3. Macaque offspring that form permanent bonds with the

mother are _____(male / female).

3. female

4. Two examples that illustrate the role of culture in

macaque behavior are (a)_____,

and (b)_____.

4. (a) potato
washing;
(b) rolling
snowballs

5. True or False: In macaque society, a female may refuse
the advances of a male.

5. True

6. True or False: A male and female mating pair in macaque
society stay together for at least a 3-6 month period.

6. False

Summary

1. The basis for all social interactions is _____

_____(reproduction / communication).

1. communication

2. True or False: Agonistic behavior is associated only with

398

fighting or aggression.

2. False

PRACTICE QUIZ

1. Which of the following is a disadvantage incurred by animals that form social groups?
   a. Herds are more noticeable to predators than an individual would be.
   b. There is too much competition for mates.
   c. A herd of animals is defenseless against a predator.
   d. There is less chance for the animals in the group to get food.

2. A social group of _____ would have the fewest members.
   a. locusts
   b. honeybees
   c. primates
   d. driver ants

3. Male huias open logs while the female picks out insect larvae. This is an example of:
   a. courtship behavior.
   b. parental bonding.
   c. sexual bonding.
   d. division of labor.

4. Which of the following statements is not true of vocalization?
   a. It is the most common form of communication.
   b. In birds, it is an indication of territoriality.
   c. It is a major form of communication in insects.
   d. It is part of courtship behavior in frogs.

5. Which of the following gives the proper order from the least inclusive term to the most inclusive term?
   a. personal space, territory, home range
   b. personal space, home range, territory
   c. territory, home range, personal space
   d. home range, personal space, territory

6. _____ establish "group territories."
   a. Palm warblers
   b. Prairie dogs
   c. Ants
   d. Lizards

7. The fact that a dolphin will help another injured dolphin is an example of:
   a. agonistic behavior.
   b. altruism.
   c. division of labor.
   d. parental bonding.

8. Dominance hierarchies are not common in _____ societies.
   a. herring gull
   b. primate
   c. chicken
   d. wolf

399

9. Division of labor is <u>most</u> pronounced in:
   a. bird flocks.
   b. primates.
   c. social insects.
   d. reptiles.

10. Diploid female honeybees are:
    a. workers and queens.
    b. workers and drones.
    c. queens and drones.
    d. queens, workers, and drones.

11. Which of the following are means of communication in honeybees?
    a. dances and sounds only
    b. vision, scents, and dances only
    c. sounds, scents, and vision only
    d. scents, sounds, vision, and dances

12. "Grass pulling" in herring gulls is:
    a. related to courtship behavior.
    b. a part of nest building.
    c. a stimulus to initiate copulation.
    d. a kind of displacement activity.

13. Behavior patterns in herring gulls are explained as primarily:
    a. altruistic
    b. learned through experience.
    c. a series of FAPs.
    d. cultural innovations.

14. Which of the following statements is <u>not</u> true of the social behavior of Japanese macaques?
    a. They display a dominance hierarchy with males at the top.
    b. Closer, more lasting bonds are formed between mothers and daughters.
    c. Mating occurs without regard to a male's position in the dominance hierarchy.
    d. Most of their behavior revolves around FAPs.

15. An example of an innovation in macaque societies that is passed along by learning is:
    a. choosing the alpha male.
    b. the display of aggressive behavior.
    c. potato washing.
    d. peripheral males leaving one group to join another.

REVIEW QUESTIONS

I. Consider the following statement, "Social behavior entails more advantages than disadvantages for a species." Support this statement, in terms of the process of natural selection, with a brief statement of your own.

_____

_____

II. There are different methods of communication among animals. Some of these are listed below. Match each of the particular behaviors listed with the proper method of communication.

                                   a.   chemical
                                   b.   auditory
                                   c.   visual

_____ 1. Defining the boundaries of a territory in birds

_____ 2. Attraction of a male silkworm to a female

_____ 3. Species recognition signals in fireflies

_____ 4. Threat display in a dog

_____ 5. Species recognition in birds

_____ 6. Location of a food source discovered by a foraging ant

_____ 7. Mating behavior in male sticklebacks

_____ 8. A male cat's attraction to and location of a female cat in heat

_____ 9. Communication by a scouting honeybee to other worker bees information about quality of a food source and its direction and distance from the hive

_____ 10. Failure of worker bees to nurture more than one queen at a given time

III. Here are a number of terms that are applicable to social behavior in animals. To show your understanding of their meaning, give a specific example of each one.

1. Parental bonds _____

2. Territoriality _____

3. Personal spacing _____

4. Altruism _____

5. Agonistic behavior _____

6. Displacement activity _____

7. Dominance hierarchy _____

IV. Briefly criticize the knowledge gained from studying the behavior of primates in an artificial setting.

401

_____

_____

_____

_____

ANSWERS TO CHAPTER EXERCISES

Practice Quiz

1. a	4. c	7. b	10. a	13. c
2. c	5. a	8. a	11. d	14. d
3. d	6. b	9. c	12. d	15. c

Review Questions

I.   Animals with characteristics that make them better able to meet environmental conditions survive, reproduce, and pass those characteristics on to offspring. The fact that social orders still exist inidcates their overall advantage for survival.

II.

1. b	3. c	5. b, c	7. c	9. a, b, c
2. a	4. c	6. a	8. a	10. a

III. 1. Parent/offspring relationship, nuclear family of society
     2. Bird, claiming an area
     3. Bird, equidistant spacing on utility line
     4. Porpoise, saving the life of a human or porpoise
     5. Wolf, defending territory
     6. Birds, grass pulling
     7. Primates, alpha male; chicken, pecking order

IV. Studying the behavior of primates necessitates an unnatural setting for the social group--that is, studies in captivity or in the presence of the human experimenter. The behavior of the primates may be altered, to a certain extent, by the unnatural setting.

Chapter 30

SEXUAL BEHAVIOR AND REPRODUCTION

WHAT'S IN THIS CHAPTER

This chapter covers sexual reproduction of animals, with an emphasis on humans. It shows the range of mechanisms used for bringing together the gametes of a species, from attraction between gametes to extensive rituals performed by courting individuals to ensure intraspecific matings. The development and function of male and female external and internal genitalia are explained, and hormonal influences on their development are included. The events of the four phases of human coitus are explained by contrast to the fixed action patterns associated with mating rituals and copulation in most other animals. Emphasis is placed on the gonads as endocrine glands and the hormonal relationships associated with the functional state of the human gonads--in particular, the hormones associated with the menstrual cycle in the female. All phases of the menstrual cycle are explained in terms of the functional activities of the pituitary gland, the ovarian structures, and changes in the endometrium. A comparison is made between ovulation in humans and in other animals, with reference to spontaneous and induced ovulation. The chapter concludes with the process of fertilization; implantation of the blastocyst in the endometrial wall; formation of the placenta, an endocrine organ in itself; and hormones that facilitate birth and stimulate growth, development, milk production, and secretion of the breast.

By the end of this chapter you should be able to:

1. Explain how sex pheromones assure that the right kinds of gametes get together, and give examples.

2. Explain the importance of intraspecific matings compared to interspecific matings.

3. Describe the mating "ceremony" of the great crested grebe in terms of a series of fixed action patterns.

4. Describe the functional anatomy of the human male and female internal and external genitalia, and explain what is meant by their developing from "indifferent" embryonic structures.

5. List some homologous male and female reproductive structures for the human.

403

6. Explain what is meant by copulation and comment on variation among animals in sexual behavior associated with it.

7. List and give characteristics of the four phases of human copulation; compare men and women with respect to the events that characterize these phases.

8. Describe the functional histology of the testis and ovary; name the endocrine portions of each, the hormones produced, and the effects of the hormones.

9. List the pituitary gonadotropins; describe the target tissue and the action of the hormone on the target tissue.

10. Describe the different roles played by LH and FSH in the human male and female.

11. Describe the events of the female menstrual cycle, correlating the activities of the anterior pituitary, ovary, and endometirum. Include all hormonal relationships.

12. Describe changes involved in the passage of a fertilized ovum to the endometrium, its implantation, hormone production, placenta formation, and placental hormone.

13. Relate the events of pregnancy, birth, breast development, milk production, and milk "let-down" to particular hormones and nervous mechanisms involved.

WHAT YOU SHOULD ALREADY KNOW

You should know the definition of a species (Chapter 2). You should be able to define and explain the role of pheromones (Chapter 6). You should be familiar with the processes of spermatogenesis and oogenesis and with the production of gametes (Chapter 10) as well as with fertilization and basic embryology (Chapter 16). You should know also the role of the pituitary, the hypothalamus, and hormones in general in integrative processes (Chapter 21 and 26). Finally, you should know the meaning of FAP and releasing stimuli (Chapter 28) and understand how complex behavior patterns may be chains of simpler FAPs.

Pre-Test

1. A sexual species is defined as a group of organisms that

are _____ isolated from other such groups.

1. reproductively   2. What type of receptor is stimulated by a pheromone?

_____

2. chemoreceptor   3. The human male gamete is the (a)_____, the female

gamete is the (b)_____. Gametes are (c)_____ (haploid / diploid) and are formed by the process of cell

division called (d)_____.

3. (a) sperm;
   (b) ovum;
   (c) haploid;
   (d) meiosis

4. Cell division and development of the embryo are initiated with the process of (a)_____, which results in the formation of a (b)_____.

4. (a) fertilza-
   tion;
   (b) zygote

5. Three extraembryonic membranes developed by embryos of higher vertebrates are the (a)_____, (b)_____, and (c)_____.

5. (a) amnion;
   (b) chorion;
   (d) allantois

6. Blood-borne substances produced by endocrine glands which affect target tissues elsewhere in the organism are called _____.

6. hormones

7. The "master" endocrine gland in humans is the (a)_____. The part of this endocrine that secretes tropic hormones is the (b)_____(anterior / posterior) portion. The part of the brain that directly or indirectly controls the function of this endocrine gland is the (c)_____.

7. (a) pituitary;
   (b) anterior;
   (c) hypothalamus

8. A basic concept of animal behavior is a behavior pattern called a (a)_____ which is performed only in the presence of a (a)_____ stimulus.

8. (a) FAP (fixed
   action pattern);
   (b) releasing

GUIDED REVIEW OF THE CHAPTER

30-1 Gametes of the same species must be brought together in reproduction.

1. _____ isolation is the basis of evolution.

1. Reproductive

2. Hybrids produced by interspecific matings are usually _____(more / less) fit than nonhybrids.

2. less

3. True or False: The most primitive mechanisms which assure that only gametes of the same species will get together are physical.

3. False

4. List three known pheromones that are important in ensuring that correct intraspecific gametes get together. Also

405

indicate what species produce them.

(a)_____

_____

(b)_____

_____

(c)_____

_____

5. Sex pheromones are recognized by means of _____

_____.

30-2 *A complex mating ritual may have to precede copulation.*

1. The courting ritual in the great crested grebe is a series

of (a)_____. This ritualistic courting behavior

has been described by (b)_____.

30-3 *Vertebrate genitals develop from indifferent embryonic
structures.*

1. In humans, the glans region becomes either a clitoris or a
penis depending on what two courses of instructions?

(a)_____ and (b)_____.

2. In the human male and female genitalia, the male counter-

part of the female labia majora is the _____.

3. Human male genitals are specialized for (a)_____
of sperm, whereas female genitals are specialized for

(b)_____.

4. List in order, beginning with the source of sperm, the
tubular structures through which sperm pass in the male
reproductive system.

(a)_____   (b)_____

(c)_____   (d)_____

(e)_____   (f)_____

4. (a) testis;
   (b) collecting
   ducts; (c)
   epididymis; (d)
   vas deferens;
   (e) ejaculatory
   duct; (f)
   urethra

5. List three glandular structures that join the tubular component of the male reproductive system and the role of their secretions.

   (a)_____   _____

   (b)_____   _____

   (c)_____   _____

5. (a) seminal
   vesicle, sperm
   motility; (b)
   prostate,
   volume; (c)
   Cowper's
   glands, lubri-
   cation

6. List the structures through which an ovum passes, beginning with the site of ovum release, in the female reproductive system.

   (a)_____   (b)_____

   (c)_____   (d)_____

6. (a) ovary; (b)
   abdominal cavi-
   ty; (c) Fallo-
   pian tube or
   oviduct; (d)
   uterus

7. The structures that guide the ovum into the oviduct are the (a)_____. Fertilization usually occurs in the (b)_____(lower / upper) part of the oviduct.

7. (a) fimbria;
   (b) upper

8. The human embryo develops in the _____.

8. uterus

9. Glands in the female that are homologous to the male Cowper's glands are the _____ glands.

9. vestibular
   or Bartholin's

10. A special bone called the _____ helps support the penis in some mammals.

10. os penis

30-4 Copulation entails a regular sequence of acts in each species.

1. Copulation behavior in mice seems to be only a series of (a)_____. The female mouse who is receptive to mating will assume a posture referred to as (b)_____

_____.

1. (a) FAPs;
   (b) lordosis

30-5 Human copulation can be divided into four phases of response.

1. Major studies on human sexual behavior have been conducted by (a)_____, (b)_____, and (c)_____.

1. (a) Kinsey;
   (b) Masters;
   (c) Johnson

2. According to Masters and Johnson, there are four phases in a sexual cycle in humans; these are the (a)_____ _____, (b)_____, (c)_____, and (d)_____ phases.

2. (a) excitement;
   (b) plateau;
   (c) orgasmic;
   (d) resolution

3. True or False: The most effective stimuli for the arousal phase of the sexual cycle are visual.

3. True

4. An indication of sexual arousal in the human male is (a)_____. Along with this is contraction of the (b)_____, which pulls the testes closer to the body.

4. (a) erection of the penis; (b) spermatic cord

5. The Cowper's glands begin to secrete during the _____ _____ phase of the sexual cycle in the human male.

5. plateau

6. True or False: Sexual excitement reaches its peak during the resolution phase.

6. False

7. True or False: The same set of muscles in males produce both orgasm and ejaculation.

7. False

8. A difference between the human male and female sexual response is that the _____(male / female) can experience multiple orgasms.

8. female

30-6 Internal sexual organs also develop from a common primordium.

1. The embryological development of the reproductive system is connected to that of the _____.

1. kidney

2. The Wolffian duct of the embryo turns into the (a)_____ _____ in human males. The Müllerian duct in the early embryo becomes the (b)_____ and (c)_____ in females.

2. (a) vas deferens;
   (b) uterus;
   (c) uterine tube or

3. The region in the embryo from which gonads develop is the (a)_____. The germ cells (b)_____(do / do not) develop in the latter.

408

Fallopian tube
or oviduct

30-7 The gonads produce steroid sex hormones.

3. (a) genital
ridge;
(b) do not

1. The two endocrine organs that produce hormones involved in

human sexual activity are the (a)_____ and

(b)_____.

1. (a) pituitary;
(b) gonads

2. The endocrine portions of the testis are the (a)_____

_____. They produce a group of

hormones called (b)_____, the main one

of which is (c)_____.

2. (a) Leydig
cells; (b)
androgens;
(c) testos-
terone

3. Androgens produce what secondary sex characteristics in
the following animals?

(a) lion _____   (b) rooster _____

(c) deer _____   (d) human larynx _____

3. (a) mane;
(b) comb; (c)
antlers; (d)
Adam's apple

4. The release of an ovum from a follicle is called _____

_____.

4. ovulation

5. List the two endocrine structures of the human ovary and
the hormones they secrete.

(a)_____ _____

(b)_____ _____

5. (a) follicle,
estrogens; (b)
corpus luteum,
progesterone
and estrogen

6. What hormone serves as the precursor for estradiol,

cortisol, and aldosterone? _____

*30-8 Luteinizing hormone stimulates testosterone production in
males.*

6. testosterone

1. List the gonadotropins produced by the anterior pituitary
in human males, their target, and their effect on the
target.

(a)_____ _____ ___ _____

(b)_____ _____ _____

1. (a) LH, inter-
stitial cells,
testosterone

409

30-9 The female cycle results from an interplay of hormones.

1. The first menstruation in a human female is termed

    _____.

2. Development of a follicle in the ovary is stimulated by

    the pituitary hormone (a)_____. Ovulation
    and formation of the corpus luteum occur under the in-

    fluence of the hormone (b)_____.

3. The follicular phase of the ovary corresponds to the

    _____ phase of the endometrium.

4. Proliferation of the cells of the endometrium is

    stimulated by (a)_____, whereas the vascu-

    larity is maintained by (b)_____.

5. The luteal phase of the ovary corresponds to the _____

    _____ phase in the endometrium.

30-10 Other mammals ovulate on a different schedule.

1. Estrus in nonhuman animals begins when (a)_____
    levels are high. Animals that ovulate as a result of

    copulation are called (b)_____.

30-11 A new set of hormonal pathways opens up during pregnancy.

1. In humans, fertilization must occur within (a)_____
    hours of ovulation. The hostile acid environment of the
    female reproductive tract is made more alkaline by

    (b)_____ fluid from the male.

2. A hormone produced as a result of implantation of the

    blastocyst in the endometrium is (a)_____

    _____. The effect of this hormone is to

    maintain the (b)_____ in order

    to keep levels of the hormone (c)_____
    high.

2. (a) chorionic
   gonadotropin;
   (b) corpus
   luteum; (c)
   progesterone

3. (a) relaxin;
   (b) oxytocin

4. (a) prolactin;
   (b) oxytocin

3. Two hormones that facilitate the birth process are
   (a)_____ and (b)_____.

4. The hormone that stimulates milk production is (a)_____
   _____, whereas (b)_____ stimulates
   milk "let-down."

PRACTICE QUIZ

1. Hybrids produced by interspecific animal breedings are:
   a. usually heartier and stronger.
   b. more fertile than nonhybrids.
   c. usually weaker than nonhybrids.
   d. impossible to produce.

2. The criterion for defining a species is _____ isolation.
   a. territorial
   b. reproductive
   c. psychological
   d. mechanical barrier

3. Pheromones are important in the proper pairing of gametes in:
   a. great crested grebes.
   b. humans.
   c. rhesus monkeys.
   d. herring gulls.

4. The _____ is not an "indifferent" reproductive structure in the human embryo.
   a. scrotum
   b. labioscrotal swelling
   c. genital ridge
   d. glans

5. The center of the embryonic labioscrotal swelling becomes the _____ in the female.
   a. scrotum
   b. labia minora
   c. labia majora
   d. vaginal opening

6. The structure into which sperm pass after their production in the seminiferous tubule is the:
   a. urethra.
   b. ejaculatory duct.
   c. epididymis.
   d. vas deferens.

7. Which of the following is part of the tubular portion of the male reproductive

411

system?
a. prostate
b. epididymis
c. seminal vesicles
d. Cowper's glands

8. Hormones that stimulate mitosis of epithelial cells of the endometrium are:
a. secreted from the anterior pituitary.
b. classified as tropic hormones.
c. estrogens.
d. nonsteroidal.

9. Which of the following is(are) not an endocrine structure?
a. spermatogenic epithelium
b. mature ovarian follicle
c. corpus luteum
d. interstitial cells of testis

10. The entrance to the uterus is called the:
a. fimbria.
b. hymen.
c. introitus.
d. cervix.

11. Which of the following statements is not true of the blastocyst?
a. It is formed during passage down the oviduct.
b. It forms during the second month of pregnancy.
c. It results from mitosis of the zygote.
d. It implants in the endometrium.

12. The first to publish studies in human sexual behavior was:
a. Masters.
b. Johnson.
c. Kinsey.
d. McGill.

13. Which of the following gives the proper sequence of phases of the human sexual cycle?
a. excitement, plateau, orgasmic, resolution
b. resolution, excitement, plateau, orgasmic
c. excitement, resolution, plateau, orgasmic
d. plateau, orgasmic, excitement, resolution

14. FSH and LH:
a. are secreted from the posterior pituitary.
b. have no effect in males.
c. are secreted in both males and females.
d. are secreted from the hypothalamus.

15. Estrogen, progesterone, and testosterone are:
a. amino acid derivatives.
b. steroids.
c. peptides.
d. proteins.

16. The corpus luteum in humans secretes:
a. luteinizing hormone.

      b. estrogen only.
      c. progesterone only.
      d. estrogens and progesterone.

17. Vascularity of the endometrium is maintained by:
      a. estrogen.
      b. LH.
      c. progesterone.
      d. FSH.

18. The endometrial phase that corresponds to the follicular phase in the ovary
      is:
      a. characterized by an increase in vascularity.
      b. the phase that follows ovulation.
      c. the proliferative phase.
      d. a response to high progesterone levels.

REVIEW QUESTIONS

I. The menstrual cycle in human females includes changes in pituitary hormone
levels, changes in ovarian structures, and changes in the endometrium of the
uterus. This carefully balanced cycle requires four major hormones. Show the role
of each of these hormones in the cycle by completing the following chart, listing
hormones in order of their appearance in the cycle.

Hormone	Source	Target Tissue	Effect	Control
1. _____	_____	_____	_____	_____
2. _____	_____	_____	_____	_____
3. _____	_____	_____	_____	_____
4. _____	_____	_____	_____	_____

II. Birth control pills consist of estrogens and progesterone. The pills are
generally taken for around 24 days and then discontinued, after which menstruation
begins. Explain this in view of the chart you just completed and your knowledge of
the menstrual cycle, using the following guides for your answer.

      1. Effect of high levels of estrogen on FSH _____

      _____

      2. Effect of high levels of estrogen on ovarian follicle _____

      _____

      3. Effect of high levels of estrogen on ovulation _____

      _____

413

4. Effect of estrogen on endometrial lining _____

_____

5. Effect of progesterone on endometrium _____

_____

6. Effect of drop in progesterone when pills are discontinued _____

_____

III. Why does ovulation not occur during pregnancy, and why does sloughing of the endometrium not occur?

1. First few months _____

_____

_____

2. Three to nine months _____

_____

IV. Trace the path of a spermatozoan from its point of formation in the male to its role in fertilizing the ovum in the female.

_____

_____

_____

V. The primordia for the human male and female genitalia are "indifferent," meaning that they could become either male or female genitalia. List the homologous male and female structures.

Indifferent Structure	Male	Female
1. glans	_____	_____
2. labioscrotal swelling	_____	_____
3. central region of labioscrotal swelling	_____	_____
4. Wolffian duct	_____	_____
5 Müllerian duct	_____	_____
6. yolk sac endoderm	_____	_____

VI. Development of the breast, lactation, and release of milk require hormonal and other stimuli. Explain the entire mechanism, in terms of the appropriate stimuli, using the following guide.

Event	Stimulatory or Inhibitory Influence
1. growth of mammary tissue	_____ _____
2. inhibition of milk formation during pregnancy	_____ _____
3. inhibition of prolactin secretion during pregnancy	_____ _____
4. production of milk following birth	_____ _____
5. decreased synthesis of PIF	_____ _____
6. "let-down" of milk	_____ _____
7. oxytocin secretion	_____ _____

ANSWER TO CHAPTER EXERCISES

Practice Quiz

1. c	4. a	7. b	10. d	13. a	16. d
2. b	5. d	8. c	11. b	14. c	17. c
3. c	6. c	9. a	12. c	15. b	18. c

Review Questions

I.	1. FSH	anterior pituitary	ovary	follicle development	estrogen levels
	2. LH	anterior pituitary	ovary	ovulation and corpus luteum formation	estrogen-progesterone levels

415

3.	estrogens	ovarian follicle, corpus luteum	endometrial lining	cell proliferation	FSH levels
4.	progesterone	corpus luteum	endometrium	increased vascularity	LH levels

II. 1. Inhibit FSH secretion
    2. No FSH, no follicle development
    3. No mature follicle, no ovulation
    4. Proliferation of lining cells
    5. Increased vascularity
    6. Vascularity cannot be maintained without progesterone, therefore sloughing occurs.

III. 1. Chorionic gonadotropin maintains the corpus luteum, which continues to secrete the estrogens and progesterone that inhibit FSH secretion and maintain endometrial vascularity.
     2. The placenta secretes progesterone, which does the same thing.

IV. Seminiferous tubules, collecting ducts, epididymis, vas deferens, ejaculatory ducts, urethra, vagina, cervix, uterus, Fallopian tube

V. 1. penis   clitoris
   2. scrotum   labia majora
   3. raphe   vaginal opening
   4. vas deferens   –
   5.   –   uterus, uterine tubes
   6. testicular   ovarian germ cells
      germ cells

VI. 1. estrogen and progesterone levels
     2. lack of prolactin hormone, high levels of progesterone
     3. presence of prolactin inhibitory factor (PIF)
     4. lack of synthesis of PIF
     5. neural signal resulting from sucking reflex
     6. presence of oxytocin
     7. neural signal resulting from sucking reflex

Chapter 31

THE BIOSPHERE AND ECOSYSTEM STRUCTURE

WHAT'S IN THIS CHAPTER

No one is an island; no organism lives alone. Each plant and animal is part of an ecosystem that is affected by the interaction of many physical factors, including the sun, wind patterns, and the major bodies of water and their currents. This chapter introduces such physical factors and the relationship among climate, vegetation, and soil. In addition, this chapter includes a survey of the biogeochemical cycles found in ecosystems, focusing on the water, sulfur, and nitrogen cycles. What is the significance of these cycles? What drives them? What organisms are involved? These questions will be answered here, and you will be provided some insight into what happens to an ecosystem that is drastically altered. Finally, you will learn about the movement of energy through an ecosystem--which does not cycle like water or carbon--and how organisms are involved with this one-way energy flow.

By the end of this chapter you should be able to:

1. Name the most important factors that determine wind patterns on earth and describe their influence.

2. Compare the movement of wind on the face of the earth to the flow of water currents in the oceans.

3. Explain how continents and mountains affect precipitation.

4. Define biome.

5. Explain how climate, vegetation, and soil are interrelated.

6. Describe the water cycle.

7. Explain how soil is formed from solid bedrock.

8. Name three different and important soil types, and tell where each is found.

9. Give an example of an organism that creates many microfilaments.

10. Define ecoline and give an example.

417

11. Compare the nitrogen cycle to the sulfur cycle.

12. Explain what happens to water and biogeochemical cycles when organisms are removed from the ecosystem.

13. Differentiate between succession and turnover.

14. Relate successional changes within an ecosystem to changes in productivity, diversity, stability, and species composition.

WHAT YOU SHOULD ALREADY KNOW

You have already been introduced to the cast of characters that one can find within a community (Chapter 5), so you should be familiar with the kinds of organisms that inhabit a community and what their fundamental roles are. You have also been introduced to the kinds of biological molecules that make up an organism and the kinds of atoms that make up biological molecules.

In this chapter you will see that, as organisms are eaten, atoms and energy are passed along but that only the chemical elements are returned to their original source--the soil or the atmosphere. Energy is continually being used by and lost from living organisms and must be replenished by the energy from the sun. To understand this interrelationship between the physical and the biological worlds, you should review Chapters 4 and 5.

Pre-Test

1. The four most important chemical elements found in biological systems are (a)_____, (b)_____, (c)_____, and (d)_____.

1. (a) carbon;
   (b) hydrogen;
   (c) oxygen;
   (d) nitrogen

2. All organisms consist largely of the compound (a)_____. Give two reasons why this molecule is important to life on earth. (b)_____

_____

and (c)_____

_____

2. (a) water; (b) and (c) Water is a universal solvent. It boils at a higher temperature and freezes at a lower

3. A community is _____

_____.

temperature
than many other
solvents. Che-
mical reactions
take place in
water. When
water freezes,
it expands
and floats.

3. a collection
of different
species living
in the same
habitat and in-
teracting with
each other

4. Ecosystems operate on a flow of energy that comes from the

(a)_____. Energy can be neither (b)_____

_____ nor (c)_____, but it can

be (d)_____.

4. (a) sun;
(b) created;
(c) destroyed;
(d) transformed

GUIDED REVIEW OF THE CHAPTER

*31-1 The sun and the earth's rotation create prevailing wind
patterns.*

1. Prevailing wind patterns on earth are created by the

earth's (a)_____ and by unequal (b)_____

_____.

1. (a) rotation;
(b) heating of
the earth

2. The earth receives more energy per unit of area at the

(a)_____ than anywhere else. This

is because (b)_____

_____.

2. (a) equator;
(b) sunlight
strikes the
earth most
directly there

3. Hadley cells are _____

_____.

3. rotating cells
of air in the
atmosphere
created by the
movement of
meridional
winds

4. Because of the Coriolis force, in the Northern Hemisphere
a low-pressure center acquires a counterclockwise movement

around it, creating a (a)_____. In
the same hemisphere, a high-pressure center acquires a

clockwise movement around it, creating an (b)_____.

4. (a) cyclone; (b) anticyclone

31-2 *Ocean currents flow in similar rotation patterns.*

1. Because water is much denser and more viscous than air, the flow of water differs from that of air in that

(a)_____

_____. Also, because solar heat is delivered only to the upper level of the ocean, there is much circulation in the (b)_____(upper / lower) level and little circulation (c)_____(above / below).

1. (a) water circulates vertically much more slowly than air; (b) upper; (c) below

2. A water current is (a)_____

_____.

Water currents are reservoirs of (b)_____

_____.

2. (a) a great mass of water whose temperature does not change quickly; (b) heat or cold

3. The Gulf Stream current flows in the (a)_____

Ocean and has a (b)_____(warming / cooling) influence. The Humboldt current flows in the

(c)_____ Ocean and has a (d)_____ (warming / cooling) influence.

3. (a) Atlantic; (b) warming; (c) Pacific; (d) cooling

31-3 *Precipitation falls in a zonal pattern across the continents.*

1. (a)_____(Warm / Cool) air can hold more water.

Precipitation occurs as water-saturated air (b)_____

_____

_____.

1. (a) Warm; (b) rises and cools until it can no longer hold all of its water vapor

2. In North America, the chief influences on rainfall patterns are the (a)_____. If there were no continents, rainfall would be distributed

over the earth (b)_____

_____.

2. (a) mountain ranges; (b) in several uniform belts

3. How are rain shadows formed? _____

_____

_____

_____ .

3. Moisture-laden winds are forc- ed upward on the western mountain slopes where they cool and deposit their moisture. The dry winds then cross over to the eastern slopes of these mountains, leaving little precipitation

31-4 The relationship between climate, vegetation, and soil.

1. Climate is determined by the pattern of (a)_____

_____ in combination with the (b)_____

_____ .

1. (a) precipita- tion; (b) temperature

2. The climate determines the major types of (a)_____

_____ , which, in combination with climate, is the

major determinant of (b)_____ .

2. (a) vegetation; (b) soil type

3. The earth's major ecosystem types, or (a)_____ ,

are characterized mainly by their (b)_____ .

3. (a) biomes; (b) vegetation

4. Around the North Pole, the major climate determinant is

(a)_____ . The three

broad climatic zones around the North Pole are the

(b)_____ , which is perpetual

ice and frost; the (c)_____ , which is

dominated by grasses and mosses; and the (d)_____ ,
which is made up of coniferous forest.

4. (a) the low temperature; (b) polar ice cap; (c) tundra; (d) taiga

31-5 The biosphere operates on a flow of water.

1. About 95% of all the earth's water is bound (a)_____

_____ ; the other 5% freely circu-

lates in the water, or (b)_____ , cycle. Of

this circulating water, 97% is in the (c)_____ ,
and most of the rest is bound up for long times in

(d)_____ .

1. (a) chemically in rocks; (b) hydrologic;

2. Evapotranspiration is _____

_____ .

(c) oceans;
(d) glaciers or ice caps

2. the combination of evaporation from the earth's surface and transpiration from plants into the atmosphere

3. There is more evaporation than precipitation of water over the (a)_____(land / ocean). The evaporation of water is powered by the (b)_____.

3. (a) ocean;
(b) sun

4. Water is a primary agent in soil formation because it is involved in (a)_____, wherein large pieces of rock are broken down into tiny fragments and because, as it seeps down through the soil, it (b)_____

_____

_____.

4. (a) weathering;
(b) transforms soil minerals chemically, leaching some elements from higher levels and depositing them at lower levels

31-6 Climate and vegetation largely determine soil types.

1. The underlying bedrock may be (a)_____, which is formed upon the cooling of molten magma from the earth's core; (b)_____, which is formed by the deposition of layers of sediment from water and wind; or (c)_____, which has been formed by the action of heat and the enormous pressure of other rock masses.

1. (a) igneous rock; (b) sedimentary rock; (c) metamorphic rock

2. Water is an effective weathering agent because as it passes through the atmosphere, it becomes _____

_____.

2. a dilute carbonic acid solution containing H^+ and HCO_3^- ions

3. Humus is _____

_____.

3. a black or brown complex of decaying plant and animal material

4. If a soil that is rich in ions such as potassium, magnesium, and iron is continually subjected to mildly acid rainfall, the soil will become (a)_____

_____

because (b)_____

_____.

4. (a) poor in
mineral ions
and acidic;
(b) the
mineral ions
are displaced
by the more
strongly bind-
ing hydrogen
ions

5. A common soil of the western mountains is (a)_____, which has few minerals in the upper layer. A common soil of American plains is (b)_____ with a deep humus layer. A common soil of the tropics is the deep, loose, red (c)_____ with extensive leaching.

5. (a) podzol;
(b) chernozem;
(c) latosol

6. Plants play an important role in nutrient cycles because they continually absorb minerals through their (a)_____ _____ and bring them up above the surface; they are eventually deposited on the ground as (b)_____ and then (c)_____ back into the soil.

6. (a) roots;
(b) litter;
(c) leached

31-7 An ecosystem creates its own microclimate and micro-habitats.

1. Forests are (a)_____ (warmer / cooler) during the winter than the surrounding areas. Inside the forest it is (b)_____(more / less) humid than the surrounding areas.

1. (a) warmer;
(b) more

2. Give an example of an organism that can be a cluster of microhabitats. _____

_____

2. a tree can
offer micro-
habitats to
birds,
squirrels,
algae, moss,
insects, and
plants on its
bark or leaves
or under its
shade.

3. In a symbiotic mycorrhizal association, the fungus provides the plant with (a)_____

_____ while the plant provides the fungus with (b)_____ _____.

3. (a) a means for
the uptake of
water and

31-8 Species distribute themselves along environmental gradients.

1. Each plant species is distributed in its own way along the

423

minerals;
(b) organic
nutrients

gradients of (a)_____, (b)_____ and

(c)_____.

1. (a) tempera-
ture; (b)
altitude; (c)
soil types

2. An _____ is a gradual change in ecosystem type.

31-9 Nitrogen cycles primarily as a component of protein.

2. ecoline

1. Matter flows through an ecosystem in a series of _____

_____ cycles.

1. biogeochemical

2. Nitrogen is a component of the macromolecules (a)_____

_____ and _____.

About (b)_____% of our atmosphere is nitrogen gas.

2. (a) protein and
nucleic acid;
(b) 80

3. The three major flows of the nitrogen cycle are the

(a)_____, as one organism eats another; (b)_____

_____, wherein nitrate and nitrite are

converted to atmospheric nitrogen; and (c)_____

_____, wherein atmospheric nitrogen is
converted to ammonia.

3. (a) food chain;
(b) denitrifi-
cation; (c)
nitrogen
fixation

4. *Nitrosomonas* is a chemautotroph that lives by oxidizing

(a)_____ to (b)_____. *Nitrobacter*

lives by oxidizing (c)_____ to (d)_____.

4. (a) ammonia;
(b) nitrite;
(c) nitrite;
(d) nitrate

31-10 Sulfur undergoes complex oxidations and reductions.

1. Sulfur cycles through the biosphere as a component of

(a)_____. Most of the rest of the sulfur is

found in (b)_____ (the atmosphere /
rock deposits).

1. (a) proteins;
(b) rock depo-
sits

2. Sulfides (a)_____ (inhibit / stimulate) the
growth of most organisms. Some bacteria oxidize sufide

to (b)_____ and phototrophic bacteria can

oxidize sufide to (c)_____.

2. (a) inhibit;
(b) sulfur;
(c) sulfate

3. Some sulfur enters the atmosphere as (a)_____

when (b)_____ is burned. This sulfur compound

then combines with rainwater to form (c)_____

_____.

3. (a) SO_2; (b)
coal or oil;
(c) acid rain

<p>

31-11 *Components of the ecosystem are always turning over,
sometimes rapidly.*

1. "Turning over of nutrients" is _____

_____.

1. the process
whereby nu-
trients are
removed from
a tissue
or ecosystem
and replaced
by new
molecules

2. Nutrient turnover in a lake occurs more quickly in

(a)_____ (winter / summer). Nutrient turnover

occurs more quicly in a (b)_____ (tropical /
temperate) forest.

2. (a) summer;
(b) tropical

3. Most of the nutrients taken up from the soil in a forest

accumulate as (a)_____, while

10-20% accumulate in (b)_____.

3. (a) ground
litter;
(b) trees

31-12 *The ecosystem is always losing nutrients.*

1. In the Hubbard Brook experiments, it was found that most

of the nutrients come from (a)_____

and a small input from salts carried by (b)_____

_____.

1. (a) weathered
bedrock; (b)
airborne sea-
water droplets

2. After clearcutting at Hubbard Brook, the total runoff of

nutrients (a)_____ (increased / decreased) by

about (b)_____ times.

2. (a) increased;
(b) eight

3. In an undisturbed forest, about 40% of the water leaves

the ecosystem by (a)_____; in a

cleared forest, most water leaves by (b)_____.

3. (a) transpira-
tion; (b)
runoff

31-13 *Communities replace one another in succession.*

1. An ecosystem changes through time. In (a)_____

_____ one community gradually replaces

425

another, whereas in (b)_____,
some community members are replaced by new species. The
series of plant types that replace one another through

time is called (c)_____.

1. (a) ecological
succession; (b)
species turn-
over; (c) sere

2. Beginning with a newly formed beaver pond, some of the

first organisms to arrive are (a)_____,
small floating plants and animals. After a few years, in
the open water at the middle of the pond, you will find

(b)_____ plants with roots in the mud
below and shoots emerging from the water.

2. (a) plankton;
(b) emergent

3. Distinguish between primary and secondary succession.

_____

_____

_____

3. Primary suc-
cession begins
with a lifeless
physical envi-
ronment such as
bare rock; sec-
ondary succes-
sion begins
with an eco-
system that has
been disturbed

4. How are the activities of organisms in a community the
driving force for succession and species turnover?

_____

_____

_____

_____

4. Every change
leads to fur-
ther changes.
The activities
of organisms
change environ-
mental condi-
tions so it is
easier for
other organisms
to move in.

31-14 Communities become more diverse in successions.

1. The community at the beginning of a sere is (a)_____
(more / less) diverse than the one at the end. The

community at the beginning lasts for (b)_____
(more / fewer) years than the one at the end.

1. (a) less;
(b) fewer

2. According to Hutchinson and MacArthur, the greater the di-

versity of a community, the greater its _____.

2. stability

*31-15 The species in a community may be continually replacing
one another.*

1. According to MacArthur and Wilson, the species on an

island should become extinct at a rate proportional to the

(a)_____

and the island should be colonized by immigration at a

rate proportional to the (b)_____

_____.

1. (a) number of
species already
there; (b) the
number of
species al-
ready there

2. When Wilson and Simberloff fumigated the Florida Keys islands, they found that the islands were recolonized by a

number of species to a level (a)_____

_____(comparable to / vastly different from) what had originally been there and that the species composition was (b)_____(similar to / different from) the original composition.

2. (a) comparable
to; (b) dif-
ferent from

*31-16 Producers use only small amounts of the available light
energy for growth.*

1. Distinguish between gross primary productivity and net primary productivity.

_____

_____

_____

_____

1. Gross primary
productivity
is the amount
of light cap-
tured in photo-
synthesis; net
primary pro-
ductivity is
the gross pro-
ductivity minus
the amount of
energy used by
the plant in
respiration.

2. The gross primary productivity of most ecosystems is about

_____(75 / 30 / 2) percent of the incoming light.

31-17 Higher trophic levels have low conversion efficiencies.

1. As energy is passed from one trophic level to the next,

there is about (a)_____ percent decrease in the biomass due in large part to the energy lost through

(b)_____ and (c)_____

_____.

2. 2

1. (a) 90; (b)
respiration;
(c) decomposi-
tion

2. The number of trophic levels in a community _____(is / is not) related to the productivity of the community.

2. is not

31-18 Seral stages show certain trends in productivity.

1. Early seral stages have a (a)_____(high / low)

   productivity and a (b)_____(great / small)
   biomass compared to later seral stages.

1. (a) high;
   (b) small

2. The net productivity of seral stages _____
   (increases / decreases) through the sere.

2. decreases

PRACTICE QUIZ

1. Which of the following has the <u>least</u> to do with prevailing wind patterns over
   the face of the earth?
   a. vegetation
   b. Coriolis force
   c. sunlight
   d. rotation of the earth

2. Ocean currents affect world climate because:
   a. currents create wind patterns.
   b. currents carry plants and animals great distances from their native lands.
   c. currents hold heat and cold.
   d. water circulates much more slowly than air.

3. Much of Hawaii is covered with a lush forest, but there are very dry areas on
   certain islands. This is because:
   a. the islands stretch across many climatic zones.
   b. the soil is very porous in the dry areas.
   c. a rain shadow has been created by certain mountains.
   d. the wind is so strong in certain places that the soil dries out.

4. Which of the following is a biome?
   a. all of the chernozem soil around the world
   b. a large grass plant
   c. a field of corn
   d. a short grass prairie

5. _____ would increase if all of the plants were to be removed from a
   community.
   a. Transpiration
   b. Runoff
   c. The herbivore population
   d. The nutrient content in the soil

6. _____ is <u>not</u> an important part of soil formation from bedrock.
   a. Sedimentation
   b. Weathering
   c. Carbonic acid action
   d. Plant growth and decay

7. _____ is a characteristic of tropical latoscl soils.
   a. Deep humus

    b. Extensive leaching
    c. Rich farmland
    d. Brown or black color

8. In which of the following biogeochemical cycles do bacteria and fungi play an insignificant role?
    a. water cycle
    b. sulfur cycle
    c. nitrogen cycle
    d. carbon cycle

9. Which of the following is a characteristic of the plants early in succession?
    a. perennial
    b. large biomass
    c. reproduce infrequently
    d. quick reproducers

10. Which of the following is a characteristic of the community early in succession?
    a. large biomass
    b. high net productivity
    c. high diversity
    d. great stability

REVIEW QUESTIONS

I. Fill in all the blanks in the following table, which concerns the interaction of climate, vegetation, and soil types.

Climate	Vegetation	Soil Type
(a)_____	rain forest	(b)_____
(c)_____	(d)_____	chernozem
arid	(e)_____	(f)_____
(g)_____	(h)_____	waterlogged and frozen soil

II. Use the following key to answer the next eight items.

        Key: a. I is greater than II.
              b. II is greater than I.
              c. I and II are nearly equal.

_____ 1. Turnover rate of phosphates in lakes in (I) summer or (II) winter

_____ 2. Turnover rate of phosphates in (I) lakes or (II) oceans

_____ 3. Turnover rate of nutrients in (I) forests or (II) lakes

_____ 4. Turnover rate of nutrients in (I) tropical forests or (II) temperate forests

_____ 5. Accumulation of nutrients in (I) forests or (II) plowed fields

_____ 6. Diversity in (I) early seral stages or (II) late seral stages

_____ 7. Ratio of gross productivity to biomass in (I) early seral stages or (II) late seral stages

_____ 8. Biomass of (I) all producers in a community or (II) all herbivores in a community

III. Use the following diagram, which illustrates pond succession, to answer the next eight items. Choose A, B, C, or D.

_____ 1. Where plankton would be found

_____ 2. Where emergent plants would be found

_____ 3. An autotrophic community

_____ 4. Next community to be invaded by trees

_____ 5. Where most different kinds of annual flowering plants would be found

_____ 6. Where most different kinds of birds are found

_____ 7. Youngest seral stage

_____ 8. Climax community

IV. Use the following table to answer the next seven items.

Biome	Annual Precipitation	Annual Rainfall Pattern	Average Annual Temperature
A	250 cm	regular	30°C
B	25 cm	regular	0°C
C	75 cm	regular	20°C
D	15 cm	irregular	30°C

_____ 1. Which represents a desert?

_____ 2. Which represents a tropical rain forest?

_____ 3. Which represents a deciduous forest in the United States?

_____ 4. Which represents a tundra?

_____ 5. In which is temperature the most important determinant?

_____ 6. In which would you find the smallest biomass at the producer level?

_____ 7. In which would you find the fastest turnover of nutrients?

V. Use the following diagram to answer the next six items about the nitrogen cycle.

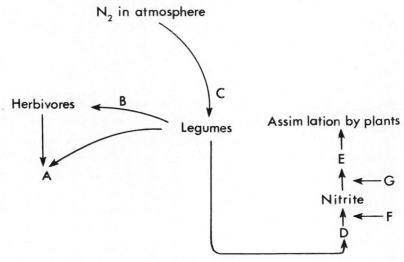

_____ 1. Letter that represents ammonia

_____ 2. Letter that represents *Nitrobacter*

_____ 3. Letter that represents nitrogen fixation

_____ 4. Letter that represents nitrate

_____ 5. Letter that represents *Nitrosomonas*

_____ 6. Letter that represents decay and excretion

ANSWERS TO CHAPTER EXERCISES

Practice Quiz

1. a	3. c	5. b	7. b	9. d
2. c	4. d	6. a	8. a	10. b

Review Questions

I. (a) superhumid, (b) laterite, (c) subhumid dry, (d) midgrass prairie, (e) desert plants, (f) sierozems, (g) tundra, (h) mosses and lichens

II.	1. a	3. b	5. a	7. a
	2. a	4. a	6. b	8. a

431

III. 1. A   3. A or B   5. C   7. A
     2. B   4. C   6. D   8. D

IV. 1. D   3. C   5. B   7. A
    2. A   4. B   6. D

V. 1. D   3. C   5. F
   2. G   4. E   6. A

Chapter 32

THE STRUCTURE AND GENETICS OF POPULATIONS

WHAT'S IN THIS CHAPTER

Individuals take in energy, grow, and reproduce. Each individual's genetic makeup
determines its ability to take in energy and its success at producing offspring.
In the long-term evolutionary sense, the individual's importance is secondary to
that of the population. Populations evolve, not individuals, and in this chapter
you will be introduced to the interface between ecology and evolution: population
genetics. The chapter begins with a description of an idealized population, one
that never exists in the real world. This is necessary to develop a model that
will allow us to predict what will happen to the population once the selective
forces of the real world are applied. The genetic makeup of populations will be
related to the genes found in individuals, including how genetic variation arises
in individuals and how this affects populations. You will learn how to predict the
growth of populations and why populations are limited in size.

By the end of this chapter you should be able to:

1. Explain the difference between random mating and assortative mating.

2. Calculate the gene frequency of a population.

3. State the Hardy-Weinberg equilibrium law.

4. Define _fitness_ and relate it to the coefficient of selection.

5. Give an example of hybrid vigor.

6. Explain the significance of a supergene.

7. Describe the effect of inversions and translocations.

8. Define balanced polymorphism.

9. Write and explain the general equation for growth.

10. Explain how population size is related to carrying capacity.

11. Define the birth rate and the death rate of a population.

12. Draw the survivorship curve of a human population.

13. Compare individuals produced by r selection to individuals produced by K selection.

14. Cite an example of a density-dependent factor and an example of a density-independent factor.

WHAT YOU SHOULD ALREADY KNOW

This chapter deals with individuals as parts of populations and explores how the genetic makeup of individuals manifests itself in the genetic makeup of the population. You should be familiar with the different levels of biological organizations--individuals, populations, and communities. Information about the genetic structure and function of organisms is found throughout the text, because genes are important to the functioning of an individual and to its production of offspring. The most important chapters you should review before starting this chapter are Chapter 3 (Sections 3-8 to 3-12 particularly), Chapter 13 (review Section 13-4) and all of Chapter 15.

Pre-Test

1. Genes are located on (a)_____. There may be two or more forms, or (b)_____, of each gene.

1. (a) chromo-
somes; (b)
alleles

2. A gene indirectly controls chemical reactions by coding for the formation of (a)_____. A mutation is (b)_____

_____.

2. (a) proteins;
(b) an altera-
tion in the
nucleotide or-
der or chromo-
some structure
that affects
the genotype,
and perhaps the
phenotype, of
the organism

3. The chances that two events will happen together is the (a)_____ of the chances of their happening (b)_____.

3. (a) product;
(b) indepen-
dently

4. An allele is dominant if (a)_____

_____

_____.

For a recessive allele to show up in the phenotype of an

434

organism, (b)_____

_____.

4. (a) in a heter-   5. Two genes are linked if they _____
   ozygous condi-
   tion, the
   allele deter-   _____.
   mines the pheno-
   type of the
   organism; (b)
   it must be
   found in a
   double dose

5. are found on
   the same
   chromosome

GUIDED REVIEW OF THE CHAPTER

32-1 Organisms in a Mendelian population mate at random.

1. The classical theory of population genetics is based on an

   ideal population that is (a)_____(large /

   small) in which mating occurs (b)_____.

1. (a) large; (b)   2. In (a)_____ mating, individuals show
   at random   some preference for certain other individuals. In random

                             mating, mating is subject to the laws of (b)_____

                             _____.

2. (a) assorta-   3. In a population of 40 mice with black fur and 60 mice with
   tive; (b)   white fur, the probability that two black-furred mice will
   probability

                             mate at random is (a)_____. If there is
                             assortative mating, the probability that two black-furred

                             mice will mate (b)_____.

3. (a) 16%; (b)   *32-2 The genetic composition of a Mendelian population should
   cannot be   remain constant.*
   determined

                        1. (a)_____ and (b)_____ helped lay
                            the foundation of population genetics.

1. (a) Hardy;   2. For each gene locus, an individual carries (a)_____
   (b) Weinberg
                            (how many?) alleles. p is the (b)_____

435

_____. q is the (c)_____

_____.

2. (a) 2; (b) fraction of all allelles of a gene that are dominant; (c) fraction of all alleles of a gene that are recessive

3. In a randomly breeding population, the probability (in terms of p and q) of an AA zygote being formed is

(a)_____. The probability of an Aa zygote

being formed is (b)_____. The probability of

an aa zygote being formed is (c)_____.

3. (a)p^2; (b) 2pq; (c) q^2

4. $p^2 + 2pq + q^2$ = (a)_____. In a randomly

breeding population with no (b)_____ or

(c)_____, the ratio p^2 : 2pq : q^2 will

come to an (d)_____.

4. (a) 1; (b) mutation; (c) selection; (d) equilibrium

32-3 q may be determined from the frequency of homozygous recessives.

1. In the Hardy-Weinberg analysis, homozygous recessives are

designated (a)_____. They are used to cal-

culate gene frequencies in a population because (b)_____

_____.

1. (a) aa; (b) they can be easily recognized in the population

2. If a genetic condition is determined by a recessive allele and 16 people out of 100 show the condition, what is the frequency of this allele in the populaton of 100 people?

_____.

2. p = 0.4

32-4 Gene frequencies are changed by such factors as selection and mutation.

1. Fitness of a genotype is related to its _____

_____.

1. ability to reproduce

2. If the frequency of aa individuals is q^2, what does q^2 (1 − s) indicate?

_____

_____

2. the reduced

3. Two major factors that can change the frequency of an

fitness of a genotype that is less well adapted to a particular set of conditions, where $\underline{s}$ is the coefficient of selection against $\underline{aa}$

allele in a population are (a)_____ and

(b)_____.

3. (a) selection; (b) mutation

4. The general range of mutation rates is _____ per individual per generation for each gene locus.

4. 10^{-5} to 10^{-8}

32-5 Some regimes of selection are notoriously ineffective.

1. If the fitness of an individual is zero, it will produce

(a)_____ offspring, and $\underline{s}$ will equal (b)_____.

1. (a) no; (b) 1

2. A human genetic disease that causes death in childhood and that is the result of a recessive allele is difficult to

eliminate from the population because_____

_____

_____.

2. the allele that causes the disease is carried by heterozygotes in the populaton

3. If a genetic disease is caused by a recessive allele and occurs in one person out of 100, the frequency of the

allele is (a)_____. It would take (b)_____ generations to reduce the disease to the point where only 1 person out of 10,000 has it.

3. (a) 10%; (b) 90

32-6 The heterozygote is sometimes more fit than either homozygote.

1. Heterosis, or (a)_____, occurs when a cross is made between two organisms with

(b)_____(identical / different) genotypes.

1. (a) hybrid vigor; (b) different

2. Offspring from parents that are inbred are _____

_____(heterozygous / homozygous) at more loci than hybrid offspring.

2. homozygous

3. One reason why heterozygotes may exhibit superiority over

homozygotes is that _____

_____

_____.

3. heterozygotes may have two or more slightly different forms of an enzyme and thus will have biochemical versatility to grow better

4. In sickle-cell anemia in humans, (a)_____ (heterozygotes / homozygotes) have the greatest fitness in

the tropics because (b)_____

_____.

4. (a) heterozygotes; (b) malaria parasites cannot infect heterozygotes very well

32-7 Every organism is an integrated gene complex.

1. If a species has different forms, or (a)_____,

the species is (b)_____.

1. (a) morphs; (b) polymorphic

2. The frequency of recombination between two different genes

on different chromosomes is about (a)_____.

Genes are (b)_____ if they are on the same chromosome.

2. (a) 50%; (b) linked

3. Supergenes are _____

_____

_____.

3. genes with co-ordinated functions linked tightly together on the same chromosome

32-8 Genes can be rearranged by inversions and translocations.

1. Four different types of mutations involving entire chromo-

somes or parts of chromosomes are (a)_____,

(b)_____, (c)_____,

and (d)_____.

1. (a) deletions; (b) duplications; (c) inversion; (d) translocations

2. A (a)_____ occurs when a part of one chromosome breaks off and attaches to a nonhomologous

chromosome. This event (b)_____ linkage groups.

2. (a) translocation; (b) breaks up

3. Down's syndrome is a condition in humans that results when

_____

_____

3. there is a non-disjunction of chromosome 21 so the child receives three copies of the chromosome or when a segment of chromosome 21 is translocated onto another chromosome and passed on to the child

4. An (a)_____ occurs when a segment of genes in one chromosome is cut out and turned around. The two kinds of this mutation are (b)_____ and (c)_____.

4. (a) inversion; (b) paracentric; (c) pericentric

5. One advantage of an inversion or a translocation is that _____ _____.

5. it may be advantageous for two genes to become tightly linked

32-9 *Natural populations are highly polymorphic.*

1. The first indications of polymorphism in a populaton of organisms came from studies of _____.

1. *Drosophila*

2. The sequence of genes along a chromosome may be important because the expression of a gene may be influenced by its _____.

2. position

3. (a)_____ is the condition wherein two or more forms coexist in a population. This condition can occur because each form (b)_____ _____ _____ _____.

3. (a) Balanced polymorphism; (b) has a relatively high fitness under some condition, and the population survives

4. Electrophoretic analyses show that wild populations have allelic forms of many (a)_____. Some variation in a population is selectively neutral, meaning that the different alleles of a gene are carried along in the population because (b)_____

because these
forms are adap-
ted to differ-
ent conditions
_____.

4. (a) enzymes;
(b) there is
no selection
against any
of them

5. Give an example of a "balanced lethal" condition. _____

_____

_____

_____.

5. In *Drosophila*
the mutations
curly wing and
plum eye are
both lethal
genes by them-
selves, but the
recombinant
with curly wing
and plum eye
survives

32-10 Populations tend to grow exponentially.

1. Define each of the following symbols that are used to describe the growth of populations: $\underline{R}$ (a) $\underline{R}$ = _____

_____;

$\underline{N}_0$ (b) $\underline{N}_0$ = _____

_____; $\underline{g}$ (c) $\underline{g}$ = _____

_____

1. (a) replacement
rate, which is
the ratio of
numbers in one
generation to
the numbers in
the previous
generation; (b)
number of indi-
viduals in the
starting popu-
lation; (c)
number of
generations

2. $\underline{r}$ is the (a)_____

of a population. As long as $\underline{r}$ has a (b)_____
(positive / negative) value, the population will grow
exponentially.

2. (a) intrinsic
growth rate;
(b) positive

3. $\underline{N} = \underline{N}_0 e^{rt}$

3. The general equation for growth is _____.

32-11 All real populations are held to a maximum size.

1. _____(All / No) population(s) can continue to
grow forever.

1. No

2. Carrying capacity is _____

_____.

2. the maximum

3. When $\underline{N}$ = $\underline{K}$, the growth rate of the population is

440

number of in-
dividuals in
a population
that can be
supported in   _____.
a given
environment   *32-12 Survivorship curves show different patterns of repro-*
                              duction.

3. zero   1. The intrinsic growth rate of a population is the

                            difference between (a)_____ and

                            (b)_____ _____.

1. (a) fertility,   2. A survivorship curve is _____
   or birth rate;
   (b) mortality,   _____.
   or death rate

2. a graph showing   3. One kind of survivorship curve is demonstrated by oysters
   how many off-   and plants. Describe such a curve.
   spring of one
   generation in a   _____
   population sur-
   vive to reach   _____
   different ages
                            _____

                            _____

3. Huge numbers of   4. From an ecological point of view, there are three periods
   zygotes are
   produced, but   in an organism's life: (a)_____,
   the majority of
   them die very   (b)_____, and (c)_____
   quickly. The
   curve falls   _____.
   quickly and
   then levels
   off, with only
   a small frac-
   tion of zygotes
   growing to
   maturity and
   reproducing.

4. (a) prerepro-   5. In a graph of different age structures in a population, a
   ductive; (b)
   reproductive;   stable population is (a)_____ in
   (c) post-
   reproductive   shape, whereas a graph of a growing population has a very

                            broad base, indicating (b)_____

                            _____.

5. (a) rectangu-
   lar; (b) a

large number
of prerepro-
ductive in-
dividuals who
will soon be
reproducing

32-13 Two general ways of life.

1. An organism that lives in a short-lived habitat is an

   (a)_____ or a fugitive

   organism. An organism tha lives in a stable environment

   is an (b)_____ species.

1. (a) opportu-
   nistic; (b)
   equilibrium

2. <u>r</u> selection favors species that reproduce (a)_____

   _____(rapidly / after several years),

   that are (b)_____(short-lived /

   long-lived), and that reproduce (c)_____
   (several times / once).

2. (a) rapidly;
   (b) short-
   lived; (c)
   once

3. <u>K</u> selection produces species that reproduce (a)_____

   _____(rapidly / after several years), that

   are (b)_____(short-lived /

   long-lived), and that reproduce (c)_____
   (several times / once).

3. (a) after se-
   veral years;
   (b) long-lived;
   (c) several
   times

32-14 Population size is limited by many factors.

1. Density-independent factors are those that (a)_____

   _____.

   An example of such a factor is (b)_____

   _____.

1. (a) affect
   large and small
   concentrations
   of organisms
   equally; (b)
   harsh weather
   or fire

2. Density-dependent factors are those that (a)_____

   _____.

   An example of such a factor is (b)_____.

2. (a) affect a
   crowded popula-
   tion much more
   than a sparse
   one; (b)
   disease

32-15 Populations may be limited by physiological pressures
       associated with high density.

1. Fecundity is (a)_____

   _____. As the density of an animal

   population increases, its fecundity (b)_____
   (increases / decreases).

1. (a) the number

2. Animal populations may stop growing because of (a)_____

of offspring
produced by
each female;
(b) decreases

or   because   (b)_____

_____.

2. (a) the accumu-
   lation of sub-
   stances that
   inhibit their
   reproduction;
   (b) some animal
   populations are
   limited by hor-
   monal changes
   that result
   from the stress
   of crowding or
   from scarce
   food supplies

PRACTICE QUIZ

1. If 4 out of 100 individuals have a genetic disease caused by a double
   recessive, what is the gene frequency of the recessive allele?
   a. .20
   b. .04
   c. .16
   d. .40

2. Gene frequencies are defined so that, for a pair of alleles:
   a. $p = q$.
   b. $2pq = p + q$.
   c. $p^2 + q^2 = 2pq$.
   d. $p = 1 - q$.

3. Which of the following organisms has the greatest fitness?
   a. an individual with dominant alleles
   b. an individual whose coefficient of selection is 1
   c. an individual whose coefficient of selection is 0
   d. an individual with a mutation

4. Hybrid vigor may be the result of:
   a. isoenzymes.
   b. extra genes.
   c. homozygosity.
   d. sickle-cell anemia.

5. If the order of genes along a chromosome is ABCDEFGHI, which of the following
   represents an inversion?
   a. ABCDABCDEFGHI
   b. ABCIHGFED

c. IHGFEDCBA
d. ABFGHI

6. A population will increase exponentially if:
a. N_0 is large.
b. e is positive.
c. r is positive.
d. $t = 0$.

7. When a population approaches its carrying capacity, its:
a. birth rate becomes zero.
b. death rate becomes infinite.
c. birth rate minus its death rate becomes zero.
d. replacement rate becomes zero.

8. The survivorship curve of plants resembles that of:
a. humans.
b. birds.
c. oysters.
d. bacteria.

9. _____ are shaped most strongly by r selection.
a. Insects
b. Humans
c. Trees
d. Birds

10. In which of the following communities would you expect density-dependent factors to be least important?
a. tropical rain forest
b. temperate decidous forest
c. corn field
d. desert

REVIEW QUESTIONS

I. Use the following diagram to help you match each description on the left with the most appropriate order of genes on the right.

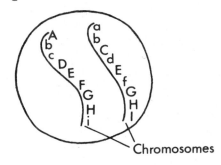

Chromosomes

_____ 1. a normal gamete

_____ 2. a translocation chromosome

_____ 3. an inversion chromosome (single)

_____ 4. a double inversion (no overlap of inversion)

a. adCbEfIHG

b. abCdEfGHIGHi

c. AbcDEFGHi

d. AbcGFEDHi

_____ 5. a double inversion (with overlap)   e. aHGfEIbCd

_____ 6. a deletion   f. AbcFGHi

II. Use the following key to answer the next six items.

> Key: a. The frequency of the dominant allele would increase.
> b. The frequency of the dominant allele would decrease.
> c. There would be no change in the frequency of the dominant allele.
> d. It cannot be determined.

What would happen to the gene frequency if...

_____ 1. ...the recessive allele were lethal?

_____ 2. ...no mutations occurred in the populations?

_____ 3. ...no selection pressures were found in the population?

_____ 4. ...individuals with the recessive trait produced fewer offspring than those with the dominant trait?

_____ 5. ...individuals with the recessive trait produced fewer gametes than those with the dominant trait?

_____ 6. ...all the individuals with the recessive trait were killed?

III. Suppose that, in a population of 100 individuals, there are 64 red-flowered plants and 36 white-flowered plants. Red is dominant to white in this case.

1. What is the frequency of the dominant allele? _____

2. What is the frequency of the recessive allele? _____

3. What is the p? _____

4. What is the q? _____

5. How many heterozygotes would you expect to find in the population of 100? _____

6. How many homozygous dominants would you expect to find in the population of 100? _____

7. What is the fitness of the homozygous recessive if s = 0.1? _____

IV. Use the following diagram to answer the next seven questions.

445

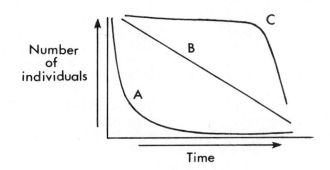

1. Which curve represents an insect population? _____

2. Which curve represents a human population? _____

3. Which curve represents a plant population? _____

4. Which population is most likely to be affected by density-dependent factors early in the lives of the individuals? _____

5. Which population would show the most rapid growth rate if no mortality occurred? _____

6. Which is a population of individuals produced by r selection? _____

7. Which is a population of individuals produced by K selection? _____

ANSWERS TO CHAPTER EXERCISES

Practice Quiz

1. a	3. c	5. b	7. c	9. a
2. d	4. a	6. c	8. c	10. d

Review Questions

I.	1. c	2. b	3. d	4. a	5. e	6. f
II.	1. a	2. d	3. c	4. a	5. d	6. a

III.	1. 0.4	3. 0.4	5. 48	7. 0.9
	2. 0.6	4. 0.6	6. 16	

IV.	1. A	3. A	5. A	7. C
	2. C	4. A	6. A	

Chapter 33

RELATIONSHIPS IN THE COMMUNITY

WHAT'S IN THIS CHAPTER

In this chapter you will learn about the interactions that take place in communities. Many different kinds of organisms live within a community and in close proximity to one another. In addition, almost all communities are based on plants that provide a source of energy and nutrients for all the other community members. These factors are partly responsible for the many interactions between organisms. The different classes of interactions will be outlined here, and you will see how these interactions help shape and change a community. Some inter-actions benefit both of the organisms involved, some benefit only one individual, and some benefit neither. The benefits and drawbacks from these interactions are driving forces for the evolution of species, and adaptations to attract, repel, defend against, eat, mimic, or hide from other organisms will be discussed. This chapter will emphasize certain relationships including the predator-prey relationship and those that keep two species from occupying the same ecological niche.

By the end of this chapter you should be able to:

1. Describe a coral reef community.

2. Define mutualism, commensalism, parasitism, and predation.

3. Give an example for each of the relationships listed above.

4. Give an example of a morphological, a behavioral, and a biochemical adaptation.

5. Explain how predators may have a long-term beneficial effect on the prey population.

6. Describe a natural predator-prey cycle.

7. Define niche.

8. State the Principle of Competitive Exclusion.

9. Name one plant allomone and one animal allomone that are used in chemical warfare against another species.

10. Differentiate between Mullerian and Batesian mimicry, and explain how mimics benefit.

447

11. Differentiate between cryptic and disruptive coloration patterns.

12. Explain how pheromones or allomones could also be kairomones.

WHAT YOU SHOULD ALREADY KNOW

This chapter deals with the relationships among organisms found in a community. Many of these relationships are based on the need for energy and nutrients to grow and reproduce. You should be familiar with the path that energy takes as it flows through and out of a community and with the different pathways that nutrients take as they flow through a community and back to their place of origin. This information can be found in Chapters 5 and 31. Also, because the physical environment places limitations on the kinds of organisms that can live within a community, you should review those important physical factors in ecosystem structure. Finally, because communities tend to change through time, you should understand the phenomenon of succession and the changes that take place throughout a sere.

Pre-Test

1. _____ determines the major types of vegetation in any region.

1. Climate

2. Matter flows through an ecosystem in a series of (a)_____, so called because there are exchanges between the biosphere and the earth. Nitrogen cycles primarily as a component of (b)_____.

2. (a) biogeochem-
ical cycles;
(b) protein

3. One community gradually replaces another in the process known as (a)_____. On a shorter time scale, some members of a community disappear and are replaced by new species in the process called (b)_____.

3. (a) ecological
succession; (b)
species turn-
over

4. Four trophic levels found in a community, beginning at the base of the food web and going upward, are (a)_____ _____, (b)_____, (c)_____, and (d)_____ _____.

4. (a) producers
(autotrophs);
(b) primary
consumers (her-
bivores); (c)
secondary con-

sumers (carni-
vores); (d)
tertiary con-
sumers (also
carnivores)

GUIDED REVIEW OF THE CHAPTER

33-1 The structure of a coral reef community.

1. A community is _____

    _____

    _____.

1. a group of or-   2. The three types of reefs are the (a)_____ reef
    ganisms of sev-
    eral different   that runs along the edge of a continent, the (b)_____
    species that
    live together   _____ reef that is separated from land by a lagoon,
    and interact in
    a relatively   and the (c)_____ that is a circular formation.
    stable pattern
    of association

2. (a) fringing;   3. Corals live only in shallow water, yet some reefs rise
    (b) barrier;
    (c) atoll   hundreds of meters above the ocean floor. Explain how

                           these reefs could have developed. _____

                           _____

3. All reefs start   4. Corals are (a)_____, simple animals
    out as fringing
    reefs, building   with a single opening to a digestive sac that live mostly
    up as the ocean
    floor sinks.   on (b)_____. Living symbiotically with corals

                           are tiny algae called (c)_____ that use

                           nitrogenous (d)_____ for their
                           growth.

4. (a) coelente-   5. Communities, including the coral reef, change (a)_____
    rates; (b)
    plankton; (c)   _____ (very little / considerably) over a
    zooxanthellae;
    (d) animal   period of time. As coral animals die, they leave behind
    wastes
                           skeletons made of (b)_____

                           that turn into (c)_____.

5. (a) consider-
    ably; (b) cal-
    cium carbonate;

449

(c) limestone

33-2 Relationships within the community are complex.

1. Six different interactions between two species are: (a)_____, (b)_____, (c)_____, (d)_____, (e)_____, and (f)_____.

1. (a) competi-
   tion; (b) amen-
   salism; (c)
   predation; (d)
   parasitism; (e)
   commensalism;
   (f) mutualism

2. The interactions between two species in which at least one species is affected <u>negatively</u> are (a)_____, (b)_____, (c)_____, and (d)_____.

2. (a) competi-
   tion; (b)amen-
   salism; (c)
   predation; (d)
   parasitism

3. The interaction in which both organisms benefit is (a)_____, whereas the interaction in which both organisms are affected negatively is (b)_____.

3. (a) mutualism;
   (b) competition

33-3 Adaptations may be morphological, behavioral, or biochemical.

1. An adaptation is _____.

1. any structure
   or process that
   allows an indi-
   vidual to live
   in a particu-
   lar environment

2. The ability to _____ is an adaptive behavioral mechanism for dealing with relatively short-termed changes.

2. learn

3. In an _____ interaction, a chemical is made and released by one species that has an ecological effect on some other species.

3. allelochemical

33-4 Predation is a major activity in every community.

1. The activity of an animal eating a plant is called (a)_____, and that of an animal eating another animal is called (b)_____.

1. (a) herbivory;
   (b) carnivory

2. Predators are to (a)_____ as (b)_____ are to hosts.

2. (a) prey; (b)

3. In some predator-prey relationships, such as those

450

parasites

involving wolves, the predator does not adversely affect

the population of the prey because _____

_____

_____.

3. the predators eat primarily those prey individuals that would die anyway or are in some way expendable

4. Ecological efficiency is (a)_____

_____. In terms of ecological efficiency, how can predation have a beneficial effect on the prey population? (b)_____

_____

_____.

4. (a) the ratio of prey biomass to the biomass of its food; (b) Every predation increases the ecological efficiency of the prey, thus increasing the efficiency of the food chain.

33-5 Predator and prey populations may go through natural cycles.

1. (a)_____ and (b)_____ developed a set of equations that predict the interaction between a predator and its prey.

1. (a) Lotka; (b) Volterra

2. Lotka and Volterra predict that predator and prey populations should rise and fall in (a)_____

because (b)_____

_____

_____

2. (a) cycles; (b) the more predators, the fewer the prey, and the fewer the prey, the fewer the predators, and because each population takes a little time to react to the other

3. The Hudson Bay Company kept records of the interaction between a predator, the (a)_____, and a prey, the (b)_____.

33-6 Many organisms engage in symbiotic relationships.

1. Phoresis means (a)_____. In a phoretic interaction a larger animal called a (b)_____ carries a smaller (c)_____ around, but the

451

3. (a) lynx; (b) snowshoe hare

larger animal is not hurt and the smaller obtains only

(d)_____.

1. (a) carrying; (b) host; (c) phoront; (d) the benefits of mobility and a place to live

2. In a commensalistic relationship, one species, called the

(a)_____, shares the host's food as well as its living space. An example of such a relationship is that

between (b)_____.

2. (a) commensal; (b) fish and anemone, or byrozoans and clams

3. Parasitism is a relationship in which the host is (a)_____

_____. Humans are sometimes host to ectoparasites

such as (b)_____, and endoparasites such as

(c)_____.

3. (a) damaged; (b) ticks, fleas, or lice; (c) tapeworms, other worms

4. The termite-flagellated protozoan interaction is a

(a)_____ interaction. The protozoans

(b)_____ for the termites.

4. (a) mutualistic; (b) digest wood into glucose

5. The lichen relationship is mutualistic. The two organisms involved are a (a)_____, which benefits

from the relationship because it receives (b)_____

_____, and an (c)_____,

which benefits from the relationship because it obtains a

(d)_____.

5. (a) fungus; (b) high energy organic molecules; (c) alga; (d) site for its growth

6. A crocodile may allow a bird to enter its mouth free of

harm because _____

_____.

6. the bird may be picking out parasitic leeches from the crocodile's mouth

7. American cowbirds and European cuckoos are sometimes

parasitic of other bird species in that they _____

_____

_____.

7. lay their eggs in the nests of other bird species, and sometimes the parasitic nest-

33-7 Two species cannot occupy the same niche.

1. A niche is _____

_____

ling pushes the
host nestling
out of the nest

_____.

1. the combination
of a species
habitat and its
way of life
within that
habitat; an
n-dimensional
space wherein
each dimension
affects the
life of the
species

2. What is the Principle of Competitive Exclusion? _____

_____

_____.

2. Stable popu-
lations of two
or more species
cannot continue
to occupy the
same niche
indefinitely.

3. It is difficult to falsify Gause's Competitive Exclusion

Principle because _____

_____.

3. there are so
many variables
that can define
a niche

*33-8 Many organisms employ allomones in chemical warfare
against other species.*

1. An (a)_____ is a substance whose sole function
is to hurt, inhibit, or repel some other species, giving

some (b)_____ to the organisms
that make the substance.

1. (a) allomone;
(b) selective
advantage

2. Two examples of plants that contain allomones are (a)_____

_____ and (b)_____.

2. (a) and (b)
foxgloves,
buttercups,
larkspurs or
St. John's wort

3. A chemical produced by one organism to be used as a
defense against another does not affect the producer

because _____

_____

_____.

3. the chemical is
made in the in-
active form,
and then through
the addition of
an enzyme it is
activated and
released only
when needed

4. Many allomones are only effective against predators if the

predator can (a)_____ because (b)_____

_____

_____.

4. (a) learn; (b)

5. Some plants produce phytoecdysones that mimic animal

453

once the predator experiences the allomone, it will learn to avoid the organism that produces the allomone

hormones known as (a)_____ that regulate (b)_____.

5. (a) ecdysones; (b) the metamorphosis of insects

6. Two examples of animals that produce allomones are (a)_____ and (b)_____.

6. (a) and (b) skunks, wasps, pufferfish, ants, meloid beetles, millipedes

33-9 *Some organisms create intolerable conditions for others.*

1. When light is a limiting growth factor, one adaptation that plants may exhibit is a tall growth habit. This not only provides a (a)_____ but also (b)_____ competitors.

1. (a) region for trapping light; (b) shades out any lower-growing

2. Both the black walnut and the common sunflower produce chemicals that (a)_____ of other plants. Both the grasses *Aristida oligantha* and *Sorghum halepense* produce allochemicals that inhibit the growth of (b)_____ and _____ _____.

2. (a) inhibit the growth; (b) nitrogen-fixing bacteria and cyanobacteria

3. Both guayule and creosote bush produce chemicals that inhibit their own (a)_____. This may be advantageous to these plants because (b)_____ _____ _____.

3. (a) seedlings; (b) water is a limiting factor in the desert, and seedling inhibition around the parent helps to space plants farther apart from each other

4. Fungi and certain bacteria produce chemical regulators called (a)_____ that inhibit the growth of the (b)_____.

33-10 *Many animals evolve protective forms and colors.*

1. Pepper moths are an example of (a)_____ coloration, which disguises the organism by means of

4. (a) antibio-
tics; (b)
microorganisms

(b)_____.

1. (a) cryptic;
(b) camouflage

2. Leopards and zebras are examples of (a)_____ coloration. Such animals are difficult to see because of their (b)_____.

2. (a) disruptive;
(b) coloration
against a
broken back-
ground

33-11 Some animals are protected by warning coloration.

1. A skunk is an example of (a)_____ coloration, which is a message to other animals that (b)_____.

1. (a) aposematic;
(b) they should
stay away

2. The situation in which several species of animals have evolved a common coloration pattern is called (a)_____ _____. An example of this occurs between wasps and (b)_____.

2. (a) Müllerian
mimicry; (b)
bees

33-12 Mimics may survive by imitating warning coloration.

1. In (a)_____ mimicry, a harmless or palatable (b)_____ survives through a kind of "false advertising" by evolving the coloration of a dangerous or distasteful (c)_____.

1. (a) Batesian;
(b) mimic; (c)
model

2. Monarch butterflies offer an example of Batesian mimicry, with the (a)_____ butterfly as the model and the (b)_____ butterfly as the mimic.

2. (a) monarch;
(b) viceroy

3. Blue jays that have never seen butterflies before will eat (a)_____(monarch butterflies / viceroy butterflies / either). If the first butterfly eaten by a blue jay is a viceroy, the blue jay would be expected to (b)_____
(eat any butterfly / avoid all such butterflies).

3. (a) either; (b)
eat any butter-
fly

4. Mimics are usually found in (a)_____ (greater / lesser / equal) numbers compared to models in a popula-tion. This is because (b)_____
_____

455

_____

_____.

4. (a) lesser; (b)   *33-13 Many species react to kairomones produced by other*
   if the number   *animals.*
   of mimics is
   high, predators   1. (a)_____ are chemicals that give selective
   will be re-
   warded too   advantage to those animals that produce them. (b)_____
   often with
   "good" food   _____ are chemicals that give selective advantage to

                        those animals that detect them.

1. (a) Allomones;   2. When a predator learns to recognize a pheromone of its
   (b) Kairomones
                       prey, a(an) (a)_____ (kairomone / allomone) has

                       been converted into a(an) (b)_____ (kairomone /
                       allomone).

2. (a) allomone;   3. Fungi that trap nematode worms catch the worms in loops
   (b) kairomone
                       that are made only when _____

                       _____

3. the fungi are   _____.
   stimulated by
   the presence of
   the nematodes
   themselves

PRACTICE QUIZ

1. In a coral reef community, the most important producers are:
   a. corals.
   b. plankton.
   c. bacteria.
   d. echinoderms.

2. In _____ both of the organisms involved benefit.
   a. mutualism
   b. commensalism
   c. amensalism
   d. neutralism

3. A major difference between predation and parasitism is that:
   a. A predator's prey moves, whereas a parasite's host does not.
   b. A prey crganism is a plant, whereas a host organism is an animal.
   c. A predator is usually larger than its prey, whereas a parasite is usually
      smaller than its host.
   d. Parasitism is beneficial to the host organism, whereas predation is not
      beneficial to the prey organism.

4. Production of ecdysone by plants is a _____ adaptation.
    a. morphological
    b. anatomical
    c. behavioral
    d. biochemical

5. A predator may be called "prudent" if it:
    a. kills its prey just before it eats the prey.
    b. kills sick or disabled prey.
    c. kills female prey, which are weaker than males.
    d. kills only when the prey population is high.

6. Which of the following statements is true of a predator-prey cycle?
    a. Both populations drop simultaneously.
    b. The prey population drops before the predator population.
    c. The predator population drops before the prey population.
    d. The prey population drops before the predator population rises.

7. An n - dimensional volume describes an organism's:
    a. niche.
    b. habitat.
    c. way of living.
    d. size.

8. If two different species are occupying the same niche, which of the following is not a likely occurrence?
    a. Both species will be eliminated.
    b. One species will be eliminated.
    c. Both species' populations will increase in size.
    d. One species's population will increase in size.

9. If two different species resemble each other and both are poisonous, they provide an example of:
    a. cryptic coloration.
    b. disruptive coloration.
    c. Batesian mimicry.
    d. Müllerian mimicry.

10. If a mountain lion is hunting a deer and the deer smells the lion's scent, the lion's scent is a(an):
    a. allomone to the deer.
    b. kairomone to the deer.
    c. pheromone to the deer.
    d. allomone to the lion.

REVIEW QUESTIONS

I. Use the following diagram to answer the next six question.

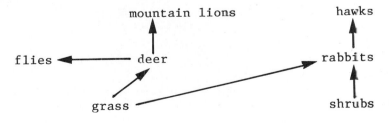

457

1. The predators are the _____

_____.

2. The parasites are the _____.

3. The organisms that are competing directly with each other are the _____

_____.

4. The herbivores are the _____.

5. The carnivores are the _____.

6. The producers are the _____.

II. Use the following graphs of population changes through time to answer the next five questions.

A   B   C   D   E

_____ 1. Which graph shows the population of a predator without prey?

_____ 2. Which graph shows the population of a prey without a predator and with no limitations?

_____ 3. Which graph shows the populations of predator and prey living together in the same area?

_____ 4. Which graph shows a population that has reached its carrying capacity?

_____ 5. Which graph shows the population of parasites that kill their host?

III. Use the following key to answer the next six items.

    Key: a.   disruptive coloration
              b.   cryptic coloration
              c.   Müllerian mimicry
              d.   Batesian mimicry

_____ 1. monarch and viceroy butterflies

_____ 2. zebras and shrubs

_____ 3. leaf hoppers and thorns

_____ 4. pepper moths and bark

_____ 5. wasps and bees

_____ 6. leopards and grasses

ANSWERS TO CHAPTER EXERCISES

Practice Quiz

1. b	3. c	5. b	7. a	9. d
2. a	4. d	6. b	8. c	10. b

Review Questions

I. 1. deer, rabbits, mountain lions, hawks
    2. flies
    3. deer, rabbits
    4. deer, rabbits
    5. mountain lions, hawks
    6. grass, shrubs

II. 1. E   2. D   3. B   4. A   5. C

III. 1. d   2. a   3. b   4. b   5. c   6. a

Chapter 34

THE MECHANISMS OF EVOLUTION

WHAT'S IN THIS CHAPTER

Biological, or organic, evolution is a major theme of biology that has been stressed throughout the book. The major evidence that evolution does occur was summarized in Chapter 2, along with a general outline of how the process works, and in Chapter 3 it was shown that evolution is a natural and necessary consequence of self-reproduction with occasional errors (mutations). But evolution is a property of populations, not of individual organisms; and with the background of population biology and ecology laid in the previous three chapters, we are ready to discuss the mechanisms of evolution in more detail.

The chapter begins with a brief outline of evolutionary mechanisms, which you should already know from earlier chapters. A convenient device is then introduced: the use of an imaginary landscape to represent the fitnesses of genomes. Those genomes that are highly fit for existence in some niche are on peaks; those with low fitness are in valleys. Natural selection tends to drive populations toward the peaks, but the peaks shift as the environment changes, so most populations are probably "struggling" to keep up. And eventually every population falls so far behind that it becomes extinct. Speciation also occurs, primarily through geographic isolation; but plants have special mechanisms, and there is good reason to think that selection can maintain differences even with little isolation. Finally, the results of evolution on earth are discussed briefly, with an emphasis on the geographic distribution of organisms, which is shown to be a consequence of the drifting of continents over many millions of years.

By the end of this chapter you should be able to:

1. Summarize the basic evolutionary process.

2. Discuss the relative fitness of various genotypes.

3. Explain why organisms in similar niches have similar adaptations and why two different species do not occupy the same niche.

4. Relate evolution to extinction, selection and hybridization to speciation, and unique biogeographic realms to continental drift.

5. Correlate geographic variations with genotypic variations within a species.

6. List isolating mechanisms and describe the role of each one in the process of speciation.

7. Compare genetic and species stability in large and small populations.

WHAT YOU SHOULD ALREADY KNOW

Chapter 2 provided a basic overview of evolution and related topics. You should have a firm idea of what evolution is before beginning to study its mechanisms. Meiosis (Section 10-8), mutations (Chapter 13), inheritance (Chapter 15), and Chapters 31-33 all offer background information that you will need to understand evolutionary mechanisms.

Pre-Test

1. On a geological time scale, evolution appears to consist of three main processes. First, in the process of (a)_____ _____, one species divides into two or more. Second, a species may gradually change its features in the process of (b)_____ evolution. Third, a species may die out in the process of (c)_____.

1. (a) speciation;
   (b) phyletic;
   (c) extinction

2. However, a controversy is now raging between two factions, because some people insist that the process of _____ _____ is of little or no importance.

2. phyletic evolution

3. Whatever its details are, evolution certainly depends on variation in population produced by (a)_____ and (b)_____.

3. (a) mutation;
   (b) recombination

4. As Darwin realized, a major driving force in evolution is (a)_____. This process is primarily a matter of differential (b)_____.

4. (a) natural selection; (b) reproduction

5. We commonly say that a species is (a)_____ to a particular way of life. To describe a specific way of life, we use the term (b)_____ for all the factors that govern the way a particular population lives; this has been conceptualized as a space with (c)_____ dimensions.

461

5. (a) adapted;
   (b) niche;
   (c) n

6. For sexually reproducing organisms, a (a)_____ can be defined as all the individuals that live within a certain geographic range and are actually or potentially capable of (b)_____ with one another.

6. (a) species;
   (b) interbreed-
       ing

7. A subdivision of a species that has a more limited range, and perhaps distinctive features, is called a (a)_____ _____ or (b)_____.

7. (a) subspecies;
   (b) race

GUIDED REVIEW OF THE CHAPTER

34-1 Review: The major mechanisms of evolution.

1. Populations become more (a)_____ as a result of mutation and recombination.   Meiosis and fertilization produce (b)_____ genetic combinations.

1. (a) diverse;
   (b) new

2. Variations among genomes means variations in the (a)_____ of the organisms that bear those genomes.   Greater fitness means a greater ability to (b)_____.

2. (a) fitness;
   (b) survive

3. Surviving individuals pass their successful (a)_____ on to future (b)_____.

3. (a) genomes;
   (b) generations

4. When subgroups of a population become (a)_____ _____ isolated, they are then considered separate (b)_____.

4. (a) reproduct-
       ively;
   (b) species

34-2 Every genotype has a certain relative fitness.

1. Every population contains (a)_____(many / very few) different genotypes, each with its own degree of (b)_____ for the environment it exists in.

1. (a) many;
   (b) fitness

2. Adaptive peaks in the genetic (a)_____ represent (b)_____(successful / unsuccessful) genotypes for some way of life.

2. (a) landscape;

3. Valleys in the genetic landscape contain (a)_____

(b) successful   (less / more) fit genotypes, which could , however, be

(b)_____(less / more) fit under other conditions.

3. (a) less;
   (b) more

4. True or False: All possible genotypes have appeared at some time, and the successful ones remain.

4. False

5. Phylogenetically close organisms have similar (a)_____

_____ and their adaptive peaks (b)_____
(will be / will not be) close.

5. (a) genotypes;
   (b) will be

6. Adaptive peaks sometimes move back and forth with the

(a)_____, (b)_____(maintaining / reducing) diversity in the population's gene pool.

6. (a) seasons;
   (b) maintaining

7. True or False: Each peak in the genetic landscape represents a living or fossil genotype.

7. False

34-3 Related populations occupy similar niches.

1. True or False: Each species defines a niche.

1. True

2. Distantly related species occupying very similar niches

may undergo (a)_____ evolution and may

thus have (b)_____(similar / dissimilar) forms.

2. (a) convergent;
   (b) similar

3. When there is a significant overlap between two populations, there is _____ between them.

3. competition

4. Evolutionary change is one result of the overlapping of

_____.

4. niches

5. A population in an unstable situation has three "choices":

It may _____: _____, or become

_____.

5. adapt, move,
   extinct

6. Populations typically adapt to overlapping niches by

evolving so they reduce _____, allowing better sharing of resources.

6. competition

7. True or False: Gause's Principle of resource sharing explains why considerable niche overlap is seen in some populations.

7. False

34-4 Species tend to adapt for a time and then become extinct.

1. Evolution appears to consist primarily of two processes: (a)_____ and (b)_____.

1. (a) speciation; (b) extinction

2. True or False: The vast majority of species that have ever existed are extinct.

2. True

3. The end of life is death. Every life eventually ends. The eventual death of a species is _____.

3. extinction

4. Most species come and go in less than (a)_____ million years. Persistent species occur in (b)_____ _____(slowly / rapidly) changing environments.

4. (a) 10; (b) slowly

5. Name each type of selection and star (*) the one most likely to lead to speciation. (a) Elimination of those on one extreme: _____, (b) Elimination of those in the middle: _____, (c) Elimination of those on both extremes: _____.

5. (a) directional; (b) *disruptive; (c) stabilizing

6. Much of selection is (a)_____, but species apparently become extinct at a (b)_____ rate, regardless of how long they have been in existence.

6. (a) stabilizing; (b) constant

7. As an environment changes, adaptive peaks move and populations are always _____(right on / to the side of) the peak.

7. to the side of

8. Populations "struggle" to _____(stay on / follow) the moving adaptive peak.

8. follow

9. Following the peak depends on (a)_____ within the population and the process of (b)_____ _____.

9. (a) variability; (b) natural selection

10. As a population falls farther behind the adaptive peak, its (a)_____ declines. Falling behind produces failure or (b)_____.

10. (a) fitness; (b) extinction

11. Human intervention generally _____(decreases / increases) the lifetime of a species.

11. decreases

12. True or False: Changes in the genetic structure of popu-

lations are reflected in niche changes.

12. True

13. The phenomenon of species replacing one another through time is called species _____.

13. turnover

34-5 Adaptive peaks generally shift geographically.

1. Different geographic populations of the same species are races or (a)_____. A continuum of variation in a species is called a (b)_____.

1. (a) subspecies;
   (b) cline

2. True or False: A cline shows a gradual continuous change in adaptive peaks and genotypes.

2. True

3. Moore's studies indicate that frogs have adapted to the average _____ at each point across eastern North America.

3. temperature

4. Clinal differences are a response to different _____ _____ pressures.

4. environmental

5. Populations with overlapping geographic ranges are (a)_____; those with nonoverlapping ranges are (b)_____.

5. (a) sympatric;
   (b) allopatric

6. True or False: Sympatric populations always interbreed with each other, as stated in Gause's Principle.

6. False

7. Noninterbreeding sympatric populations occupy _____ niches.

7. different

34-6 Speciation occurs primarily through geographic isolation.

1. Most long-term changes occur over many (a)_____ of years and result from many (b)_____, in which one species replaces another.

1. (a) millions;
   (b) speciations

2. Long-lasting species have enough (a)_____ potential to respond to changing (b)_____ demands.

2. (a) genetic;
   (b) environ-
   mental

3. True or False: Sibling species are separated primarily on the basis of morphological characteristics.

3. False

4. Geographic isolation can lead to _____

465

isolation.

4. reproductive

5. A mountain, a river, an interstate freeway could be a _____ barrier.

5. geographic

6. True or False: One can determine whether allopatric populations are separate species only after they have enlarged their ranges and have become sympatric again.

6. True

7. Sibling species become sympatric only if their (a)_____ do not overlap strongly, so there is little (b)_____ between them.

7. (a) niches;
   (b) competition

8. Character displacement means that two species are more dissimilar where they are (a)_____ than where they are (b)_____.

8. (a) sympatric;
   (b) allopatric

9. Character displacement may serve as a means of maintaining _____ isolation.

9. reproductive

34-7 Gene frequencies may change rapidly in small populations.

1. Random changes in gene frequencies are called _____ drift.

1. genetic

2. Genetic drift can occur _____(faster/ more slowly) in small populations.

2. faster

3. An allele with a frequency of 1 is said to be _____.

3. fixed

4. The _____ effect refers to the establishment of new isolated populations by individuals with atypical genotypes.

4. founder

5. True or False: Populations genetically drifting from one adaptive peak to another play a major role in evolution.

5. False

6. Rapid genoptyic changes in isolated populations may be due to a relaxation of _____.

6. selection

34-8 Isolating mechanisms may be prezygotic or postzygotic.

1. Reproductive isolating mechanisms are divided into two categories: (a)_____ and (b)_____ _____.

1. (a) prezygotic;
   (b) postzygotic

2. True

3. against

4. (a) Breeding
   occurs at dif-
   ferent times.
   (b) Copulation
   is structural-
   ly impossible.
   (c) Species
   occupy differ-
   ent habitats.

5. (a) Hybrids are
   sterile. (b)
   Hybrids abort
   or die. (c) F_2
   is of lower
   viability.

1. demes

2. do not

3. (a) selection;
   (b) much

4. is

2. True or False: Breeding between animal species wastes reproductive potential because hybrids are genetic dead ends, but for plants new species often arise.

3. Selection generally works _____(against / for) hybridization.

4. Briefly describe <u>prezygotic</u> isolating mechanisms of the following kinds:

   (a) temporal: _____

   (b) structural: _____

   (c) habitat: _____

5. Briefly describe <u>postzygotic</u> isolating mechanisms of the following kinds:

   (a) sterility: _____

   (b) inviability: _____

   (c) breakdown: _____

34-9 Both gene flow and selection influence speciation.

1. Neighboring populations of a cline are called _____.

2. Individuals that wander into other demes generally _____(do / do not) contribute to the gene pool of their neighbor.

3. Parapatric demes may have different features, maintained by (a)_____, even though there may also be (b)_____(little / much) gene flow between them.

4. Parapatric speciation _____(is / is not) possible with substantial gene flow where fitness variables change smoothly.

34-10 Plant evolution frequently involves hybridization and polyploidy.

1. The process by which genes of one plant species work their way into the genome of another is called _____ _____.

467

1. introgression

2. Introgression probably involves _____(chromosomes/ genes) being replaced between plant species.

2. chromosomes

3. Continued introgression can move sympatric species to _____ status.

3. semispecies

4. Autopolyploidy results from (a)_____ n gametes and

(b)_____-fertilization producing (c)_____ n and

(d)_____ n zygotes.

4. (a) 2n; (b) self; (c) 3n; (d) 4n

5. Polypolidy in which a diploid hybrid produces a fertile

(a)_____ n plant species is called (b)_____

_____, and the plant is called an (c)_____

_____.

5. (a) 4n; (b) allopolyploidy; (c) allotetraploid

6. Which has a better chance for survival, an autopolyploid

or an allopolyploid? _____

6. an allopolyploid

7. True or False: *Spartina angelica* (2n = 122) arose as an allotetraploid by autopolyploidy of *S. townsendii* (2n = 61), which was a hybrid between *S. maritima* (2n = 60) and *S. alterniflora* (2n = 62).

7. True

34-11 The evolution of higher taxa does not require special mechanisms.

1. True or False: Given vast expanses of time, continuing series of small changes can produce large differences.

1. True

2. It is more difficult to accept very different major taxa

having evolved through small changes, because the _____

_____ forms are extinct.

2. intermeditate

3. *Archaeopteryx* was an intermediate between (a)_____

and modern (b)_____.

3. (a) reptiles; (b) birds

4. Evolution in many directions from an ancestral form is

called _____.

4. adaptive radiation

34-12 Species that occupy similar niches generally have similar structures.

1. Fishes, seals, and whales illustrate _____ evolution.

1. convergent

2. Adaptation to similar niches generally produces a _____ _____ morphology.

2. similar

34-13 The world is divisible into several biogeographic realms.

1. Continental isolation has allowed different organisms to occupy _____ (different / similar) niches on each continent.

1. similar

2. Curious distributions of living and fossil forms can be explained by Wegner's theory of _____.

2. continental drift

3. The longer two continents have been separated, the more _____ (sinilar / dissimilar) the organisms they harbor.

3. dissimilar

4. Europe and North America have been separated for about (a)_____ million years; North and South America rejoined only (b)_____ million years ago.

4. (a) 45; (b) 2

34-14 Each biogeographic realm contains similar organisms in similar niches.

1. As birds and mammals filled niches vacated by extinct reptiles, the number of species _____ _____ (increased / decreased / remained relatively constant).

1. remained relatively constant

2. Adaptive radiation of mammals on separate continents has resulted in each having about _____ (how many?) families of mammals.

2. 20 to 25

3. Mammals of each continent show _____ evolution.

3. convergent

4. True or False: After North and South America were connected, interchange of fauna produced permanently larger faunas for both.

4. False

5. When faunas mix, the dominant ones tend to be those that evolved in the (a)_____ (larger / smaller) area because they are more (b)_____.

5. (a) larger; (b) specialized

469

34-15 All evolution occurs within structured communities.

1. All evolution is really _____, because all
   populations in a community have some impact on each other.

1. coevolution

2. Evolution causes the world's communities to be in a
   constant state of _____.

2. flux

PRACTICE QUIZ

1. Which of the following statements is <u>not</u> true of the peaks in the genetic
   landscape?
   a. Each is occupied by some genotype.
   b. Each represents a potential for existence.
   c. All have valleys between them of less fit genotypes.
   d. They tend to shift with time.

2. Gause's Principle states that two species:
   a. can occupy the same niche if they share resources.
   b. cannot occupy the same niche.
   c. will become one if they occupy the same niche.
   d. occupying the same niche will forever be in a state of conflict.

3. _____ do <u>not</u> cause adaptive peaks to shift.
   a. Human intervention
   b. Polyploidy
   c. Seasons
   d. Ice Ages

4. A species with a wide range has divided into a number of allopatric
   populations; they could now be considered any of the following <u>except</u>:
   a. subspecies of the whole species.
   b. semispecies of a superspecies.
   c. races of the whole species.
   d. separate species of a genus.

5. The <u>most</u> important factor in speciation is:
   a. directional selection.
   b. convergent evolution.
   c. mutation and recombination.
   d. geographic isolation.

6. The random change of gene frequencies:
   a. is the founder effect.
   b. causes adaptive peaks to slowly change.
   c. is called genetic drift.
   d. is caused by reproductive isolating mechanisms.

7. _____ reproductive isolation exists between a male dachshund and a female
   greyhound.
   a. Temporal
   b. Structural

470

c. Behavioral
d. Hybrid sterility

8. Chromosome doubling ($2n$ to $4n$) in a sterile diploid hybrid is called:
   a. allopolyploidy.
   b. autopolyploidy.
   c. introgression.
   d. hybridization.

9. Rabbits and kangaroos best illustrate:
   a. continental drift.
   b. adaptive radiation.
   c. convergent evolution.
   d. parapatric demes.

10. Continental animals carried to far-away islands usually compete favorably with island forms because they:
    a. are larger.
    b. are more specialized.
    c. evolved under reduced selective pressures.
    d. don't have to be held in check by coevolution.

REVIEW QUESTIONS

I. Answer each of the following questions.

   1. How is the success or fitness of a genotype determined in an evolutionary sense?

   _____

   _____

   2. What value is there in populations containing some less fit genotypes?

   _____

   _____

   3. What relationship exists between genotypes and phylogeny?

   _____

   _____

   4. What effect does seasonal shifting of adaptive peaks have on the genotypes of a population?

   _____

   _____

   5. How are adaptive peaks and niche similarity related?

   _____

471

6. Are populations on adaptive peaks that are close together always closely related?

_____

_____

7. Why can't two species coexist in the same area and niche (Gause's Principle)?

_____

_____

8. What results from strong competition between species?

_____

_____

9. Speciation and extinction are like birth and death. What causes extinction to be such a rule in nature?

_____

_____

10. Name and explain the three types of natural selection.

_____

_____

_____

_____

11. How is natural selection related to changing adaptive peaks?

_____

_____

12. What produces the variability for natural selection to operate on?

_____

13. What is a cline and what causes it?

_____

_____

14. What is the difference between allopatric and sympatric populations?

_____

_____

15. What are morphologically identical, reproductively isolated populations called?

_____

16. How do geographic barriers play a role in speciation?

_____

_____

17. Of what value is character displacement?

_____

_____

18. Why does genetic drift occur faster in small populations?

_____

_____

19. Of what value are (a) prezygotic and (b) postzygotic isolating mechanisms?

_____

_____

II. Match each isolating mechanism in the left column with the correct characteristic in the right column.

_____ 1. behavioral isolation   a. F_2 offspring of low fitness

_____ 2. gametic incompatibility   b. different breeding seasons

_____ 3. habitat isolation   c. hybrid aborts

_____ 4. hybrid breakdown   d. different courtship patterns

_____ 5. hybrid inviability   e. horse x donkey = sterile mule

_____ 6. hybrid sterility   f. adapted to different types of soil

_____ 7. structural isolation   g. copulation impossible

_____ 8. temporal isolation   h. sperm cells die in female

473

III. Answer each of the following questions.

1. What are demes, and why and how can they have different characteristics?

   _____

   _____

2. How does introgression provide a source of variability in plants?

   _____

   _____

3. How would you produce a seedless squash?

   _____

   _____

4. Why are triploids sterile?

   _____

   _____

5. How does allopolyploidy produce new species?

   _____

   _____

6. Why do intermediate species, such as *Archaeopteryx*, have a brief geologic existence?

   _____

   _____

7. Apes and tuna are very different. How could all vertebrates have possibly evolved from a common ancestral form?

   _____

   _____

8. Sharks, whales, and submarines are drastically different, but all possess the same body shape. Why?

   _____

   _____

9. Why is there a greater difference between organisms in India and Central Asia than between organisms in Australia and South America?

   _____

10. How did North America get the opossum? (North America separated from Australia before marsupial evolution.)

_____

_____

11. What is a biogeographic realm?

_____

_____

12. How do flowering plants and insects show coevolution?

_____

_____

ANSWERS TO CHAPTER EXERCISES

Practice Quiz

1. a	3. b	5. d	7. b	9. c
2. b	4. d	6. c	8. a	10. b

Review Questions

I. 1. The success of a genotype is determined by the number of offspring it produces.

2. They may contain genes allowing survival if the environment changes.

3. Organisms that are closely related phylogenetically will have similar genotypes.

4. It maintains a variety of similar, but slightly different, genotypes.

5. Adaptive peaks that are close together reflect similar niches.

6. Usually, except for convergent evolution by less than closely related forms.

7. There is too much competition for the same resources.

8. One species will move or die out. Or, one or both will adapt (evolve) in such a way that competition is reduced or absent.

9. Extinction is caused by changing environmental conditions and failure to adapt successfully. Successful adaptation also leaves species that divide into other species.

475

10. Stabilizing selection eliminates genotypes on both extremes. Directional selection eliminates genotypes on one end of the distribution. Disruptive selection eliminates genotypes in the middle of the distribution.

11. Natural selection moves the population along in the direction of the adaptive peak.

12. Mutation and recombination.

13. A cline is a continuous variation in a species across its geographic range. It is caused by different environmental pressures.

14. Sympatric populations have overlapping geographic ranges; allopatric populations do not.

15. Sibling species.

16. Geographic barriers stop gene flow. The separated populations can drift so far apart genetically that, if reunited, they would be reproductively isolated.

17. It promotes sharing of resources and, perhaps, mate recognition.

18. With fewer fertilization events, there is a greater chance that the average genotype will deviate from that expected from random fertilization.

19. Prezygotic mechanisms eliminate wasting reproductive potential. Post-zygotic mechanisms make less fit genotypes dead ends.

II. 1. d   3. f   5. c   7. g
    2. h   4. a   6. e   8. b

III. 1. Demes are local populations of a species. Selection can apparently keep neighboring deme different, even if there is gene flow between them.

   2. Hybridization and backcrossing add or change chromosomes in plant species.

   3. Chemically induced autotetraploids crossed with normal diploid plants would produce 3n offspring unable to make seeds.

   4. Normal synapsis does not occur in meiosis.

   5. A diploid hybrid, reproducing only vegetatively, becomes a tetraploid capable of both sexual and asexual reproduction.

   6. With their new unspecialized features, they generally do not compete very well and must specialize (evolve) quickly or die out.

   7. Given vast expanses of time and continuing series of small changes, almost anything is possible.

   8. For the habitat they exist in, this is a very successful form. Other shapes obviously don't work so well for this life style, or we would see them among ocean dwellers.

9. India and Central Asia have been separated much longer than Australia and South America. Evolution along different lines takes time and won't produce differences if different lines compete. One line becomes extinct.

10. It entered from South America, which was connected to Australia when the evolution of marsupials began.

11. It is a continental area with a unique assemblage of organisms.

12. Flowers evolve mechanisms that attract insects, which disseminate pollen. Insects evolve mechanisms for finding flowers and obtaining nectar.

Chapter 35

ORIGINS AND EARLY LINES OF EVOLUTION

WHAT'S IN THIS CHAPTER

We start this chapter 15 billion years ago with the "Big Bang" that explains the origin of our universe, stars, and planets. Our planet's early atmosphere, in which life began, is examined, as are the earliest life forms. Once established, organisms began to explore various life styles and evolved into unique groups that taxonomists have labeled kingdoms. The remainder of this chapter and the next two are surveys of these kingdoms.

The Kingdom Monera includes the various groups of procaryotes, most of which are called bacteria. The Kingdom Protista consists primarily of unicellular eucaryotes, including several algae groups, protozoans, and slime molds. Each is briefly described, along with other interesting facts about their life styles. An examination of morphological characteristics, physiological features, and metabolic pathways provides evidence for some evolutionary relationships among members of these two kingdoms and the other more advanced kingdoms.

By the end of this chapter you should be able to:

1. Explain the "Big Bang" theory and the origin of galaxies, stars, and planets.

2. Describe the early earth's atmosphere, the origin of the first organic molecules, and the nature of the first organisms.

3. Discuss any weak points in the story of the origin of life.

4. Name and differentiate among the major groups of bacteria.

5. Characterize the major protistan groups, describing unique features of each.

6. Suggest a moneran group that may be a protistan ancestor, and provide evidence to support your suggestion.

7. Describe evolutionary lines or tendencies in moneran and protistan kingdoms.

8. Cite features of evolutionary significance among monerans and protistans that relate them phylogenetically to each other and to the other kingdoms.

WHAT YOU SHOULD ALREADY KNOW

This chapter and the next two touch on many aspects of the previous chapters, so you may need to remind yourself of a variety of subjects from time to time. However, it does not demand much detailed information from the rest of the book, and you may very well be reading this chapter quite early in your course. You should understand general biological organization (Chapter 3) and the cell and sexual cycles (Chapter 10). The early evolution of organisms, and especially the evolution of the genome, will make sense only if you understand the major ideas presented in Chapter 9; however, most of the chapter can be understood without touching on those points. To fully understand the probable evolution of the protista, you ought to understand the structure of chloroplasts (Chapter 8) and of cilia (Chapter 12).

Pre-Test

1. taxonomy or
   systematics

1. The science of classification is called _____.

2. Closely related organisms share (a)_____(few / many) of the same characteristics and are placed in the same

   (b)_____.

2. (a) many;
   (b) taxa

3. There are two major superkingdoms of organisms: The

   (a)_____ are apparently the more

   primitive and are characterized primarily by (b)_____

   _____.

3. (a) procar-
   yotes; (b) hav-
   ing no nucleus
   (nuclear enve-
   lope)

4. The more advanced superkingdom consists of (a)_____

   _____, which are characterized primarily by (b)____

   _____.

4. (a) eucaryotes;
   (b) having a
   nucleus (nu-
   clear envelope)

5. On the basis of their energy source, organisms may be

   characterized as (a)_____, which get their

   energy from light, or as (b)_____, which
   get their energy from chemical compounds.

5. (a) photo-
   trophs; (b)
   chemotrophs

6. Organisms may also be characterized as (a)_____,
   which can make all of their organic molecules with carbon

   dioxide as a carbon source, or as (b)_____,
   which require an organic carbon source.

6. (a) autotrophs;
   (b) hetero-
   trophs

7. In eucaryotes, the organelle in which photosynthesis is

   carried out is the (a)_____, while respira-

   tion occurs in the (b)_____.

479

7. (a) chloro-
plast; (b)
mitochondrion

8. In organisms that reproduce sexually, there is a cycle of

four phases or processes. In (a)_____,

cells have one set of chromosomes. In (b)_____

_____, two gametes fuse. In (c)_____,

cells have two sets of chromosomes. In (d)_____

_____, cells divide to make some with only one set of
chromosomes again.

8. (a) haplo-
phase; (b)
fertilization
or syngamy;
(c) diplophase;
(e) meiosis

9. Ordinary cell division in eucaryotes, producing two cells
with the same chromosome numbers as the original, is

(a)_____. The chromosomes are separated

with the aid of a spindle made of (b)_____.
(The information about chloroplasts, mitochondria, and
microtubules is not essential to understanding the major
points of this chapter. However, if you want to understand the chapter more fully, you should consult pages
193-194, 179, and 304-308, respectively.)

9. (a) mitosis;
(b) micro-
tubules

GUIDED REVIEW OF THE CHAPTER

*35-1 The elements are formed through the natural evolution of
stars.*

1. Our universe originated about (a)_____ billion
years ago. At that time all matter and energy was in a

tight, dense mass which then (b)_____(action).

1. (a) 15; (b)
exploded

2. Localized condensation produced galaxies and (a)_____,

in which reactions produce heavier elements and (b)_____

_____.

2. (a) stars;
(b) light

3. Eventually all stars (a)_____(action), releasing

heavy (b)_____ into space.

3. (a) explode;
(b) elements

4. Condensation of this star "dust" produces new (a)_____

and some orbiting (b)_____ such as Earth.

4. (a) stars;
(b) planets

5. Our sun is about (a)_____ billion years old. It
formed through condensation of matter in a rotating mass

called a (b)_____.

5. (a) 4.5;
(b) protostar

6. Chemical reactions leading to the development of living organisms probably take place _____(early / late) in the formation of planetary systems.

6. early

35-2 Organic molecules form in the reducing atmosphere of primitive planets.

1. Life could not again originate on earth as it did once before because of the presence of (a)_____ in the atmosphere, which would (b)_____(reduce / oxidize) any simple organic compounds.

1. (a) oxygen;
(b) oxidize

2. Primitive earth had a (a)_____ atmosphere of H_2, CH_4, NH_3, N_2 and H_2O, and it had no free (b)_____ (gas).

2. (a) reducing;
(b) oxygen

3. This reducing atmosphere, with energy sources of ultraviolet light and lightning, produced _____ molecules which formed a "primitive soup."

3. organic

4. Stanley Miller subjected a mixture similar to a primitive reducing atmosphere to (a)_____ and produced organic compounds, including (b)_____.

4. (a) electricity; (b) amino acids

5. True or False: Repeating Miller's experiment with various initial mixtures always produces organic compounds.

5. True

6. Heating dry mixtures of amino acids with an excess of acidic or basic types produces small (a)_____, some having the ability to (b)_____ chemical reactions.

6. (a) proteins;
(b) catalyze

7. Proteinoids dissolved in hot salt solutions and allowed to cool form (a)_____ with many properties of modern (b)_____ cells.

7. (a) microspheres; (b) procaryotic

8. If the pH surrounding these microspheres is changed, they form (a)_____, indicating that celllike objects can form under (b)_____ planetary conditions.

481

8. (a) buds;
   (b) primitive

35-3 The evolution of a functioning genome is still a problem.

1. Refinement through Darwinian mechanisms requires a (a)_____ to inform structure, and evolution of structure depends on (b)_____ that selection can act upon.

1. (a) genome;
   (b) variations

2. A genome must be able to (a)_____ and direct (b)_____ synthesis.

2. (a) replicate;
   (b) protein

3. A difficult problem is to explain how nucleic acids get control over protein stucture and are able to _____ _____ that structure.

3. specify or
   inform

4. The first nucleic acid to become functional was probably (a)_____ and was of (b)_____(how many?) kinds.

4. (a) RNA;
   (b) two

5. One kind was a type of RNA that could (a)_____ itself; others could have been a primitive (b)_____ _____ RNA, so together the two might be able to catalyze a kind of protein synthesis.

5. (a) copy or
   replicate;
   (b) transfer

35-4 The earliest organisms must have been heterotrophs.

1. Autotrophy involves (a)_____(complex / simple) metabolic machinery that was (b)_____ (absent from / present in) the first organisms.

1. (a) complex;
   (b) absent from

2. The early heterotrophs fed on _____ in the primitive soup until an essential one was depleted.

2. monomers

3. Many heterotrophs then died; the survivors possessed an _____ for converting other molecules into the essential one.

3. enzyme

4. Repetition of this process developed (a)_____ pathways and produced (b)_____(less / more) independent organisms.

4. (a) metabolic;
   (b) more

5. The earliest heterotrophs appeared at least (a)_____ billion years ago (BY) and probably obtained energy by a (b)_____ process.

5. (a) 3.4; (b)
   fermentation

6. Carbon isotope evidence suggests the existence of _____

   _____ at about the same time (3.35 BY) as early
   heterotrophs.

6. autotrophs

7. If these autotrophs used light as an energy source, they

   must have possessed some kind of _____.

7. chlorophyll

8. Electron transport systems of photosynthesis and respira-

   tion must have been (a)_____(aerobic /
   anaerobic) because there was little, if any, free

   (b)_____.

8. (a) anaerobic;
   (b) oxygen

9. The first cells were (a)_____(eucaryotic /

   procaryotic) and appeared over (b)_____ BY.

9. (a) procaryo-
   tic; (b) 3.3

10. Oxygen accumulation in the atmosphere about (a)_____
    BY allowed the development of aerobic respiration

    mechanisms, which are much (b)_____(more / less)
    efficient than anaerobic mechanisms.

10. (a) 2.0-1.8;
    (b) more

11. Eucaryotic cells appear about _____ BY.

11. 1.3

12. Cells became larger with the evolution of two organelles:

    (a)_____ and (b)_____.

12. (a) mitochon-
    dria; (b)
    chloroplasts

35-5 Some problems of phylogeny and taxonomy.

1. In establishing phylogenetic relationships, investigators

   first assumed that each feature evolved _____
   time(s).

1. one

2. Groups sharing the same feature presumably (a)_____

   _____(have / do not have) a common ancestor; those not

   sharing a feature are presumed to have (b)_____
   before that feature appeared.

2. (a) have;
   (b) diverged

3. Taxonomic systems are based on apparent features, which

   _____(always / do not always)
   reflect phylogeny accurately.

3. do not always

4. Which is easier to determine, phylogeny or descriptors?

   _____

483

4. descriptors

5. No group of living organisms can be the ancestor of any other living group, but both could have evolved from an extinct (b)_____.

5. common ancestor

35-6 Most procaryotes are designated "bacteria."

1. Bacteria are commonly named for their (a)_____ and are found virtually everywhere.

1. shapes

2. Of the many beneficial bacterial activities, fixation of _____ gas is one of the most important.

2. nitrogen

3. Most procaryote cell walls are built of (a)_____, or peptidoglycan, which is composed of amino acids and (b)_____ sugars.

3. (a) murein; (b) amino

4. The peptide chains run (a)_____(what direction?) to the polysaccharides, forming an extendable (b)_____.

4. (a) crosswise; (b) amino

5. Penicillin weakens the (a)_____ of a growing cell, causing it eventually to (b)_____.

5. (a) murein; (b) burst

6. Bacteria that take the gram stain are called (a)_____-_____; (b)_____-_____ bacteria do not take the stain.

6. (a) gram-positive; (b) gram-negative

7. Methanogens and halophiles are primitive types of procaryotes that lack (a)_____ in their walls and are known as (b)_____.

7. (a) murein; (b) archaebacteria

8. Procaryotes move by means of either (a)_____ or an obscure (b)_____ mechanism.

8. (a) flagella; (b) gliding

9. Cell walls may be either (a)_____ or (b)_____.

9. (a) flexible; (b) rigid

10. The Myxobacteria have (a)_____ walls and move by (b)_____.

10. (a) flexible; (b) gliding

11. Soft-walled corkscrew-shaped procaryotes are known as the _____.

11. spirochetes

12. Motile eubacteria move by (a)_____; members of

the other rigid-walled group, the cyanobacteria, move via

(b)_____.

12. (a) flagella;
(b) gliding

35-7 Some bacteria have unusual forms.

1. Actinomycetes are unusually (a)_____ bacteria

whose cellular organization is (b)_____.

1. (a) large;
(b) coenocytic

2. Important antibiotics, such as streptomycin, are produced

by _____(what bacterial group?).

2. actinomycetes

3. Rickettsias are unusually (a)_____(large / small)

and are usually carried by (b)_____ vectors,
which transmit various rickettsial diseases through their

(c)_____.

3. (a) small;
(b) arthropod;
(c) bite

4. The smallest cells are (a)_____ with

diameters of (b)_____ micrometers.

4. (a) myco-
plasmas;
(b) 0.1-0.3

35-8 Cyanobacteria show some features of eucaryotic cells.

1. The (a)_____- _____ (color) bacteria obtain

their energy through (b)_____,

and some can fix (c)_____ gas.

1. (a) blue-green;
(b) photosyn-
thesis; (c)
nitrogen

2. Under unfavorable conditions filamentous forms produce

_____ that can remain dormant for long periods
of time.

2. spores

3. (a)_____ are sites of nitrogen fixation,

using the enzyme (b)_____ which only works

(c)_____(aerobically / anaerobically).

3. (a) Hetero-
cysts; (b)
nitrogenase;
(c) anaero-
bically

4. Cyanobacteria possess chlorophyll (a)_____ but

lack organized (b)_____. Some of their

light-gathering pigments are (c)_____.

4. (a) a; (b)
chloroplasts;
(c) phycobilins

5. Phycobilins are found in structures called (a)_____

_____. Such features in cyanobacteria

485

appear to closely link them with (b)_____
(color) algae.

5. (a) phycobili-
   somes; (b) red

35-9 *Some phototrophs have evolved other modes of nutrition.*

1. Because of chlorophyll <u>a</u>, (a)_____ as a photosynthetic by-product, phycobilins, and (b)_____,
   cyanobacteria are probable ancestors of eucaryotic algae.

1. (a) oxygen;
   (b) sterols

2. An apochromatic daughter cell lacks (a)_____
   _____ but obtains nourishment as an (b)_____
   _____ or as a phagotroph.

2. (a) chloro-
   plasts; (b)
   osmiotroph

3. Some apochromatic protistan groups probably originated
   from nearly identical _____ algal groups.

3. phototrophic

35-10 *The photosynthetic apparatus provides good clues to
      phylogeny.*

1. Two evolutionary lines among protists are the (a)_____
   _____- line (color) and the (b)_____-line
   (color).

1. (a) green;
   (b) brown

2. The thylakoids of green-line algae occur (a)_____
   _____(in bundles / singly); they have similar
   carotenoids, and possess chlorophylls (b)_____ and
   _____.

2. (a) singly;
   (b) <u>a</u> and <u>b</u>

3. The thylakoids of brown-line algae occur in bundles of
   three; they possess a different group of carotenoids, and
   some have only chlorophyll (a)_____; most
   also have chlorophyll (b)_____.

3. (a) <u>a</u>; (b) <u>c</u>

4. Food-storage products in the green-line and brown-line
   algae are _____(the same / different).

4. different

35-11 *Flagella also have characteristic structures.*

1. Green-line algae generally have (a)_____(how many?)
   (b)_____(what type?) flagella.

1. (a) two;

2. Brown-line algae usually have one (a)_____(what

486

(b) whiplash

type?) flagellum and one (b)_____(what type?) flagellum pointed in (c)_____(the same / opposite) direction(s).

2. (a) whiplash;
   (b) tinsel;
   (c) opposite

35-12 Metabolic pathways provide other clues to phylogeny.

1. The metabolic pathway of lysine links (a)_____ (group) flagellates and most (b)_____(group).

1. (a) euglenoid;
   (b) fungi

2. The lysine pathway of euglenoids and fungi probably evolved _____(after / before / at the same time as) the pathway used by other eucaryotes.

2. after

35-13 The red algae have many primitive features.

1. The red algae constitute the phylum (a)_____, containing about (b)_____(how many?) species that live mainly in (c)_____ water.

1. (a) Rhodophyta;
   (b) 4,000;
   (c) marine

2. The inner cell wall of red algae cells is of (a)_____ _____; the outer one is of (b)_____ materials.

2. (a) cellulose;
   (b) pectic

3. Secondary pit connections following mitosis, and complex life cycles, link red algae phylogentically with _____ _____.

3. fungi

4. A spore resulting from meiosis is a (a)_____; one resulting from mitosis is a (b)_____.

4. (a) meiospore;
   (b) mitospore

35-14 The primitive eucaryote probably had no flagella.

1. Two large taxonic groups without cilia, flagella, or centrioles are the (a)_____ and the (b)_____.

1. (a) red algae;
   (b) fungi

2. This lack of cilia, flagella, and centrioles indicates that they diverged from the eucaryotic ancestor _____ (after / before) the evolution of such structures.

2. before

487

35-15 Some algae retain very primitive nuclei and mitotic apparatus.

1. Dinoflagellate chromosomes look like the nuclear bodies of

    (a)_____, and they lack the (b)_____ that are characteristic of eucaryotic chromosomes.

1. (a) bacteria;
   (b) histones

2. In dinoflagellates, mitosis occurs by division of the nucleus into two halves, without breakdown of the

    _____.

2. nuclear
   membrane

3. Chromosomes are attached to the inner surface of the nuclear membrane, which elongates with the aid of

    _____.

3. microtubules

4. Dinoflagellates and euglenoid flagellates retain primitive

    (a)_____ (organelle) and mitosis, which may

    be characteristic of the hypothetical ancestral (b)_____

    _____.

4. (a) nuclei;
   (b) eucaryote

5. Euglenoids are difficult to place phylogenetically because

    they possess chlorophylls (a)_____ and _____

    of the green algae and (b)_____ materials of the brown algae.

5. (a) <u>a</u> and <u>b</u>;
   (b) storage

6. Euglenoids also have a unique (a)_____ (loco-

    motor organelle) and a peculiar method of (b)_____

    _____.

6. (a) flagellum;
   (b) locomotion

35-16 The brown-line algae come in many shapes.

1. The phylum (a)_____ includes the

    diatoms, which are enclosed in a pair of (b)_____ that overlap like a petri dish and its cover.

1. (a) Bacilla-
   riophyta;
   (b) shells

2. The brown-line algae also include the yellow-green (phylum

    (a)_____) and the (b)_____

    - _____ (phylum Chrysophyta) algae.

2. (a) Xantho-
   phyta; (b)
   golden-brown

3. Some Xanthophyta are coenocytic and are probable ancestors

    of certain _____.

3. fungi

4. The Phaeophyta, or (a)_____ (color) algae, are (b)_____(multicellular / unicellular) seaweeds.

4. (a) brown; (b) multicellular

5. Whereas brown algae have independently evolved structures parallel to those of (a)_____ plants, none have the equivalent of (b)_____ tissue.

5. (a) vascular; (b) xylem

6. Advanced brown algae emphasize the (a)_____ (gametophyte / sporophyte) phase, an evolutionary trend repeated in (b)_____ plants.

6. (a) sporophyte; (b) green or vascular

35-17 *Several types of protozoans must have evolved from algae.*

1. Flagellate protozoans appear to have evolved from _____ _____ algae.

1. apochromatic

2. Amebalike protozoans are called (a)_____. They use (b)_____ for locomotion and food collection.

2. (a) Sarcodina; (b) pseudopods

3. Most of the Sarcodina are shelled; foraminiferans secrete shells of (a)_____, and radiolarians secrete shells of (b)_____.

3. (a) $CaCO_3$; (b) silica

4. Flagellates and sarcodines appear to be _____ (closely / distantly) related.

4. closely

5. The (a)_____ are a group of parasitic protozoans, one of which is *Plasmodium*, which causes (b)_____ (disease) in humans.

5. (a) sporozoans; (b) malaria

6. Some sporozoans use flagellated gametes, some ameboid, suggesting an evolutionary derivation from both (a)_____ and (b)_____ ancestors.

6. (a) flagellate; (b) sarcodine

7. Ciliates possess (a)_____ for locomotion and probably arose from (b)_____ ancestors.

7. (a) cilia; (b) flagellate

8. Ciliate trichocysts are used for (a)_____, food collection, or for (b)_____ the cell.

489

8. (a) defense;
   (b) anchoring

9. When ciliates conjugate, the (a)_____ disintegrates; then there are meiosis and mitosis of the (b)_____, followed by exchange and fusion of haploid nuclei.

9. (a) macronu-
   cleus; (b)
   micronucleus

35-18 The slime molds are a variety of ameboid saprobes.

1. Slime molds feed and grow as (a)_____ cells and develop (b)_____-producing fruiting bodies.

1. (a) ameboid;
   (b) spore

2. True slime molds grow and move as a large coenocytic (a)_____(haploid / diploid) mass producing (b)_____(haploid / diploid) spores on fruiting bodies.

2. (a) diploid;
   (b) haploid

3. Spores develop into (a)_____ (locomotor organelle) gametes that (b)_____ and develop into a large plasmodium.

3. (a) flagel-
   lated;
   (b) fuse

4. Cellular slime molds produce an alarmone that induces cells to aggregate into a _____ that produces spores.

4. pseudoplas-
   modium

5. Cellular slime molds show no (a)_____(sexual / asexual) processes, and all stages are (b)_____ (haploid / diploid).

5. (a) sexual;
   (b) haploid

6. Eucaryotic cells have the advantage of (a)_____ (more / less) efficient energy production and can handle (b)_____(larger / smaller) amounts of DNA.

6. (a) more;
   (b) larger

7. Eucaryotic cells can have larger genomes than procaryotic cells, and this has allowed them to evolve into complex organisms that carry enough genetic information for the process of _____.

7. differentiation

PRACTICE QUIZ

1. Oparin proposed a primitive atmosphere for earth that was:
   a. reducing and made up of H_2, CH_3, NH_3, N_2, and H_2O.
   b. oxidizing and made up of H_2, CH_3, NH_3, N_2, and H_2O.

c. reducing and made up of H_2, N_2, CO_2, NH_3, and O_2.

d. oxidizing and made up of H_2, N_2, CO_2, NH_3, and O_2.

2. Electrical discharges through a mixture like the primitive atmosphere produce:
   a. phospholipid bilayers.
   b. nucleic acids.
   c. amino acids.
   d. proteins.

3. The first organisms must have been heterotrophs, because:
   a. there was no free oxygen in the early atmosphere.
   b. heterotrophs have a less complex metabolism than autotrophs.
   c. the first cells were also procaryotic.
   d. autotrophs cannot exist in a reducing atmosphere.

4. The first primitive cell fossils were probably:
   a. eucaryotic aerobes.
   b. eucaryotic anaerobes.
   c. procaryotic aerobes.
   d. procaryotic anaerobes.

5. Which is not the result of moneran activity?
   a. crown gall neoplasms
   b. malaria
   c. Rocky Mountain spotted fever
   d. fixation of nitrogen gas

6. Which is the weakest piece of evidence for considering cyanobacteria to be ancestors of eucaryotic algae?
   a. chlorophyll a
   b. phycobilins
   c. oxygen production
   d. heterocysts

7. The green line of protistan evolution is characterized by:
   a. one whiplash and one tinsel flagellum.
   b. chlorophyll b.
   c. glucose polymers with β:1-3 linkages.
   d. thylakoids occurring in bundles of three.

8. The AAA lysine pathway provides an evolutionary link between:
   a. cyanobacteria and red algae.
   b. green-line and brown-line algae.
   c. euglenoid flagellates and fungi.
   d. red algae and fungi.

9. The vascular plant feature that has no equivalent among phaeophytes is:
   a. xylem tissue.
   b. root, stem, and leaf.
   c. multicellularity.
   d. a dominant sporophyte phase.

10. Sporozoan gametes suggest that the group may have been derived from both:
    a. ciliates and sarcodines.
    b. ciliates and flagellates.

491

c. apochromatic phototrophs and osmiotrophs.
d. flagellates and sarcodines.

REVIEW QUESTIONS

I. Using numbers, arrange the following events in sequence from the earliest (1) to the most recent (8).

_____ All matter and energy of the universe are in a compact mass.

_____ Big bang occurs.

_____ First stars and galaxies form.

_____ Our sun forms.

_____ Creation of heavy elements.

_____ Creation of light elements.

_____ The planet Earth forms.

_____ Supernovae occur.

II. Using numbers, arrange the following events in sequence from the earliest (1) to the most recent (9).

_____ Aerobic respiration appears.

_____ Oxygen accumulates in the atmosphere.

_____ Autotrophs appear.

_____ Eucaryotic cells appear.

_____ The primitive soup forms.

_____ Heterotropic cells are present.

_____ Metabolic pathways develop.

_____ Mitochondria appear as cell organelles.

_____ The primitive soup shows depletion of essential monomers.

III. The following chart shows the distribution of five characteristics among five groups of arthropods. Fill in the blanks in the phylogenetic tree below the chart, placing letters across the top and numbers vertically, illustrating the sequence of characteristic divergence.

	1 Mandibles	2 Simple eyes	3 Three body regions	4 Viviparous	5 Wings
A.	0	0	+	0	0
B.	+	+	+	+	+
C.	+	0	+	0	0
D.	+	+	+	0	+
E.	+	0	+	0	+

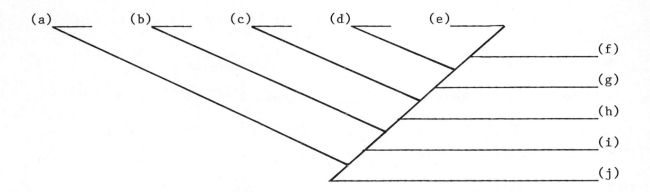

IV. Match each item in the left column with the proper taxonomic groups in the right column.

_____   1. diphtheria   a. Actinomycetes

_____   2. epidemic typhus fever   b. Archaebacteria

_____   3. flagella, true bacteria   c. Corynebacteria

_____   4. methanogens, lack murein   d. Cyanobacteria

_____   5. rigid wall, gliding, heterocysts   e. Eubacteria

_____   6. slime bacteria, gliding   f. Mycobacteria

_____   7. smallest of cells   g. Mycoplasmas

_____   8. soft-walled corkscrews   h. Myxobacteria

_____   9. streptomycin, sporulation   i. Rickettsias

_____ 10. tuberculosis and leprosy   j. Spirochetes

V. Fill in the blanks in the following chart, using a (+) for the presence of the substance and a (-) for its absence.

	Eucaryotic phototrophs	Cyanobacteria	Other photosynthetic procaryotes
Chlorophyll _a_	1.	2.	3.
Chloroplasts	4.	5.	6.
Membrane sterols	7.	8.	9.
Phycobilins	10.	11.	12.

493

VI.   Place a G in front of all green-line features and a B in front of all brown-line features in protistan evolution.

_____   1. thylakoids single   _____   7. chlorophylls <u>a</u> and <u>b</u>

_____   2. thylakoids in bundles   _____   8. α:1-4 glucose linkage

_____   3. grass-green color   _____   9. β:1-3 glucose linkage

_____   4. golden-brown color   _____ 10. paramylum

_____   5. yellow-green color   _____ 11. starch

_____   6. chlorophylls <u>a</u> and <u>c</u>   _____ 12. paired whiplash flagella

                                              _____ 13. tinsel flagellum

VII. Who are the members of the "AAA" club? _____

_____

VIII. Name each of the following groups of algae.

  1. Flexible shape, flagella with single row of hairs, chromosomes separated by
      nuclear membrane during mitosis, chlorphylls <u>a</u> and <u>b</u>, brown-line storage

      materials. _____

  2. Cellulose plates, flagella, no histones, chromosomes separated by nuclear

      membrane during mitosis. _____

  3. Phycobilins, inner cellulose wall, outer pectic wall, no flagella or cilia.

      _____

  4. Multicellular, seaweeds, plantlike development, sporophyte phases dominant.

      _____

  5. Overlapping silica shells. _____

IX. Fill in the blanks in the following chart.

	Adult locomotor organelle	Probable ancestral group	Number of different kinds of nuclei
Sarcodines	1.	2.	one
Sporozoans	none	3.	one
Ciliates	4.	5.	6.
Flagellates	7.	8.	one

X. Place an A in front of all Acrasiomycota features and an M in front of all Myxomycota features.

_____ 1. true slime mold   _____ 5. have AMP pheromone

_____ 2. cellular slime mold   _____ 6. all stages haploid

_____ 3. plasmodium   _____ 7. flagellated gametes

_____ 4. pseudoplasmodium   _____ 8. no sexual events

XI. What is the evolutionary significance of the appearance of larger cells?

_____

ANSWERS TO CHAPTER EXERCISES

Practice Quiz

1. a	3. b	5. b	7. b	9. a
2. c	4. d	6. d	8. c	10. d

Review Questions

   I. 1, 2, 4, 7, 5, 3, 8, 6

  II. 7, 6, 5, 8, 1, 2, 4, 9, 3

 III. (a) A; (b) C; (c) E; (d) D; (e) B; (f) 4; (g) 2; (h) 5; (i) 1; (j) 3

  IV. 1. c   3. e   5. d   7. g   9. a
       2. i   4. b   6. h   8. j   10. f

V. 1, 2, 4, 7, 8, 10 and 11 are (+);   3, 5, 6, 9, and 12 are (−).

VI. 1, 3, 7, 8, 11, and 12 are G;   2, 4, 5, 6, 9, 10, and 13 are B.

VII. Euglenoid flagellates and fungi with chitinous cell walls.

VIII.
1. euglenoid flagellates
2. dinoflagellates
3. red algae
4. brown algae
5. diatoms

IX.
1. pseudopods
2. flagellates
3. flagellates, sarcodines
4. cilia
5. flagellates
6. two
7. flagella
8. algae

X. 1, 3, and 7 are M;   2, 4, 5, 6, and 8 are A.

XI. Larger nuclei contain the larger amounts of DNA necessary to direct differentiation.

Chapter 36

THE FUNGAL AND PLANT KINGDOMS

WHAT'S IN THIS CHAPTER

In this chapter you will learn about two kingdoms of organisms that were at one
time lumped together in one large kingdom. After studying the groups carefully,
most biologists agree that fungi and green plants are very different from each
other and that they should be placed in separate kingdoms. You will learn about
the major differences between these two large groups and about the characteristics
that unite all the fungi and those that unite all the green plants. As you will
see, the evolutionary past of these groups has led, in both kindgoms, to a great
diversity of organisms with different life styles. You will be presented with the
major groups of fungi and plants, their life cycles, and the major structures that
distinguish each group.

By the end of this chapter you should be able to:

1. List three major differences between green plants and fungi.

2. Name three major groups of fungi and give an example of each group.

3. List three important characteristics of "true fungi."

4. Define <u>hypha</u>, <u>mycelium</u>, and <u>fruiting body</u>.

5. Distinguish an antheridium from an archegonium.

6. Name and describe the two subkingdoms of the plant kingdom.

7. Trace three major lines of evolution in the green algae.

8. Describe the typical life cycle of an embryophyte plant.

9. Compare a bryophyte to a fern.

10. Describe the evolutionary advances in the vascular tissue and in the
    development of leaves.

11. Name three adaptations plants have evolved that allow them to live on the
    land.

497

12. Compare gymnosperms to angiosperms.

13. List three examples of gymnosperms and three examples of angiosperms.

14. Describe the life cycle of a flowering plant, including all of the major structures involved.

WHAT YOU SHOULD ALREADY KNOW

Chapters 2, 18, and 35 will help greatly in your understanding of this chapter. The understanding of each chapter has been built on information you obtained from previous parts of the text. Now that we are in the final phase, you should be able to synthesize concepts and information from a variety of sources. In Chapter 2 the bases for evolution are laid down; you should have a firm grasp of this unifying theme. Chapter 18 introduced the generalities of plant life and many terms that will be useful to you here. Chapter 35 serves as an introduction to this chapter because it deals with the origins of eucaryotes, which fungi and green plants both are. In general, then, before you enter this chapter, you should understand evolution and be familiar with the basic parts and kinds of plants.

Pre-Test

1. All existing organisms are related by _____.

1. evolution

2. The driving force in evolution is (a)_____

_____, which is basically differential reproduction. Evolution consists primarily of the processes of

(b)_____, in which one species splits into two

or more species, and (c)_____, in which a species dies out.

2. (a) natural se-
    lection; (b)
    speciation; (c)
    extinction

3. Only advanced plants have an organ for absorption and

anchorage, called a (a)_____, an organ for

support and conduction, called a (b)_____, and

an organ for photosynthesis, called a (c)_____.

3. (a) root; (b)
   stem; (c) leaf

4. Only the advanced plants have vascular tissue, of which

there are two kinds: (a)_____, which conducts

high energy organic molecules from the leaves, and (b)____

_____, which conducts water and minerals from the roots.

4. (a) phloem;
   (b) xylem

5. The two major lines of evolution among eucaryotic

phototrophic algae were the (a)_____
algae, which include the ancestors of higher plants, and

498

the (b)_____ algae.

5. (a) green-line;
    (b) brown-line

GUIDED REVIEW OF THE CHAPTER

Introduction

1. The body of a fungus is a (a)_____, one without
    roots, stems or leaves. The body is made up of threads
    called (b)_____, which grow into a branching
    network called a (c)_____.

1. (a) thallus;
    (b) hyphae;
    (c) mycelium

36-1 The fungal kingdom is still polyphyletic.

1. Fungi are generally (a)_____(motile / nonmotile)
    (b)_____(heterotrophs / autotrophs) that
    live as saprobes or (c)_____.

1. (a) nonmotile;
    (b) hetero-
    trophs; (c)
    parasites

2. The true fungi share the characteristics of having cell
    walls made of (a)_____ and having (b)_____
    _____(flagella / no flagella) during the reproductive
    phase.

2. (a) chitin; (b)
    no flagella

3. Three major different groups of fungi are (a)_____
    _____, (b)_____, and
    (c)_____.

3. (a) Phycomy-
    cetes; (b) As-
    comycetes; (c)
    Basidiomycetes,
    Zygomycetes,
    Trichomycetes,
    or Chytridiomy-
    cetes

36-2 The chytrids are obscure parasites and saprobes.

1. The (a)_____ is a group of fungi that
    have chitin in their cell walls and reproductive cells
    with a whiplash flagellum. Most of them are saprobes or
    parasites on (b)_____.

1. (a) chytridio-
    mycetes; (b)
    plants or fungi

2. Zoospores may be (a)_____, made by mitosis, or
    (b)_____, made by meiosis.

2. (a) mitospores;
    (b) meiospores

3. A mitospore is important to the fungus as a means of
    (a)_____, whereas the

499

meiospores are (b)_____ made in (c)_____

_____.

3. (a) spreading
and proliferat-
ing; (b) gam-
etes; (c) game-
tangia

1. (a) bread mold;
(b) sporangio-
phores; (c) mi-
tospores

2. (a) +; (b) -;
(c) zygospore

3. (a) herbivore
wastes; (b)
sporangium; (c)
are not di-
gested but are
deposited in
the animal's
dung

1. (a) closed
sacs; (b) asci;
(c) yeast or
Neurospora

2. (a) haploid
meiospores;
(b) conidia

3. (a) fruiting
bodies; (b)

36-3 Zygomycetes have no flagella and reproduce through zygospores.

1. A zygomycete is *Rhizopus*, a kind of (a)_____

_____. It reproduces asexually when (b)_____

_____ produce haploid (c)_____.

2. In sexual reproduction in *Rhizopus*, there are (a)_____

and (b)_____ mating types, which help produce a zygote

with a heavy, thorny wall called a (c)_____.

3. *Pilobulus* grows on (a)_____.

Spores are carried away from the fungus in a (b)_____

_____ that sticks to a plant. When the plant is

eaten the spores (c)_____

_____.

36-4 Ascomycetes develop spores inside sacs (asci).

1. The Ascomycetes are known as the sac fungi because their

reproductive spores are formed within (a)_____

_____ or (b)_____. An example of an

ascomycete is (c)_____.

2. Meiosis in the ascus produces four (a)_____

_____, which then break out and grow vegetatively.
Asexual reproduction occurs by means of mitospores called

(b)_____.

3. Large, fleshy mushrooms are all (a)_____

_____, which arise from a mycelium buried below the

ground. An example of an edible ascomycete is a (b)_____

_____.

4. The powdery mildew is a _____ of fruits and
vegetables.

truffle, morel
or helvella

4. parasite or
pathogen

5. (a) ergot;
(b) alkaloids

1. (a) fruiting
bodies; (b)
Basidiomycetes

2. (a) basidio-
spores; (b)
gills

3. (a) rusts; (b)
smuts

4. (a) cellulose;
(b) starch; (c)
<u>a</u>; (d) <u>b</u>

5. (a) Thallophy-
ta; (b) Em-
bryophyta

1. (a) Chlorophy-
ta; (b) 7,000

5. A common parasite of rye is the ascomycete (a)_____

_____, which produces chemicals called (b)_____,
including the drug LSD.

36-5 Basidiomycetes include most of the common mushrooms.

1. Most of the mushrooms we know are actually (a)_____

_____ of the group of fungi, called

(b)_____.

2. Basidiomycetes reproduce by means of haploid cells called

(a)_____, which are borne externally in

their pores or on (b)_____.

3. Two exmples of a basiodiomycete that is a plant parasite

are (a)_____ and (b)_____.

4. A plant is a green phototroph whose walls are made up of

(a)_____. These organisms store (b)_____

_____ as food reserves and have chlorophylls (c)_____

and (d)_____.

5. The plant kingdom is divided into two subkingdoms,

(a)_____, which includes the green algae,

and (b)_____, which includes all other
plants.

36-6 Green algae have evolved independently along several lines.

1. The division of the green algae is the (a)_____

_____, which consists of about (b)_____(7,000 /
70,000) species.

2. A living model for a primitive alga is (a)_____

_____ which is (b)_____(unicellular /

multicellular) and has a cup-shaped (c)_____.

507

2. (a) *Chlamy-domonas*; (b) unicellular; (c) chloroplast

3. One line of evolution in the green algae is from a primitive cell to the (a)_____, which are embedded in a gelatinous matrix. The second line has led to (b)_____, or coenocytic, species. The third line has led to cells that are (c)_____(uninucleate / multinucleate), have lost their (d)_____, and have formed (e)_____ _____.

3. (a) colonial flagellates; (b) siphonous; (c) uninucleate; (d) flagella; (e) sheets or filaments

4. The Charophyta, or (a)_____, are generally found in fresh water and may be the ancestors of (b)_____ _____.

4. (a) stoneworts; (b) mosses

36-7 Plant evolution has involved a modification of the haplodiplontic cycle.

1. In the life cycle of a plant there is an alteration of (a)_____. The haploid phase is known as the (b)_____ because it produces (c)_____.

1. (a) generations; (b) gameotphyte; (c) gametes

2. The gametangia are called the (a)_____ for the male sperm-producing structure and the (b)_____ _____ for the female ovum-producing structure.

2. (a) antheridium; (b) archegonium

3. The zygote develops into the diploid (a)_____, which produces (b)_____.

3. (a) sporophyte; (b) spores

4. In a heterosporous plant the sporophyte bears (a)_____ _____, which produce a few large (b)_____ _____, and the (c)_____, which produce many small (d)_____.

4. (a) megasporangia; (b) megaspores; (c) microsporangia; (c) microspores

5. Each megaspore develops into a (a)_____ that produces (b)_____, and each microspore develops into a (c)_____ that produces (d)_____.

502

5. (a) megagameto-
phyte; (b)
eggs; (c) mi-
crogametophyte;
(d) sperm

36-8 The bryophytes are nonvascular terrestrial plants.

1. The most common bryophytes are the (a)_____.
The (b)_____ are leathery and lobed. There are
approximately 100 species of (c)_____.

1. (a) mosses; (b)
liverworts; (c)
hornworts

2. In the embryophytes, the gametangia are (a)_____
_____(unicellular / multicellular) and in cell
division a (b)_____ grows from the
center outward between newly formed cells.

2. (a) multicellu-
lar; (b) cell
plate

3. In mosses, the leafy green structure is the (a)_____
_____(sporophyte / gametophyte). (b)_____
swim in a film of water to the (c)_____,
where fertilization occurs. Within the sporophyte's
capsule, cells go through meiosis to produce a mass of
(d)_____, each of which grows into a (e)___
_____.

3. (a) gameto-
phyte;(b)
Sperm; (c)
archegonium;
(d) meiospores;
(e) protonema

36-9 Features of vascular plant evolution.

1. The development of vascular tissue solved two problems for
large, terrestrial plants: the need for (a)_____
and the need for (b)_____
_____.

1. (a) support;
(b) transport
of water and
nutrients

2. The stele of most primitive vascular plants is a (a)_____
_____. One major trend in plant
evolution is for this stele to be replaced by (b)_____
_____
_____.

2. (a) central
cylinder; (b)
multiple steles
separated by
parenchymatous
tissue

3. The most primitive xylem elements are long, spindle-shaped
(a)_____ that have evolved into (b)_____
_____, which are specialized for support, and (c)_____
_____, which are completely open at the ends.

503

3. (a) tracheids;
(b) fibers; (c)
vessels

4. Primitive vascular plants have stems that branch (a)_____

_____. These branches become flattened into

the "large leaves," or (b)_____, of modern
plants.

4. (a) dichoto-
mously; (b)
megaphylls

36-10 Early vascular plants were dichotomously branched stems.

1. The most primitive vascular plants had (a)_____

_____ branching stems with true xylem. These

plants (b)_____(were leafless /
had microphylls).

1. (a) dichoto-
mously; (b)
were leafless

2. Fossil vascular plants are the (a)_____

_____ type, which has simple dichotomous branching

with (b)_____ sporangia, and the (c)_____

_____ type, which has an H-shaped dichotomous

pattern with (d)_____ sporangia.

2. (a) *Rhynia-Cook-
sonia;* (b) ter-
minal; (c) *Zos-
terophyllum;*
(d) lateral

3. Two living genera of plants that are leafless, are

homosporous, and have true embryos are (a)_____

and (b)_____.

3. (a) *Psilotum;*
(b) *Tmesipteris*

36-11 An outline of plant evolution.

1. Primitive living plants that have true roots, stems, and

leaves and resemble small pine trees are the _____

_____.

1. lycopods

2. The three great evolutionary branches from a psilopsid

ancestor are the (a)_____, with

tough, jointed stems, the (b)_____, and the

fossil (c)_____, which are believed to
be ancestral to all other plants.

2. (a) equiseto-
phytes; (b)
ferns; (c) pro-
gymnosperms

3. The conifers have <u>pyconxylic</u> wood, meaning that the wood

is _____

_____.

3. fairly hard and
   made up of
   small cells
   with heavy
   walls

4. (a) flowering
   plants; (b)
   seed ferns

1. leaves bearing
   a single spo-
   rangium on
   their upper
   surface; (b)
   strobilus;

2. (a) biflagel-
   late sperm; (b)
   archegonium

1. (a) horsetails;
   (b) scouring
   rushes; (c)
   silica

2. (a) elators;
   (b) disperse
   the spores

1. (a) fronds; (b)
   sori

2. (a) do not
   have; (b) mega-
   phylls

3. sporophyte

4. The Magnoliophyta, or (a)_____,
   may have evolved from (b)_____.

*36-12 Lycopsids developed sporophylls but were a side branch
   of evolution.*

1. Lycopsids have sporophylls, which are (a)_____

   _____. In

   Lycopodium, these sporophylls aggregate to make a (b)_____

   _____.

2. In lycopsids, antheridia release (a)_____

   _____ that swim to the (b)_____
   where a single egg is fertilized.

36-13 Equisetophytes have jointed stems.

1. Plants in the genus *Equisetum* are commonly called (a)_____

   _____. They have also been called (b)_____

   _____, because their stems are tough and abrasive

   from the (c)_____ deposited in their stems.

2. Each spore of *Equisetum* bears four springy (a)_____

   _____ that change shape when wet or dry, which helps to

   (b)_____.

*36-14 Ferns were among the first plants to develop megaphyll
   leaves.*

1. The leaves of ferns are called (a)_____. They

   often have clusters of sporangia, or (b)_____,
   on their undersides.

2. Ferns (a)_____(have / do not have) flowers,

   and they have (b)_____(microphylls /
   megaphylls).

3. In the fern life cycle, the _____
   (sporophyte / gametophyte) is larger.

505

36-15 Seed plants evolved an important new reproductive mechanism.

1. The seed helps a seed plant bypass the need for water during reproduction. Explain why this is important.

   _____

   _____

   _____

   _____

1. In more primitive vascular plants, motile sperms swim to the archegonia in water, but in the absence of a film of water, reproduction will not occur. Those plants that can reproduce in dry conditions have an advantage.

2. The integument, the nucellus, and the egg constitute the (a)_____. After fertilization, the structure that contains the developing embryo is the (b)_____.

2. (a) ovule; (b) sperm

3. Each microgametophyte in a seed plant becomes a (a)_____ _____ that carries the (b)_____ _____ to the ovule so fertilization can occur.

3. (a) pollen grain; (b) sperm

4. (a)_____ are plants with exposed ovules and seeds; (b)_____ are plants with ovules covered by an ovary.

4. (a) Gymnosperms; (b) angiosperms

36-16 Conifers are gymnosperms with relatively simple leaves.

1. The oldest living tree is a _____ approximately (b)_____ years old, and the tallest tree is a (c)_____ approximately (d)_____ meters high.

1. (a) bristlecone pine; (b) 4,900; (c) redwood;

2. Conifer leaves are adapted to (a)_____ conditions, with such adaptations as (b)_____

(d) 100

2. (a) dry; (b) needlelike leaves, recessed stomates and thick epidermis

3. (a) pollen grain; (b) ovule; (c) cone

3. In gymnosperms, a (a)_____ carries a sperm cell to an egg inside an (b)_____ on the scale of a (c)_____.

36-17 The flowering plants have seeds enclosed in an ovary that becomes a fruit.

1. The Anthophyta or Magnoliophyta consists of approximately (a)_____ species, all of which are defined by their distinctive reproductive structures, the (b)_____ _____.

1. (a) 250,000; (b) flower

2. In a flowering plant, the ovary becomes a (a)_____ which protects the (b)_____.

2. (a) fruit; (b) seeds

3. The innermost ring of the perianth is made of (a)_____ _____ and the outermost ring is made of (b)_____.

3. (a) petals; (b) sepals

4. In angiosperms, there is double fertilization wherein one sperm from a pollen grain fertilizes the (a)_____ and the other sperm fuses with the (b)_____ _____ to make a triploid (c)_____.

4. (a) egg; (b) fusion nucleus; (c) endosperm

PRACTICE QUIZ

1. Which of the following is <u>not</u> a characteristic shared by a plant and a fungus?
   a. thallus
   b. rhizoids
   c. chitinous cell walls
   d. nucleated cells

2. Which of the following groups includes a fungus you have probably eaten?
   a. Basidiomycetes
   b. Oomycetes
   c. Phycomycetes
   d. Chytridiomycetes

3. The _____ is a structure that produces sperm.
   a. archegonium

507

b.   sporangiophore
c.   antheridium
d.   crozier

4.   A primitive alga is:
a.   colonial.
b.   coenocytic.
c.   filamentous.
d.   single-celled.

5.   Which of the following is the structure with the greatest number of
     chromosomes per cell?
a.   spore
b.   gamete
c.   sporophyte
d.   gametophyte

6.   Which of the following characteristics do a fern and a moss share?
a.   spore production
b.   vascular tissue
c.   dominant sporophyte
d.   fronds

7.   Which of the following was(were) characteristic of a primitive vascular plant?
a.   vessels
b.   macrophylls
c.   dichotomous branching
d.   seeds

8.   _____ is a fossil plant.
a.   *Psilotum*
b.   *Rhynia*
c.   *Equisetum*
d.   *Ginkgo*

9.   _____ are a unique characteristic of gymnosperms.
a.   Naked seeds
b.   Pollen grains
c.   Ovules
d.   Fruits

10. A flowering plant could <u>not</u> produce a seed without having a(an):
a.   stamen.
b.   perianth.
c.   ovule.
d.   hypocotyl.

REVIEW QUESTIONS

I.   Use the following key to answer the next eight items.

            Key: a.   fungi <u>only</u>   d.   gymnosperms <u>only</u>
                  b.   algae <u>only</u>   e.   c and
                  c.   flowering plants <u>only</u>   f.   b, c, and d

_____ 1. photosynthetic

_____ 2. possess tracheids

_____ 3. chitinous cell walls

_____ 4. seed producers

_____ 5. autotrophic

_____ 6. thallus is a mycelium

_____ 7. colonial flagellates

_____ 8. embyros

II. In each of the following pairs of organisms, which is <u>more primitive</u>?

1. fungi or flowering plants _____

2. flowering plants or gymnosperms _____

3. green algae or mosses _____

4. ferns or mosses _____

5. unicellular or multicellular algae _____

6. vascular plants or nonvascular plants _____

7. ferns or gymnosperms _____

III. In each of the following pairs of events in the life cycle of a flowering plant, which event comes first? Assume that the life cycle starts with the seed.

1. Formation of the seed or of the pollen grain _____

2. Formation of sperm or of the seed _____

3. Growth of the gametophyte or of the sporophyte _____

4. Formation of the carpel or of the endosperm _____

5. Formation of the microgametophyte or of the fruit _____

6. Formation of the epicotyl or of the flower _____

7. Formation of the perianth or of the hypocotyl _____

ANSWERS TO CHAPTER EXERCISES

Practice Quiz

1. c   3. c   5. c   7. c   9. a
2. a   4. d   6. a   8. b   10. c

Review Questions

I.   1. f   3. a   5. f   7. b
     2. e   4. e   6. a   8. e

II. 1. fungi   5. unicellular algae
     2. gymnosperms   6. nonvascular plants
     3. green algae   7. ferns
     4. mosses

III. 1. pollen grain   5. microgametophyte
     2. sperm   6. epicolyl
     3. sporophyte   7. hypocotyl
     4. carpel

Chapter 37

THE ANIMALS

WHAT'S IN THIS CHAPTER

This chapter surveys the Kingdom Animalia--those organisms that are holotropic, multicellular, and generally diploid reproducing with egg and sperm cells. Each group of animals has its unique features plus characteristics possessed by one or more other phyla. Several groups show important adaptive evolutionary innovations, some of which are retained by succeeding groups, some of which are abandoned. The general mechanisms of solving life's daily problems (food collection, excretion, reproduction, and so on) are sometimes solved in surprising, ingenious, and efficient ways. Features suggesting evolutionary connections among phyla or groups of phyla are pointed out.

By the end of this chapter you should be able to:

1. List the major animal phyla, as well as the subphyla and classes of chordates.

2. Characterize each group listed above in terms of its unique and general features.

3. Point out evolutionary characteristics linking phyla or groups of phyla to each other.

4. Explain the meaning and rationale for using eumetazoa and parazoa; radial and bilateral; acoelomate, pseudocoelomate, and eucoelomate; protostomia and deuterostomia; metamerism; vertebrate and invertebrate; and ectothermic and endothermic as characteristics in animalia taxonomy.

5. Name the major evolutionary advances occurring in the Animalia lineage, and give the phylum in which each is first observed.

6. Characterize feeding, excretory, and reproductive techniques for each major animal group.

7. Describe the problems of a terrestrial existence faced by aquatic life forms, and explain how these problems were solved by amphibians and reptiles.

WHAT YOU SHOULD ALREADY KNOW

You should have a general understanding of taxonomy and evolution, as presented in Chapter 2. You should be familiar with cycles of reproduction, as presented in Chapter 10. Most important, you should have a general understanding of animals as presented in Chapter 18; Chapter 38 is largely an expansion of that brief survey. All animals do essentially the same things to survive, and in Chapter 37 you will simply look at some of the variations on a few themes--mechanisms of circulation, respiration, feeding, and so on.

A word of warning: There is a tendency--especially with animals--to think of organisms on a scale ranging from "lower" to "higher." In itself there is nothing wrong with seeing a jellyfish, say, as being more primitive than a fish. But there is great danger in thinking like this, particularly because the animals, like all organisms, have diverged in so many different directions. There is no basis for arguing that a mammal is "higher" than an insect, especially when there are so many species of insects and they are so ubiquitous compared with the mammals.

Pre-Test

1. Animals are (a)_____(unicellular / multi-

    cellular) organisms that have (b)_____
    (autotrophic / hetertrophic) metabolism.

1. (a) multicellu-   2. They get their food (a)_____(osmio-
lar; (b) hetero-   trophically / holotrophically) which means that
trophic
                         (b)_____.

2. (a) holotrophi-   3. Animals take their food into a (a)_____
cally; (b) they
ingest solid   _____, where it is (b)_____.
food

3. (a) digestive   4. A feature of most animals is the concentration of sense
tube or alimen-
tary canal;   organs, brain, and other features at the (a)_____
(b) digested
                         end; this is known as _____.

4. (a) head; (b)   5. Animals generally exhibit a form in which the left and
cephalization   right halves of the body mirror each other, a feature

                         called _____ symmetry.

5. bilateral   6. Some animals, such as sea anemones, do not move about--in

                         other words, they are (a)_____--or they had
                         ancestors that did not move around. As an adaptation to

                         this kind of life, they have evolved (b)_____
                         symmetry.

6. (a) sessile;   7. In order to move oxygen and nutrients into their cells and
(b) radial
                         to remove wastes, most animals have (a)_____

that is moved through a system of tubes called the

(b)_____ system.

7. (a) blood; (b) circulatory or cardiovascular

8. In order to move, animals need a firm structure for their muscles to pull against. In some simple animals, the major body cavity, or _____ serves this function.

8. coelom

9. Other animals use a solid structure called a (a)_____ _____. There are two general types. An (b)_____ _____ on the inside of the body or an (c)_____ _____ on the outside serves for protection.

9. (a) skeleton; (b) endoskeleton; (c) exoskeleton

GUIDED REVIEW OF THE CHAPTER

37-1 Animals are divisible into several major taxa.

1. Sponges are in subkingdom (a)_____; most other animal groups are in subkingdom (b)_____.

1. (a) Parazoa; (b) Eumetazoa

2. Coelenterates are primitive eumetazoans, are (a)_____ _____ symmetrical, and have poorly developed (b)_____ tissue.

2. (a) radially; (b) mesoderm

3. Acoelomate eumetazoans lack a (a)_____ cavity; their body spaces are filled with undifferentiated (b)_____ cells.

3. (a) body; (b) mesenchyme

4. The pseudocoelom type of body cavity is not lined by (a)_____. This lining is present in the (b)_____ body cavity.

4. (a) peritoneum; (b) eucoelomate

5. A true coelom is a cavity in the (a)_____ (tissue) in which organs are held in place by (b)_____ _____.

5. (a) mesoderm; (b) mesenteries

513

37-2 Sponges are basically colonies with little integration.

1. Sponges are often made of small units called (a)_____

    _____, which together form a (b)_____
    with little integration between units.

1. (a) zooids;
   (b) colony

2. Water enters a sponge through (a)_____ pores and
    leaves through an excurrent osculum, being moved by the

    flagella of (b)_____ cells.

2. (a) incurrent;
   (b) collar

3. Food is (a)_____(process) out of the water by

    the (b)_____(structure) of the choanocyte
    cells.

3. (a) filtered;
   (b) collar

4. Between the inner layer of collar cells and an outer layer

    of (a)_____ cells is a (b)_____-

    like layer containing mobile (c)_____
    cells.

4. (a) epithelial;
   (b) jelly;
   (c) mesenchyme

5. Amoebocytes (a)_____(process) material between

    cells and can (b)_____ into any needed cell
    type.

5. (a) transfer;
   (b) differen-
   tiate

6. Support is provided by (a)_____(structure)

    made of $CaCO_3$ (b)_____, or a fibrous protein

    called (c)_____.

6. (a) spicules;
   (b) silica;
   (c) spongin

7. Sponge fertilization is (a)_____(external /
    internal). The zygote develops into a ciliated hollow

    (b)_____(shape) of cells that swims briefly and
    then settles.

7. (a) internal;
   (b) ball

8. Asexually, sponges produce resistant _____
    under adverse conditions.

8. gemmules

*37-3 Coelenterates are built around a central digestive
      cavity.*

1. Coelenterates are three-layered, the middle layer being a

    (a)_____-like (b)_____, the
    equivalent of mesoderm.

1. (a) jelly;
   (b) mesoglea;

2. The nervous system of coelenterates is a simple _____

    _____.

2. nerve net

3. The coelenterate polyp and (a)_____ body

   forms are (b)_____ symmetrical.

3. (a) medusa;
   (b) radially

4. A central (a)_____ cavity functions

   in both (b)_____ and circulation.

4. (a) gastro-
   vascular;
   (b) digestion

5. Special (a)_____ cells capture prey, which

   is moved into the gastrovascular cavity by (b)_____

   _____.

5. (a) nematocyst;
   (b) tentacles

6. Sexual reproduction produces a (a)_____ larva,

   which is a (b)_____(hollow / solid), ciliated
   mass of cells.

6. (a) planula;
   (b) solid

7. Hydrogen medusae result from (a)_____(asexual /

   sexual) reproduction of the (b)_____(medusa /
   polyp) stage.

7. (a) asexual;
   (b) polyp

8. Comb jellies possess eight ciliated (a)_____-like

   plates and exhibit (b)_____ symmetry.

8. (a) comb;
   (b) biradial

9. Ctenophores lack (a)_____ cells and have only

   (b)_____(how many?) tentacles around the mouth.

9. (a) nematocyst;
   (b) two

37-4 The flatworms are typical bilateral acoelomates.

1. Platyhelminthes, or (a)_____(common name), show

   (b)_____ symmetry and have bodies of (c)_____
   (how many?) tissue layers.

1. (a) flatworms;
   (b) bilateral;
   (c) three

2. Their digestive tract, if present, has one opening that

   functions as both (a)_____ and (b)_____.

   They possess a definite head and (c)_____ end.

2. (a) mouth;
   (b) anus;
   (c) tail

3. *Planaria*, in the class (a)_____, is free-
   living and excretes metabolic wastes and excess water

   through (b)_____ cells.

3. (a) Turbellar-
   ia; (b) flame

4. Hermaphroditic turbellarians (a)_____(cross / self)
   fertilize. These worms show remarkable powers of

   (b)_____(regrowing lost parts).

4. (a) cross;

5. Trematodes are all (a)_____(life style), have

515

(b) regenera-
tion

(b)_____(complex / simple) life cycles, and

are covered with coats that are resistant to (c)_____

_____.

5. (a) parasitic;
   (b) complex
   (c) digestive
   enzymes

6. Cestodes, or (a)_____(common name), lack a
   digestive tract and, as adults, are always found in the

   (b)_____ of their host.

6. (a) tapeworms;
   (b) intestine

7. The "units" of a tapeworm body are called (a)_____

   _____; they are filled with eggs and are shed in

   the (b)_____ of the host.

7. (a) proglot-
   tids; (b)
   feces

37-5 Ribbon worms are more advanced acoelomates.

1. Two advances seen in nemertines are a (a)_____

   system and a(an) (b)_____(complete / incomplete)
   digestive tract with separate mouth and anus.

1. (a) circula-
   tory; (b)
   complete

2. Ribbon worms harpoon prey with an eversible (a)_____

   _____, which then (b)_____(process),
   pulling prey into the mouth.

2. (a) proboscis;
   (b) contracts

*37-6 The coelom, the gonads, and the kidneys--a story of
changing form.*

1. A coelom provides a (a)_____ skeleton and

   a water space permitting (b)_____ to move freely.

1. (a) hydrosta-
   tic; (b) organs

2. It also satisfies the need for an (a)_____

   system in large animals that lack an efficient (b)_____

   _____ system.

2. (a) excretory;
   (b) circulatory

3. Wastes can be dumped into a coelom only if there is an

   (a)_____ through which they can be

   (b)_____.

3. (a) opening;
   (b) removed

4. The gonocoel theory of coelom origin suggests that there

   was an enlargement of (a)_____ cavities

   opening to the outside through (b)_____.

4. (a) gonadal;

5. Removal of coelomic fluid wastes is the primary function

(b) coelomo-
ducts

of the (a)_____, which is basically

(b)_____(germ layer) and grows (c)_____

_____(inward / outward).

5. (a) nephridium;
   (b) ectodermal
   (c) inward

6. A protonephridium has (a)_____(how many?) opening(s);

a metanephridium has (b)_____. A (c)_____

_____ is a fused coelomoduct and nephridium, carrying
both waste and gametes.

6. (a) one;
   (b) two; (c)
   nephromixium

*37-7 Embryological features distinguish major groups of
animals.*

1. In protostomes, the blastopore becomes the (a)_____;

in deuterostomes it becomes the (b)_____.

1. (a) mouth;
   (b) anus

2. The protostome larval type is the (a)_____;

the deuterostome larva is a (b)_____.

2. (a) trocho-
   phore ; (b)
   dipleurela

3. Spiral cleavage is characteristic of (a)_____;

(b)_____ cleavage is characteristic of deuterostomes.

3. (a) proto-
   stomes; (b)
   radial

4. Protostomes are also distinguished from deuterostomes by

having (a)_____(determinate / indeterminate)

cleavage and (b)_____(enterocoelous /
schizocoelous) coelom formation.

4. (a) determinate;
   (b) schizo-
   coelous

37-8 The pseudocoelomates share an unusual body structure.

1. Roundworms and (a)_____(group) have a (b)_____

_____ for a body cavity.

1. (a) rotifers;
   (b) pseudocoe-
   lom

2. The nematode body wall is a tough (a)_____
(substance) covering a layer of longitudinally arranged

(b)_____ cells.

2. (a) cuticle;
   (b) muscle

3. _____ is a serious disease caused by
nematodes and acquired by eating poorly cooked pork.

3. Trichinosis

4. Rotifers possess two (a)_____ cells for excre-

tion and are abundant in (b)_____ habitats.

4. (a) flame;
   (b) fresh water

517

37-9 Three phyla of animals feed with the aid of a lophophore.

1. A lophophore is a (a)_____ (function) device

    possessed by three small phyla of (b)_____(motile
    / sessile) marine animals.

1. (a) feeding;
   (b) sessile

2. The lophophorate group are the _____,

    _____, and _____ (comm_n
    group names).

2. (a) phoronids,
   brachiopods,
   bryozoans

3. A lophophore consists of a pair of (a)_____(shape)

    ridges fringed with ciliated (b)_____ that

    direct a current of water toward the (c)_____.

3. (a) spiral;
   (b) tentacles;
   (c) mouth

37-10 The articulate animals have a definite metamerism.

1. A body plan consisting of a series of similar units is

    called _____.

1. metamerism

2. Uniform metamerism is characteristic of the phylum

    _____.

2. Annelida

3. Once uniform metamerism is attained, _____
    (process) of segments for specific functions may evolve.

3. specialization

37-11 The annelids have rather uniformly metamerized bodies.

1. Annelids are (a)_____(body cavity con-

    dition) and have a(an) (b)_____(complete /
    incomplete) digestive system.

1. (a) eucoelo-
   mate; (b)
   complete

2. Their circulatory system is (a)_____(closed / open);

    the nerve cord is (b)_____(dorsal / ventral);

    excretion is by (c)_____.

2. (a) closed; (b)
   ventral; (c)
   metanephridia

3. Earthworms are (a)_____(habitat) annelids

    of the class (b)_____. Other members of

    this class are found in (c)_____
    environments.

3. (a) terrestrial;
   (b) Oligochaeta
   (c) fresh water

4. Parapodia are found on (a)_____(group name)

    which live on the ocean floor or in (b)_____
    made of mud and sand cemented together by mucus or lime.

4. (a) poly-
   chaetes; (b)
   tubes

5. While attached to hosts, leeches suck (a)_____

   with an anterior and posterior (b)_____
   (structure).

5. (a) blood;
   (b) sucker

6. The class (a)_____ contains the leeches.

   They possess the anticoagulent (b)_____, used
   in feeding.

6. (a) Hirudinea;
   (b) hirudin

37-12 Arthropods have metameric bodies with jointed limbs.

1. The nervous and excretory systems of *Peripatus* are like

   those of (a)_____(group), but its circulatory

   system is (b)_____(closed / open) like that of
   arthropods).

1. (a) annelids;
   (b) open

2. And, like anthrcpods, blood is collected in cavities

   called (a)_____ and is pumped by a (b)_____

   _____(dorsal / ventral) heart).

2. (a) hemocoels;
   (b) dorsal

3. Features of *Peripatus* suggest that it is a link between

   _____ and _____ (phyla).

3. annelids,
   arthropods

4. The largest animal phylum is the phylum (a)_____

   _____, (b)_____ percent of which are insects.

4. (a) Arthropoda;
   (b) 90

5. The arthropod leg is a series of (a)_____.

   These appendages are modified in (b)_____(a few /
   many) ways for special functions.

5. (a) joints;
   (b) many

6. Modified appendages have been a key factor in arthropod

   success in _____(many / several) different ways
   of life.

6. many

7. The _____ constitute an extinct subphylum of
   arthropods that have bodies divided into three lobes.

7. trilobites

8. The chelicerates have chelicerae and (a)_____ as

   head appendages, (b)_____(how many?) body regions,

   and (c)_____(how many?) pairs of legs.

8. (a) pedipalps;
   (b) two;
   (c) four

9. Mandibulates have mandibles, one or two pairs of (a)_____

   _____ and (b)_____ as head appendages.

519

9. (a) antennae;
   (b) maxillae

10. _____ (process) of segments into larger units is a tendency in arthropod evolution.

10. Fusion

11. The insect body consists of _____ (how many?) major units.

11. three

12. The ancestral arthropod excretory and reproductive systems are a series of (a)_____ that divide into (b)_____ and ventral portions.

12. (a) cavities;
    (b) dorsal

13. Gas exchange in aquatic arthropods is via (a)_____; terrestrial forms have (b)_____ systems and some spiders use (c)_____ lungs.

13. (a) gills;
    (b) tracheal;
    (c) book

14. The arthropod body is covered with an exoskeleton made of (a)_____, which is flexible in the joints and elsewhere may be hardened with (b)_____ salts.

14. (a) chitin;
    (b) calcium

15. The exoskeleton protects against predators, prevents (a)_____ (substance) loss or gain, and serves as a place for (b)_____ (tissue) attachement.

15. (a) water;
    (b) muscle

16. A disadvantage of an exoskeleton is that it must be _____ to allow for growth.

16. molted

17. A collection of many eye units in one spot is called a (a)_____ eye; each individual unit is an (b)_____.

17. (a) compound;
    (b) ommatidium

37-13 Molluscs are unsegmented but their ancestors were metamerized.

1. The mollusc body exhibits (a)_____ symmetry and consists of a (b)_____, a visceral mass, and the mantle.

1. (a) bilateral;
   (b) foot

2. A unique feeding structure, the (a)_____, scrapes bits of food into the mollusc's (b)_____ (complete / incomplete) digestive tract.

2. (a) radula;
   (b) complete

3. Clams (a)_____ (process) food out of the water with their (b)_____.

520

3. (a) filter;
   (b) gills

4. Except for cephalopods, the circulatory system of molluscs is _____(closed / open), like that of arthropods.

4. open

5. *Neopilina* links molluscs with (a)_____(phylum) because of its (b)_____(feature).

5. (a) annelids;
   (b) segmenta-
   tion or meta-
   merism

37-14 The echinoderms are basically adapted to a sessile life.

1. Larval echinoderms are bilateral, but adults are (a)_____ _____ and built on a plan of (b)_____(how many?) or multiples thereof.

1. (a) radial;
   (b) five

2. Sea star respiratory, circulatory, and (a)_____ systems are taken care of by (b)_____ fluid.

2. (a) excretory;
   (b) coelomic

3. Extensions of the water vascular system, the (a)_____ feet, are controlled by (b)_____ that fill or empty and thus create movement.

3. (a) tube;
   (b) ampullae

4. Sea stars feed on (a)_____ by pulling them slightly open and dumping in (b)_____ enzymes.

4. (a) bivalves;
   (b) digestive

37-15 The chordates share three main characteristics.

1. All chordates have a (a)_____ that becomes part of the backbone in (b)_____(group).

1. (a) notochord;
   (b) vertebrates

2. Chordates also possess a dorsal hollow (a)_____ cord and (b)_____ gill slits at some time in their life cycle.

2. (a) nerve;
   (b) pharyngeal

3. The single chordate feature retained by adult tunicates is the (a)_____; all three features are present in the (b)_____ stage.

3. (a) gill slits;
   (b) larval

4. Cephalochordates possess (a)_____(all / one / two) chordate characteristics and clearly show the (b)_____ _____ (feature) seen in vertebrates.

4. (a) all;
   (b) metamerism

37-16 Vertebrates are defined primarily by their backbone.

1. Vertebrates are so named because of the (a)_____ made of bone or (b)_____.

2. The vertebrate circulatory system is of the (a)_____ (closed / open) type; blood is pumped by a ventral (b)_____.

3. Paired organs in vertebrates are the (a)_____ organs, kidneys, and (b)_____ used in locomotion.

4. Primitive vertebrate fishes lack (a)_____ (structure). Other fishes are either (b)_____ _____ or bony fishes.

37-17 The most primitive vertebrates are fishes.

1. Jawless (a)_____ (group) fishes appeared about 400 MY. They were (b)_____ feeders covered with (c)_____ plates.

2. Living ostracoderm descendants are (a)_____ and hagfish, both of which lack (b)_____ fins, but retain a persistent (c)_____ (chordate feature).

3. Jawed fishes, or (a)_____, appeared (b)_____(after / before) jawless fishes and (c)_____(had / had not) evolved paired fins.

4. Placoderms were ancestral to living cartilaginous and (a)_____ fishes in which (b)_____ (structure) replace bony plates.

5. Another line of placoderm evolution led to the (a)_____ _____-finned fishes, which were ancestral to (b)_____.

6. Lobe-finned fishes have both (a)_____ and (b)_____ (gas exchange devices).

1. (a) vertebrae; (b) cartilage

2. (a) closed; (b) heart

3. (a) sex; (b) appendages

4. (a) jaws; (b) cartilaginous

1. (a) ostracoderm; (b) filter; (c) bony

2. (a) lampreys; (b) paired; (c) notocord

3. (a) placoderms; (b) after; (c) had

4. (a) bony; (b) scales

5. (a) lobe; (b) amphibians

6. (a) gills;
   (b) lungs

37-18 *The amphibians have made a partial transition to the land.*

1. Amphibians ventured onto land _____ MY.

1. 350-200

2. A sexually mature larval form illustrates _____ (phenomenon).

2. neoteny

3. Adult amphibians lack gills and use (a)_____ and lungs to obtain oxygen. The ancestral lobe fins evolved into (b)_____,

3. (a) skin;
   (b) limbs

4. Limb support required development of pectoral and (a)_____ girdles and stronger (b)_____.

4. (a) pelvic;
   (b) muscles

5. Most amphibians spend much of their time in or near (a)_____, but their descendants, the (b)_____, do not.

5. (a) water;
   (b) reptiles

37-19 *Reptiles conquered the land through the amniote egg.*

1. Reptile dependence on aqueous environments is eliminated by their (a)_____ skin and (b)_____ egg.

1. (a) scaly;
   (b) shelled

2. Independence of water allowed a great _____ radiation among reptiles.

2. adaptive

3. An amniote egg possesses everything needed to develop a new individual except (a)_____, which enters through the porous (b)_____.

3. (a) oxygen;
   (b) shell

4. Reptiles appeared about (a)_____ MY and eventually gave rise to (b)_____ and (c)_____ (major vertebrate groups).

4. (a) 250;
   (b) birds;
   (c) mammals

37-20 *The birds are essentially modified dinosaurs with feathers.*

1. Endothermy, or (a)_____-bloodedness, may have been present in the (b)_____ (group) ancestors of birds and mammals.

1. (a) warm;
   (b) reptilian

2. Feathers could have evolved for _____ before they were used for flight.

2. insulation

3. Everything about a bird is designed for one purpose: _____.

3. flight

4. Reptiles have a three-chambered heart; a bird's heart has _____ chambers.

4. four

37-21 Mammals have body hair and suckle their young.

1. Hair is derived from reptilian _____.

1. scales

2. Only mammals have hair, (a)_____(how many?) ear bones, (b)_____ glands, and (c)_____ _____ teeth.

2. (a) three; (b) mammary; (c) differentiated

3. Egg-laying mammals are called (a)_____, kangaroos and their relatives are (b)_____, and the rest are (c)_____.

3. (a) monotremes; (b) marsupials; (c) placentals

4. Mammals arose from (a)_____ reptiles, (b)_____(a different / the same) group as(from) that which birds evolved from.

4. (a) therapsid; (b) a different

PRACTICE QUIZ

1. The annelid body cavity, lined by peritoneum, is:
   a. acoelomate.
   b. eucoelomate.
   c. pseudocoelomate.
   d. filled with mesenchyme cells.

2. The most specific description of the sponge food-gathering method is that it is:
   a. saprozoic.
   b. holozoic.
   c. filter feeding.
   d. phagocytosis.

3. A unique feature of coelenterates is:
   a. two different phases in some of the life cycles.
   b. their three-layered construction.
   c. their possession of nematocysts.
   d. radial symmetry in the adult.

4. Which characteristic is shared by all sponges, coelenterates, and flatworms?
   a. acoelomate
   b. incomplete digestive systems
   c. life in a marine environment
   d. hermaphroditic

5. Which of the following is a deuterostome feature?
   a. spiral cleavage
   b. determinate cleavage
   c. dipleurula larva
   d. schizocoelous

6. The function of the phoronid lophophore is:
   a. reproduction.
   b. locomotion.
   c. gas exchange.
   d. nutrition.

7. Which group of animals all show metamerism?
   a. rotifers, earthworms, birds
   b. leeches, lizards, lophophorates
   c. flatworms, *Peripatus*, leeches
   d. insects, earthworms, salamanders

8. Which "taxon – example" pairing is correct?
   a. Cephalochordata – tunicates
   b. Urochordata – sharks
   c. Chondrichthyes – salmon
   d. Vertebrata – caecilian

9. Ostracoderms are the probable ancestors of:
   a. lampreys.
   b. trout.
   c. sharks.
   d. *Latimera*

10. Which modification for a terrestrial existence was evolved by amphibians?
    a. an air-breathing lung
    b. a closed circulatory system
    c. scale loss, permeable skin
    d. lobe fins for support

REVIEW QUESTIONS

I. Mark each of the following A for acoelomate, E for euoelomate, or P for pseudocoelomate.

_____ 1. annelids

_____ 2. arthropods

_____ 3. body cavity is blastocoel remnant

_____ 4. body cavity lined by a peritoneum

_____ 5. body spaces filled with mesenchyme

_____ 6. chordates

525

_____ 7. coelenterates   _____ 11. molluscs

_____ 8. echinoderms   _____ 12. ribbon worms

_____ 9. flatworms   _____ 13. roundworms

_____ 10. lophophorates   _____ 14. sponges

II. Provide a one- or two-word function for each term.

1. Amphibian skin _____   16. metanephridia _____

2. chelicerae _____   17. notochord _____

3. chorion _____   18. ocelli _____

4. coelomoducts _____   19. nematocysts _____

5. comb jellies' ciliated plates _____   20. ommatidia _____

6. coxal gland _____   21. osculum _____

7. flame cells _____   22. parapodia _____

8. gemmules _____   23. pectoral girdle _____

9. gill slits _____   24. placenta _____

10. hair _____   25. primitive feathers _____

11. hemocoel _____   26. proglottids _____

12. lobe fins _____   27. radula _____

13. lophophore _____   28. spicules _____

14. keeled sternum _____   29. tracheal system _____

15. maxillae _____   30. tube feet _____

III. What is the major reason for placing sponges in the Parazoa, separating them from the Eumetazoa?

_____

_____

IV. Match each item in the left column with the correct animal group in the right column. Answers may be used more than once.

_____ 1. bony fishes   a. amphibians

526

_____ 2. cartilaginous fishes

_____ 3. chitin, jointed legs

_____ 4. choanocyte cells

_____ 5. ciliated comblike plates

_____ 6. cuticle, lacks body wall, circular muscles

_____ 7. ectothermic, amniote egg

_____ 8. endothermic, amniote egg

_____ 9. flame cells, proglottids

_____ 10. hair

_____ 11. lobe-finned fishes

_____ 12. lophophore

_____ 13. mesoglea

_____ 14. nematocyst cells

_____ 15. neoteny

_____ 16. nerve net

_____ 17. nervous system absent

_____ 18. parapodia, hirudin

_____ 19. planula larva

_____ 20. radula

_____ 21. spicules

_____ 22. water vascular system

b. annelids

c. arthropods

d. birds

e. brachiopods

f. chondrichthyes

g. coelenterates

h. crossopterygians

i. ctenophores

j. echinoderms

k. mammals

l. molluscs

m. nematodes

n. osteichthyes

o. platyhelminthes

p. reptiles

q. sponges

V. Which two phyla are linked by *Peripatus*? _____

VI. Which two phyla are linked by *Neopilina*? _____

VII. Fill in the blanks in the chart. Use the following symbols for each column.

Column 1
CD = complete digestive tract
ID = incomplete digestive tract
DL = digestive tract lacking

Column 2
OC = open circulatory system
CC = closed circulatory system
CL = circulatory system lacking

Column 3
P = protostome
D = deuterostome

Column 4
S = segmented
N = not segmented

Column 5
RS = radial symmetry
BS = bilateral symmetry

Column 6
EX = exoskeleton
EN = endoskeleton
SL = skeleton lacking

	Col. 1 CD, ID, DL	Col. 2 OC, CC, CL	Col. 3 P, D	Col. 4 S, N	Col. 5 RS, BS	Col. 6 EX, EN SL
asteroids	1.	9.	17.	25.	33.	41.
chitons	2.	10.	18.	26.	34.	42.
coelenterates	3.	11.	19.	27.	35.	43.
mandibulates	4.	12.	20.	28.	36.	44.
nematodes	5.	13.	21.	29.	37.	45
oligochaetes	6.	14.	22.	30.	38.	46.
reptiles	7.	15.	23.	31.	39.	47.
trematodes	8.	16.	24.	32.	40.	48.

VIII. Which came first, the chicken or the egg? Support your answer!

_____

_____

IX. Give the probable evolutionary or embryonic origin of each of the following.

1. amphibians _____   8. jawed fishes _____

2. arthropods _____   9. jaws _____

3. birds _____   10. limbs _____

4. bird's anus _____   11. mammals _____

5. cyclostomes _____   12. pseudocoelom _____

6. feathers _____   13. reptiles _____

7. hair _____   14. turbellarian mouth _____

X.   On the right are listed major animal groups. The left column lists
evolutionary advances (or characteristics) seen in the animals. Place in front of
each advancement or characteristic the number for the group in which it first
appears in living form.

_____ 1. amniote egg   a. sponges

528

_____ 2. bilateral symmetry   b. coelenterates

_____ 3. circulatory system   c. flatworms

_____ 4. deuterostome   d. ribbon worms

_____ 5. digestive system   e. aschelminths

_____ 6. digestive system with mouth and anus   f. lophophorates

_____ 7. endothermy   g. annelids

_____ 8. eucoelom   h. arthropods

_____ 9. excretory system   i. molluscs

_____ 10. exoskeleton   j. echinoderms

_____ 11. heart   k. fishes

_____ 12. jaws   l. amphibians

_____ 13. jointed appendages   m. reptiles

_____ 14. metamerism   n. birds

_____ 15. nervous system   o. mammals

_____ 16. pelvic girdle of bone

_____ 17. pseudocoelom

_____ 18. scales

_____ 19. skeletal support

_____ 20. terrestrial existence

_____ 21. three ear bones

_____ 22. vertebral column

_____ 23. wings

ANSWERS TO CHAPTER EXERCISES

| 1. b | 3. c | 5. c | 7. d | 9. a |
| 2. c | 4. a | 6. d | 8. d | 10. c |

Practice Quiz

I. A: e, g, i, l, n,   E: a, b, d, f, h, j, k;   P: c, m

II. Gas exchange: 1, 3, 9, 29; feeding: 2, 13, 15, 27; gamete passage: 4;
    locomotion: 5, 22; excretion: 6, 7, 16; reproduction: 8, 26; insulation:

Copyright © 1983 by Harcourt Brace Jovanovich, Inc. All rights reserved.

10, 25; blood collection: 11;   support: 12, 17, 23, 28;   muscle attachment: 14;   light detection: 18;   food capture: 19;   sight: 20;   water exit: 21; embyro development: 24;   attachment: 30

III. Sponges do not show the high degree of integration that is seen in eumentazoans.

IV.
1. n	5. i	9. o	13. g	17. q	21. q
2. f	6. m	10. k	14. g	18. b	22. j
3. c	7. p	11. h	15. a	19. g	
4. q	8. d	12. e	16. g	20. 1	

V. Annelids and arthropods

VI. Annelids and molluscs

VII.
1. CD	9. CL	17. D	25. N	33. RS	41. EN
2. CD	10. OC	18. P	26. N	34. BS	42. EX
3. ID	11. CL	19. P	27. N	35. RS	43. SL
4. CD	12. OC	20. P	28. S	36. BS	44. EX
5. CD	13. CL	21. P	29. N	37. BS	45. SL
6. CD	15. CC	22. P	30. S	38. BS	46. SL
7. CD	15. CC	23. D	31. S	39. BS	47. EN
8. ID	16. CL	24. P	32. N	40. BS	48. SL

VIII. Dinosaurs were laying eggs long before they evolved into chickens.

IX.
1. crossopterygian fishes	8. placoderms
2. annelids	9. gill supports
3. reptiles	10. lobe fins
4. blastopore	11. reptiles
5. ostracoderms	12. blastocoel
6. scales	13. amphibians
7. scales	14. blastopore

X.
1. m	6. d	11. g	16. 1	21. o
2. c	7. n	12. h	17. e	22. k
3. d	8. f	13. h	18. k	23. h
4. j	9. c	14. g	19. a	
5. b	10. h	15. b	20. h	

Chapter 38

HUMAN ORIGINS AND EVOLUTION

WHAT'S IN THIS CHAPTER

A key feature throughout this text has been the postulated evolutionary
relationships between various taxa. This evolutionary thread runs through all
living groups and helps tie them together. We have now reached the point where it
is time to examine ourselves and our evolutionary history. Speculation on human
origins has been, and still is controversial. The information in this chapter is a
simple presentation of facts and realistic analyses of them.

Starting with the earliest known mammals thought to be on a line leading to modern
humans, a step-by-step procedure examines a series of fossils. Similarities in
skeletal structures reveal basic anatomical correlations. Associated behavioral
and cultural features are determined by examining artifacts and ancient living
areas. Some of the environmental changes over the past four million years
correlate with observed developments in our evolution. Woven together, these three
aspects reveal a logical, credible, and fascinating story of human evolution.

By the end of this chapter you should be able to:

1. Compare modern humans to their closely related living relatives and to each of
   the major groups of fossil ancestors, noting similarities and differences.

2. Correlate environmental conditions with changes that have occurred in the
   lineage of forms leading to humans.

3. Give examples of artifacts and explain how each is used to provide information
   about the nature of the form that used them.

4. Cite evidence for major cultural advances (tools, clothes, fire, language,
   agriculture, and the like) developed by human ancestral groups, naming each
   group and giving its contribution.

5. List sequentially the forms on the line to modern humans, and give their
   approximate existence in years before present.

6. Speculate on the consequences of such cultural advances as clothes, fire,
   language, tools, agriculture, and medicine.

WHAT YOU SHOULD ALREADY KNOW

You really need to know very little to read this chapter; it is almost independent of the rest of the book, except for some fundamental ideas contained in Chapter 2. You should understand the process of evolution in general, particularly the meaning of natural selection. You should also understand the taxonomic system for classifying organisms.

Pre-Test

1. Sexually reproducing organisms are considered different species if they do not _____.

1. interbreed

2. Similar species are classified by means of a hierarchy of categories called (a)_____; the singular is (b)_____.

2. (a) taxa;
   (b) taxon

3. The taxa above species, in ascending order are _____ _____ _____.

3. genus, family, order, class, and phylum

4. The most general, fundamental meaning of natural selection is _____.

4. differential reproduction

5. The most important methods used today to determine the age of a stratum or rock depend on the process of (a)_____ _____. These methods depend on measuring the relative amounts of two different (b)_____.

5. (a) radio-active decay;
   (b) isotopes

GUIDED REVIEW OF THE CHAPTER

Introduction

1. Miocene times were cooler and dryer, allowing _____ (plant form) to spread across the plains.

1. grasses

2. This new habitat placed a premium on _____ (activity) rather than climbing.

2. running

3. A small ape, _____(genus), adopted this life style.

3. *Ramapithecus*

4. Darwin did not discuss human evolution in (a)_____

_____, published in 1859, but he later did

in his (b)_____.

*38-1 Primates are generalized mammals adapted to an arboreal
life.*

1. Primates includes humans, apes, and (a)_____.

Their common ancestor arose about (b)_____ MY.

2. Primates evolved from (a)_____ during the

adaptive radiation of mammals about (b)_____ MY.

3. The _____ appear to be transitional between insectivores and primates.

4. A frugivorous animal eats (a)_____; an omni-

vorous one eats (b)_____.

5. Primate adaptation is for an (a)_____ life.

This includes a grasping, (b)_____ thumb.

6. Primates are (a)_____(generalized /
specialized) animals. The apposable thumb can be used to

grasp (b)_____ as well as branches of trees.

7. The design of the primate limb allows for great (a)_____

_____, an adaptation to life in the (b)_____.

8. Primate features also include (a)_____(shape)
nails and sensitive digit ends, contributing to greater

(b)_____.

9. Primate eyes have (a)_____(quality) vision; and
they are aimed forward so they can work together to

produce (b)_____ perception.

10. Upright posture provides a better (a)_____ of

surroundings and frees the (b)_____ for uses
other than locomotion.

11. Poorly developed primate features include the sense of

(a)_____ and the (b)_____(structure).

11. (a) smell;
    (b) teeth

12. Primates produce (a)_____(fewer/ more) offspring than other animals and care for them (b)_____ (briefly / longer).

12. (a) fewer;
    (b) longer

13. Long periods of parental care allow for transmission of (a)_____ skills by (b)_____ means.

13. (a) survival;
    (b) cultural

38-2 Who are the primates?

1. Tree shrews and lemurs, (a)_____(suborder), were displaced by monkeys about (b)_____ MY.

1. (a) prosimians;
   (b) 40

2. Modern and fossil humans and prehumans are in the family (a)_____, and are commonly called (b)_____ _____.

2. (a) Hominidae;
   (b) hominids

3. New World monkey stock evolved (a)_____ tails and (b)_____(shape) faces.

3. (a) prehensile;
   (b) flat

4. Old World monkeys have downward-pointing _____ and lack prehensile tails.

4. snouts

5. The tooth type sequence in a dental formula is (a)_____ _____, (b)_____, (c)_____, and (d)_____.

5. (a) incisors;
   (b) canines;
   (c) premolars;
   (d) molars

6. New World monkeys have one more (a)_____(tooth type) than Old World monkeys, apes, and (b)_____.

6. (a) premolar;
   (b) humans

7. Simons considers *Aegyptopithecus* the oldest known ancestor of the _____ group.

7. hominids

38-3 Evolving populations do not conform to simple types.

1. Fossil forms of the same species show _____, just as individuals of living populations do.

1. variation

2. _____ species exist at different geologic times.

2. Allochronous

3. In a complete lineage of fossil species, it would be _____ _____(difficult / easy) to separate one species from

the next.

3. difficult

38-4 Ramapithecus was the first hominid.

1. The first ape, (a)_____

    (genus), lacked a tail and appeared about (b)_____
    MY.

1. (a) *Dryopithecus*; 2. Apes move through trees by (a)_____(pro-
   (b) 25-20

    cess). Larger apes spend most of their time on the (b)___

    _____.

2. (a) brachia-   3. Apes do not have a full (a)_____ posture and
   tion; (b)
   ground

    move by (b)_____-walking.

3. (a) upright;   4. During the Miocene many apes left the (a)_____
   (b) knuckle

    and adapted to life on the (b)_____.

4. (a) trees;   5. The earliest hominid was a late-Miocene (a)_____
   (b) ground

    named (b)_____(genus).

5. (a) ape; (b)   6. To change from frugivorous to omnivorous required
   Ramapithecus

    (a)_____ jaws and more (b)_____ on the
    teeth.

6. (a) tougher;   7. *Ramapithecus* shows these features plus a more _____
   (b) enamel

    _____ shape of the jaw, in contrast to the rectangular
    ape jaw.

7. pointed   8. Comparatively less tooth wear in *Ramapithecus* may be
                       considered evidence that its permanent teeth emerged

    (a)_____(earlier / later) than those of its

    ancestors and that it used its (b)_____ for
    tearing food.

8. (a) later;   9. Later permanent tooth eruption implies a (a)_____
   (b) hands   (longer / shorter) development period, and use of the

    hands implies an (b)_____ posture.

9. (a) longer;
   (b) upright   *38-5 Australopithecines were small, erect hominids.*

    1. *Australopithecus* fossils from Africa are dated about _____

        _____ MY and show many bipedal hominid features.

535

1. 5-3

2. gracile

3. (a) larger;
   (b) vegetarians

4. (a) brain;
   (b) body

5. (a) 500-700;
   (b) gracile

6. (a) bipedalism;
   (b) family

7. (a) upright;
   (b) 3.8

8. *Homo*

1. (a) 2;
   (b) Olduvai

2. (a) *Homo habilis*
   (b) 650-700

3. (a) more;
   (b) 800

4. (a) million;
   (b) tool

---

2. Dental and artifact evidence indicates the _____ form of the australopithecines ate meat.

3. The robust forms were (a)_____(larger / smaller) and were probably (b)_____(diet type).

4. Intelligence is correlated with the ratio of (a)_____ size to (b)_____ weight.

5. The australopithecines' brain size of (a)_____ cc suggests the (b)_____(gracile / robust) form was more intelligent.

6. Their skeletons show adaptations for (a)_____ (locomotion), and they probably lived in extended (b)_____ _____ groups.

7. *Australopithecus afarensis* stood fully (a)_____ about (b)_____ MY, although its brain size was small.

8. *A. afarensis* appears to be ancestral to at least two evolutionary lines, including one leading to _____ (genus).

38-6 Human evolution is charted partially by cultural relics.

1. The oldest tradition or industry is about (a)_____ MY and is from the (b)_____ Gorge.

2. The Olduwan tradition was probably the work of the species, (a)_____, which had humanlike teeth and a cranial capacity of (b)_____ cc.

3. The Lake Turkana *H. habilis* specimens were (a)_____ (less / more) advanced than the Olduvai forms and had a brain capacity of (b)_____ cc.

4. *H. habilis* coexisted with *Australopithecus robustus* for at least a (a)_____ years and eventually won out. It was the first hominid (b)_____ maker.

38-7 Homo erectus created Lower Paleolithic culture.

1. *Homo erectus* appeared about (a)_____ MY and had a

    brain cpacity of (b)_____ cc but retained a

    primitive skull and (c)_____.

**1. (a) 2; (b) 800–
1,100; (c) teeth**

2. *H. erectus* ranged widely across Europe, (a)_____,

    and the Near East. It was fully (b)_____
    (diet).

**2. (a) Africa;
(b) omnivorous**

3. *H. erectus* campsites contain bones of grazers and

    carnivores, along with both (a)_____ and (b)____

    _____ tools.

**3. (a) core;
(b) flake**

4. Previous hominids worked (a)_____(both / one) side(s)

    of their stone tools and learned to use (b)_____
    for cooking.

**4. (a) one;
(b) fire**

5. As the climate grew colder, *H. erectus* began using (a)____

    _____ for clothing, and some moved into (b)_____

    _____ heated by (c)_____.

**5. (a) skins;
(b) caves;
(c) fire**

6. The size and shape of various brain areas indicate that

    H. erectus used a rudimentary _____.

6. language

7. Language was important for the development of (a)_____

    _____ and for cooperation in (b)_____
    (activity).

**7. (a) culture;
(b) hunting**

8. With a selective premium on (a)_____ and
    language, evolution increased cranial capacity by at least

    (b)_____ % in less than a million years.

**8. (a) intelli-
gence; (b) 150**

9. *H. habilis* obtained food by the _____-_____

    _____ method.

**9. hunting-
gathering**

*38-8 Middle-Paleolithic culture was created by Neanderthal
(and later) humans.*

1. *H. erectus* was replaced by *H. sapiens* about _____
    thousand years ago, perhaps through a gradual change of
    features.

1. 250–150

2. The Neanderthal grade followed the (a)_____

537

grade and led to the (b)_____ grade.

2. (a) *erectus;*
   (b) *sapiens*

3. Neanderthals were fully (a)_____(posture) and were different from modern humans in two major aspects:

   (b)_____ cranial capcity and heavy (c)_____

   _____.

3. (a) erect;
   (b) larger;
   (c) brow ridges

4. Neanderthals may have been the first to consider life after (a)_____, as suggested by the practice of

   (b)_____ their dead.

4. (a) death;
   (b) burying

5. Neanderthal skulls indicate that they were (a)_____-

   handed and that the brain area governing (b)_____ was relatively small.

5. (a) right;
   (b) speech

6. The *sapiens* grade dates from _____ thousand years ago to present.

6. 35

38-9 Modern humans appeared about 35,000 years ago.

   1. Cro-Magnon existed (a)_____ thousand years ago in a

      time period called the Upper (b)_____.

1. (a) 35-10
   (b) Paleolithic

2. They made (a)_____(quality) tools and estab-

   lished the foundation of our (b)_____.

2. (a) excellent;
   (b) culture

3. Much is learned about them from their cave (a)_____

   _____, some of which probably had a (b)_____ significance.

3. (a) paintings;
   (b) ritual

4. Until 8000 B.C., all Upper Paleolithic cultures lived by

   (a)_____ and (b)_____.

4. (a) hunting;
   (b) gathering

5. Then, some tribes settled on shore lines, creating

   transitional cultures known as (a)_____

   and living by (b)_____(method).

5. (a) Mesolithic;
   (b) fishing

38-10 Agriculture created a revolution in human life.

   1. Animal (a)_____ and farming started

      about (b)_____ B.C. in Asia, India, and the (c)_____

      _____.

1. (a) domestica-   2. Agriculture marks the start of the (a)_____
   tion; (b) 8000   culture, which spread rapidly, leading to great increases
   (c) Middle East
                         in (b)_____.

2. (a) Neolithic;   3. The use of metals ushered in the (a)_____ Age
   (b) population
                         about (b)_____ B.C.

3. (a) Bronze;
   (b) 3000

PRACTICE QUIZ

1. The opposable thumb was initially an adaptation for:
    a. holding fruit while eating.
    b. tearing and shredding flesh.
    c. grasping tree branches.
    d. making and using tools.

2. Which feature is characteristic of New World monkeys?
    a. lack of prehensile tails
    b. platyrrhine faces
    c. dental formula of 2:1:2:3
    d. downward-pointing noses

3. How many premolars are in the mouth of an animal with a dental formula of
    2:1:2:3?
    a. 2
    b. 4
    c. 8
    d. 12

4. Synchronous species are those:
    a. in which one evolved from the other.
    b. that breed at the same time of the year.
    c. that show the same aging patterns.
    d. that live at the same time.

5. The first hominid was:
    a. *Ramapithecus*.
    b. *Dryopithecus*.
    c. *Australopithecus*.
    d. *Homo*.

6. Intelligence of fossil forms is determined primarily by:
    a. brain size.
    b. ratio of brain size to body weight.
    c. size of the left half of the brain.
    d. degree of upright posture.

7. Which cultural activity characterizes the Lower Paleolithic?
    a. use of simple stone tools
    b. agricultue and domestication of animals

539

c. use of fire
d. extensive cave paintings

8. The first groups to bury their dead were:
a. Neanderthals.
b. Cro-Magnons.
c. *Homo erectus.*
d. *Homo habilis.*

9. The <u>most</u> primitive tradition in tool making was the:
a. Abbevillian.
b. Acheulian.
c. Mousterian.
d. Middle-Paleolithic.

10. The Neolithic innovation that ultimately resulted in overpopulation was:
a. cooler weather and cave dwelling.
b. development of agriculture.
c. domestication of animals.
d. use of metal for tools and weapons.

REVIEW QUESTIONS

I. Match each item in the left column with the correct approximate age listed in the right column. Some answers are used more than once. (MY = million years ago; YA = years ago)

_____ 1.	australopithecine fossils	a.	70-65 MY
_____ 2.	Bronze Age	b.	40 MY
_____ 3.	Cro-Magnon	c.	40-30 MY
_____ 4.	*Dryopithecus*	d.	36-25 MY
_____ 5.	earliest hominid	e.	25-20 MY
_____ 6.	Gondwana broke apart	f.	25-7 MY
_____ 7.	first *Homo erectus*	g.	20 MY
_____ 8.	*Homo habilis*	h.	3.8-1.5 MY
_____ 9.	first *Homo sapiens*	i.	2 MY
_____ 10.	human-ape common ancestor	j.	2-1.75 MY
_____ 11.	Miocene	k.	250,000-150,000 YA
_____ 12.	monkeys evolved	l.	100,000-35,000 YA
_____ 13.	Neanderthal dominance	m.	35,000-10,000 YA
_____ 14.	Neolithic revolution	n.	10,000 YA

_____ 15. Oligocene   o. 5000 YA

_____ 16. first primates

_____ 17. *Ramapithecus*

_____ 18. first tools

II. Identify the group in which each of the following developmenst is first seen:
R = *Ramapithecus*, A = *Australopithecus*, HH = *Homo habilis*, HE = *Homo erectus*,
N = Neanderthals, HS = modern *Homo sapiens* types.

_____ 1. ate meat

_____ 2. beginning of an angular hominid jaw

_____ 3. clearly bipedal

_____ 4. clothing

_____ 5. core and flake tools

_____ 6. buried its dead

_____ 7. earliest hominid

_____ 8. extensive cave painting

_____ 9. fire use

_____ 10. first crude tools

_____ 11. Mesolithic culture

_____ 12. more heavily enameled teeth

_____ 13. Mousterian tradition

_____ 14. rotary grinding motion of the jaws

_____ 15. rudimentary language

III. Define or identify each term in a few words.

1. allochronous species _____

2. arboreal _____

3. brachiation _____

4. catarrhine face _____

5. flake tools _____

6. cosmopolitan _____

7. cranial capacity _____

8. fovea _____

9. frugivorous _____

10. insectivorous _____

11. Neolithic revolution _____

12. nomadic _____

13. omnivorous _____

14. Old Stone Age _____

15. opposable thumb _____

16. platyrrhine _____

17. prehensile tail _____

18. cones in retina _____

19. steppes _____

20. stereoscopic vision _____

21. synchronous species _____

IV. Assume you are an adult with all your teeth. What is your dental formula?

____:____:____:____ What is the Old World monkey's dental formula?

____:____:____:____

V. Give the known distribution of each group, as indicated by their fossil remains. A = Africa, EA = East Africa, SA = South Africa, E = Europe, ME = Middle East, NE = Near East, I = India, O = Orient.

_____ 1. Dryopithecine apes

_____ 2. Australopithecines

_____ 3. *Homo habilis*

_____ 4. *Homo erectus*

_____ 5. Neanderthals

Practice Quiz

1. c	3. c	5. a	7. c	9. a
2. b	4. d	6. b	8. a	10. b

Review Questions

I.
1. h	4. e	7. i	10. g	13. l	16. a
2. o	5. f	8. j	11. f	14. n	17. f
3. m	6. c	9. k	12. b	15. d	18. i

II.
1. A	4. HE	7. R	10. HH	13. N
2. R	5. HE	8. HS	11. HS	14. A
3. A	6. N	9. HE	12. R	15. HE

III.
1. live at different times
2. tree dwelling
3. swinging
4. with snout pointing downward
5. made from chips of stone
6. world wide
7. brain size
8. part of retina with clearest vision
9. fruit-eating
10. insect-eating
11. agriculture
12. roaming
13. eats wide range of food
14. Lower Paleolithic
15. used for grasping
16. flat face
17. grasping tail
18. used for color vision
19. grassy plains
20. depth perception
21. live at the same time

IV. Both are 2:1:2:3.

V. 1. E, EA, I, O   2. EA, SA   3. EA   4. E, A, NE, O   5. E, A, NE

A 3
B 4
C 5
D 6
E 7
F 8
G 9
H 0
I 1
J 2